Boundary Control
and Legal Principles

Boundary Control

and Legal

Principles

CURTIS M. BROWN, B.S.

Licensed Land Surveyor
Instructor, San Diego Junior College
and Vocational School

WITH CONTRIBUTIONS BY
H. FREDERICK LANDGRAF
Attorney at Law

NEW YORK • JOHN WILEY & SONS, INC.
London

This book is dedicated to

WILLIAM C. WATTLES

to whom "the contrary may be shown."

Preface

The purpose of this book, as the name suggests, is to discuss and enumerate legal principles that control the boundary location of real property.

To be valid, a transfer of real property must be in writing. One purpose of the writings is to distinguish the limits of a particular parcel of land from the limits of any other parcel of land. Presented herein is a summary of the legal principles that transcribe the written words of a deed into a monumented location on the ground. This book does not discuss items that affect the validity of deeds, such as insanity and legal age, nor does it tell how to use surveying equipment and mathematics. This is a textbook of legal principles of boundary control, presented for abstractors, surveyors, title engineers, attorneys, and others who interpret, insure, and locate deed descriptions.

Since many deeds are and were written from surveys, the legal principles discussed are often interwoven with the customs, habits, and methods of surveyors. The Federal law, "the boundaries of the public lands, when approved and accepted, are unchangeable," indicates the necessity of understanding how the original surveyor set the boundaries. Knowing how and why a surveyor established his lines where he did is the foundation for understanding where obliterated and lost boundaries should be reestablished.

The English language is composed of many words with dual meanings. The word "north" may mean "astronomic north," "magnetic north," or "north relative to the bearing of the monumented line," depending upon the contents of the remainder of the deed. "Blue" may mean a color or a personal feeling. Mathematics, in contrast to written English, is an exact science. Two

plus two always equals four. The surveyor, being a man of
science, is apt to develop an exact viewpoint. The attorney, on
the other hand, utilizes a language that can have various meanings,
exceptions, and modifications, depending upon the surrounding
circumstances. Law is not looked upon as an exact science. With
the same conditions and facts, two judges may render opposing
decrees. The surveyor finds it difficult to adjust his exact views to
the more flexible principles of law. In the following pages are set
forth many principles that may be subject to two criticisms: First,
the surveyor may say that they are too flexible and are subject to
too many exceptions. Second, the attorney may say that they are
too rigid. The principles as set forth are derived from law and
are, therefore, just as flexible as the law from which they were
derived.

Court records prove the prevalence of erroneous ideas in the
interpretation of deeds and deed terms. Property rights of people,
as defined by a written instrument, are all too frequently ambiguous
in meaning, thus setting the stage for litigation between adjoining
property owners. Often court action could be prevented, if the
deed author had used due care in selecting the original deed terms.

Attorneys, because of their legal skill, are eminently qualified to
compose the operative portions of deeds. Surveyors, because of
their technical and mathematical skills, are best qualified to describe
the size, shape, and location of a particular parcel of land. By
pooling their efforts, the attorney and the surveyor form a team
capable of producing a clear, unambiguous deed. Books that assist
such a team by relating real property law to surveying are indeed
scarce. Many explain the laws pertaining to real property boundaries, and many explain the techniques of surveying and mathematics, but few integrate the legal elements of title descriptions,
boundary law, and surveying. As a surveyor, I realized early that
the surveying of land boundaries is dependent upon law and that
a text book correlating law and surveying was needed. This is my
answer.

Practically all the lands of the United States have been, at one
time, surveyed. It is seldom that a property survey does not include the element of retracement of a former survey. Instructions
contained in the deed furnished, and the records of the former surveys, may have several meanings relative to monuments called for,
mathematical correctness, basis of bearings, distance, area, or plat.

Thus the surveyor can no longer depend exclusively upon his knowledge of mathematics and measurement techniques; he must have a knowledge of law to resolve latent deed ambiguities.

Title engineers and abstractors, when passing judgment upon title matters, should know the legal significance of each term contained in each deed. Innocent-looking phrases, like the controversial "due north" in the Richfield Oil Company case, may result in an explosive law suit involving hundreds of thousands of dollars. Many deed terms may not be fixed in value without field measurements. A deed call for a monument establishes the position of the monument in the spot in which it is found, not in the position called for by bearings and distances. Hence it is patent that abstractors and title engineers need to know boundary law from the viewpoint of those making the measurements.

Although the solution to a boundary problem is derived from the combined application of correct law and skillful surveying observations, it is obvious that a reprint of all the statute laws of the forty-eight states and the Federal Government is needless. As a preparation to the writing of this book, extensive research into court cases and legal books was instigated. From this vast accumulation of abstracts and notes, the pertinent facts and conclusions stated herein were sifted out. It is regrettable that space limitations do not allow a more detailed proof and discussion of the principles presented. Only a limited number of court cases are directly quoted, each quotation being selected because of its specific application to the subject matter.

The forerunner of this book was *Boundary Control for Surveyors in California*. As an aid in writing this book, H. Frederick Landgraf, attorney at law, was prevailed upon to lend technical advice and to write Chapter 2. His assistance in leading me through the research techniques of law, and his advice on legal points, materially assisted in the preparation of the book.

To William C. Wattles, an authority and dean of title matters, is my dedication for his oft-repeated sage counsel—to most legal principles the statement "the contrary may be shown" should be added. To Mr. Albert W. Daniels, I am indebted for his assistance.

La Mesa, Calif.　　　　　　　　　　　　　Curtis M. Brown
January, 1957

Contents

CHAPTER 1

Systems Used
to Describe Property

1. Contents of Book. The scope of this book is limited to the legal elements and terms that control what and where boundaries are. Where the position of a particular real property boundary is located is a fact determinable by measurements. What constitutes the boundaries of real property is a question of law that may be resolved by a fence, a measurement, a line of possession, senior considerations, or other legal matters. It is not the intent to include factors affecting the validity of ownership, such as insanity, legal age, nonpayment of taxes, deed forms, and community property. Nor is it the intent to explain the use of surveying instruments and mathematics. Many excellent textbooks exist for that purpose, and the reader is referred to them (*Principles and Practice of Surveying*, Breed and Hosmer, John Wiley and Sons; *Surveying*, Davis and Foote, McGraw-Hill Book Company; *Surveying*, R. Brinker, International Textbook Company; *Surveying Theory and Practice*, Tracy, John Wiley and Sons).

Chapter 1, "Systems Used to Describe Property," is written to acquaint the reader with the meaning of deed terms and systems used to position and describe property lines. Chapter 2, "Transfer of Real Property," written by Mr. Landgraf, considers the voluntary and involuntary methods of transferring property ownership. The *initial* right to land ownership must be acquired by a written document; but, after the original right is established by writings, land may be added to or subtracted from a person's holdings by unwritten means. Nature, by the forces of water, may alter the shape of land by erosion or accretions. Man by his acts, conduct, and verbal statements, may augment or diminish his land area. Although these methods of title transfer are questions of law, the surveyor and

1

title author must understand the elements of each to enable them to locate and describe property properly.   Chapters 3, 4, 5, 6, 7, and 8 divulge into the legal elements that determine the exact location of property, exclusive of possession considerations.   Within a written instrument terms may be in conflict.   Such questions as "Will a monument control over bearing and distance and, if it does, under what circumstances?" need answering.   After the surveyor has correctly made his measurements and observations and has found conflicting elements, what are the true deed boundaries? Which factors, the deed terms, monuments on the ground, or witness evidence, are controlling?   These questions are purely legal, and to seek an answer the records of the courts and statute laws must be examined.   The answers presented are from a legal viewpoint rather than an engineering one, but the arrangement of the subject matter is in accordance with the types of boundary problems surveyed.   Boundary location is a dual consideration; it requires the mature judgment of an attorney and the skill of a surveyor.   The surveyor needs to know the language of the attorney and the attorney needs to know the language of the surveyor.

Chapters 9 and 10, "Making the Survey" and "Writing Deeds," are of an advisory nature for those composing deeds and those making surveys.   Pitfalls to avoid, procedure to use, and dangers encountered are presented.   To eliminate interruption of thought caused by an explanation of the meaning of a word or term used, a glossary of deed terms and their definitions is presented at the back of the book.

2. Control of Location by Monuments.   Land is fixed in place. If it is to be divided among various people, it must be marked by monuments where they exist or directions must be given explaining how it is or can be monumented.   The earliest land holdings were dependent upon found or set monuments that delineate limits of ownership.   But monuments and marks on the earth's surface are subject to destruction or movement by intentional or unintentional means.   Trees die, wooden stakes rot, rivers change their course, and ploughs remove stakes.   Certainty of boundary lines dependent upon monuments may be destroyed with the destruction of the monuments marking them.   To cope with the problem of replacing lost or destroyed monuments, especially in the Nile valley of Egypt where frequent floods destroyed many land markers, man invented measuring methods that would enable him to reset new monuments reasonably close to the spot occupied by the old monuments. Measurements start from some definite point, a monument, and go a fixed distance in a given direction. By relating numerous monuments to one another by measurements, a lost monument can be replaced by distance and direction from other monuments.

Land ownerships have shape, size, and location. The shape and size of a parcel of land may be defined without the aid of monuments, i.e., a square, a parallelogram, a circle, or an irregular parcel by bearings and distances. But the place where the particular shape is located is related to a fixed monument on the face of the earth. Theoretically the position of land can be defined by latitude and longitude without the aid of monuments, but, because of technical difficulties in pinpointing a particular latitude and longitude, it is rarely done. All the advancements in land location technique have not eliminated the monument as the ultimate means by which land is controlled.

In the early days in the United States *free surveys* often existed. A surveyor could start at any point, survey a selected quantity of land, monument, and describe it. He was not limited by previous ownerships or previous surveys. Today practically all boundary surveys are dependent partly or wholly upon monuments or points previously established on the earth. If a new parcel is described, it is related to existing boundaries which in turn are related somehow to a fixed monument. If a new parcel is established by survey, it is done by measurements from fixed monuments. Monuments are the backbone in relation to which land is located.

From early Colonial times down to the present, various systems have been adopted to describe real property relative to monuments, said systems being dependent upon either local laws, common laws, state laws, Colonial laws, or Federal laws. Townships, ranges, and sections of land as first defined by the Continental Congress and later enacted into Federal law represent the most widespread system used to mark and describe land within the United States. Fundamentally two methods are used: (1) metes and bounds descriptions and (2) subdivision descriptions.

3. Metes and Bounds Descriptions. The word "mete" means to measure or to assign by measure, and the word "bounds" means the boundary of the land or the limits and extent of a property. Within the broad meaning of the term "metes and bounds" it is not necessary to measure a property as implied by the word "metes." A parcel of land can be described without a single measurement being taken as: "beginning at an oak tree, blazed on the north; thence to a large boulder located on the bank of Lake Washington; thence along the lake to . . . , etc." Usually metes and bounds descriptions are described by successive courses, said courses being fixed by monuments, direction, distance, or by all three.

Within this book, those written conveyances which have junior and senior considerations will be discussed under metes and bounds descriptions. Although this classification is broad and includes types of description that are quasi-metes and bounds descriptions, the classification does form a logical division for the purpose of discussing boundary surveys. Subdivision map descriptions, although fundamentally a shorthand method of picturing a metes and bounds description, will be considered separately because of many differences in boundary location procedure.

A landowner who, by written deed and without aid of a lot and block description, conveys to another a portion of his land, must fulfill his obligation to the other person, thus creating a *senior* (buyer's) and a *junior* (seller's remainder) *deed*. If at a later date another parcel is sold, the second parcel becomes junior to the first parcel, but senior to the seller's remainder. Likewise, the third, fourth, and fifth parcels may be sold, each being senior to those parcels created after them, but junior to those parcels created prior to them. A subdivision map, filed in accordance with statute laws, causes the creation of numerous parcels of land at the moment of filing the map. Even though the lots shown on the map may be sold in sequence, none can be said to be senior to the other since all of them were created at the same moment of time by the same subdivider. A subdivision type of description, as contrasted to true or quasi-metes and bounds description, within the limits of this book, has an absence of senior and junior rights between lots within the same subdivision.

Senior rights, once formed, may be voided or eliminated by court decree or by the acts of the neighbors. A line decreed by a competent court to be the true line between neighbors is equally binding on each and excludes any idea of seniority for either party. A line agreed upon between neighbors eliminates the old line, and any seniority that might have been applicable to the old line cannot be applied to the new line.

4. Types of Metes and Bounds Conveyances. Several types of metes and bounds descriptions, as classified above, exist, some being so closely related to subdivision descriptions that they could be considered as a quasi-subdivision description.

DESCRIBED BY SUCCESSIVE BOUNDS. In the most common metes and bounds description, and the one normally considered to be the true metes and bounds descriptive, all the bounds are described in successive order, the bounds being fixed by reference to a map or document, by bearing and distance, by monuments, or by all three. The purpose of any description is to convey, by written language, a parcel of land of the exact shape, size, and location offered for sale by the grantor. Although it is desirable to use as short a description as possible, it is often necessary, when a clear intent is expressed, to use many words describing each bound. All too often a short description can alter the meaning of a deed, and a long description written by an unskilled person frequently shows conflicts among the terms of a deed. The following quasi-metes and bounds descriptions are discussed along with true metes and bounds descriptions.

STRIP CONVEYANCES AND STATIONING. In describing a road easement or right of way by a strip deed, the form "A right of way for road purposes over and across a strip of land lying 30 feet on each side of the following described center line:" is used. Generally the *stationing system*, that of starting from an arbitrary point called 0 + 00 and assigning each point on the line a station that is dependent upon its distance from the starting point, is employed. If a point is 1,327.62 feet from the arbitrary starting point, said distance being measured along the center line of the strip, the station is 13 + 27.62. Every 100 feet *along the center line*, be it on a curve or angle, is an even station; the plus number is the added distance beyond the station. The stationing system was devised for the convenience of the surveyor in note keeping and map notations. Any object along a right of way, such as a power pole, may be located by a simple note, Sta. 13 + 12.60, 30′ rt. When looking towards increasing station numbers, right is to your right. The "30′ rt." means that the pole is located 30 feet to the right and is 90° or radial from the station indicated.

CONVEYED BY A DIVISION LINE. A portion of a lot divided by a road or a natural monument is described precisely and simply by the form "all of lot 12 lying northerly of U. S. Highway 80 as it now exists" or "all of lot 12 lying southerly of Boulder Creek." Longer descriptions result from the usage of the form "all of lot 12 lying northerly of the following described line." The bearing and distance description of the line following the general statement requires many more words than the two simplified examples above.

LAND CONVEYED BY DISTANCE. The shortest quasi-metes and bounds deed is of the type "the easterly 50 feet of lot 2" as shown in Fig. 3-9. The junior deed, "all except the easterly 50 feet of lot 2," is for the remainder of the lot. This type of deed is easy to write, but it may be misinterpreted by the parties of the deed, since the 50 feet is measured so as to give the senior deed (the buyer) the maximum area whereas the junior deed has the remainder.

PROPORTIONAL CONVEYANCES. Proportional conveyances are those which convey a fractional part of the whole area as shown in Fig. 3-21. By common law, proportional conveyances are presumed to be a proportion of the area of the lot and not a proportion of the lineal measurements. Statute law can and has altered this common law rule by differently defining proportional conveyances as in sectionalized lands. By running a line from the north quarter corner to the south quarter corner of a section of land, the section is, by statute law, divided into two halves which may or may not be equal in area.

LAND CONVEYED BY EXCEPTION. Land may be conveyed by exception as "all except the easterly 50 feet of lot 2." The normal presumption is that the grantor sold the easterly 50 feet and retained the remainder for himself, but this is not always true; conveyances have been made in the reverse order, thus changing the apparent seniority.

DESCRIBED BY ACREAGE. A parcel of land described as "the south five acres of lot 7," is clearly described as conveying 5 acres; however, the direction of the division line between the two parcels is ambiguous. The ease of writing this type of description is advantageous, but the directions of the dividing line should always be defined.

"OF" DESCRIPTIONS. Legal problems that arise from descriptions using the word "of" are similar, and for the purpose of discussion they are grouped together. "The westerly 50 feet *of* lot 2," "the south 3 acres *of* lot 7," "the east one half *of* lot 9" are examples of this type. Common descriptions are shown in Fig. 1-1.

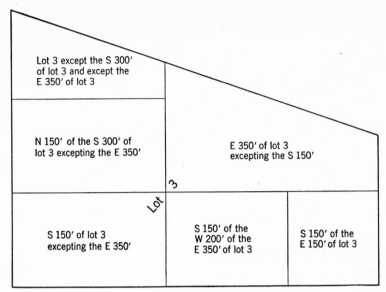

Figure 1-1.

5. Nomenclature and Units Used in Metes and Bounds Descriptions.

Deed terms commonly used in metes and bounds conveyances are best understood by examination of Fig. 1-2, by reading the glossary of deed terms given on page 253, and by the following explanations:

DIRECTION OF TRAVEL. True metes and bounds descriptions and many quasi-metes and bounds descriptions have a direction of travel. A bearing may be stated in either of two directions on a map or plat but only one can be utilized in a written perimeter description. In Fig. 1-3, starting at the point of beginning, the direction of travel is to the southeast, making the first written bearing in the description S 45° 00′ E, not N 45° 00′ W. Because the relationship of one line to another is shown by the plotting of the lines in Fig. 1-3, it is immaterial whether the bearing on the plat is written S 45° 00′ E or N 45° 00′ W.

MONUMENTS. Monuments are classified as either *natural, artificial, record,* or *legal.* Naturally occurring monuments such as rivers, lakes, oceans, bays, sloughs, cliffs, trees, hills, and large boulders are permanent objects found on the land as they were placed by nature and are usually considered controlling over *artificial monuments* (man made) such as iron stakes, wooden stakes,

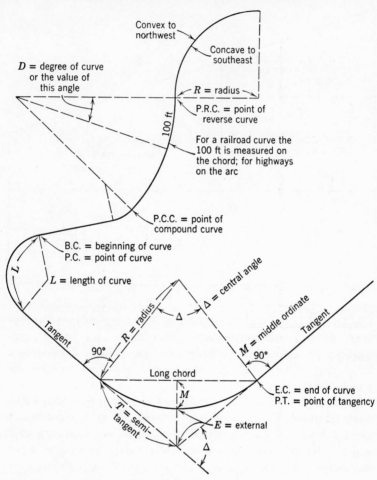

Convex to
northwest

Concave to
southeast

D = degree of curve
or the value of
this angle

R = radius

P.R.C. = point of
reverse curve

100 ft

For a railroad curve the
100 ft is measured on
the chord; for highways
on the arc

P.C.C. = point of
compound curve

B.C. = beginning of curve
P.C. = point of curve

L = length of curve

L

Tangent

Δ = central angle

R = radius

Δ

M = middle ordinate

Tangent

90°

M

90°

Long chord

T = semi-
tangent

M

E.C. = end of curve
P.T. = point of tangency

E = external

Δ

Figure 1-2.   Deed terms

rock mounds, stones and wooden fences, but, if the writings clearly
indicate a contrary intent, especially where the lines of a survey are
called for, the control might be reversed.   Some man-made monuments, because of the certainty of location, visibility, stability, and
permanence, are considered equal in rank to natural monuments.
In this classification would fall sidewalks, street paving, curbs,
wells, canals, concrete buildings, and concrete fences.

RECORD MONUMENTS OR BOUNDARIES.   These exist because of
a reference to them in a deed or legal description; thus, "to Brown's

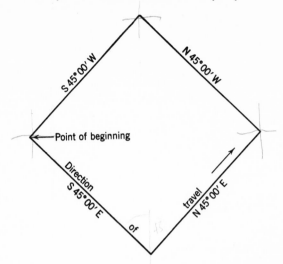

Figure 1-3.

property line" is a call for a record monument (Brown's property). Record monuments may or may not be marked upon the ground by artificial or natural monuments. Where a deed reads "to the side line of the street," the call is for the boundary of a record monument (street) which could be marked by stakes, improvements, fences, or all three, or not marked at all. A call for any record monument is a call for all the monuments, or considerations, that establish the location of the record monument. If a monument is controlling in a legal description, it is often classified as a *legal monument*. "To a stone" is a call for a legal artificial monument; "to Brown's property line" is a call for a legal record monument. The words record monument and legal monument are sometimes used synonymously.

Courts may refer to record monuments as natural monuments. The boundaries of a street are marked by man, but the dirt composing the street is naturally occurring, and, in this sense, the street is a natural monument. It is an unfortunate classification. In the order of importance of conflicting elements within deeds, natural monuments are normally considered as superior to artificial monuments. A call for a record monument, where no senior right is interfered with, is normally subordinate to a call for an artificial monument. If record monuments are classified as natural monuments, the statement that natural monuments control artificial monuments, is not exactly true.

Adjoiners, streets, and parcels of land differ from rivers, lakes, and the like, in that man marks and defines these boundary divisions. Waters and creeks always have visible boundaries, whereas a parcel of land may not be physically marked at all. A deed call for an adjoiner, is a call for a monument in the form of a parcel of land that has size, shape, and location, but there is poor foundation for classifying the monument as a natural monument. Since the limits of a parcel of land must be marked by man, why not classify the call for an adjoiner as a call for an artificial monument? Because adjoiners to a conveyance are mainly dependent upon the record for their existence and because they may have invisible lines marking their limits, the classification "record monument" is preferred. The word "natural monument" as used herein is exclusive of record monuments.

PROPERTIES OF MONUMENTS. A good monument should possess the quality of being easily visible, certain of identification, stable in location, permanent in character, and nondependent upon measurement for its location. An artificial monument possesses the qualities of a natural monument to a lesser degree. Thus, a stake placed in the ground will rust or rot with time and is less permanent than a naturally occurring large boulder. A stake is easier to move than a boulder and is therefore less stable. The visibility of record monuments is wholly dependent upon the natural or artificial monuments (fences, stakes, cultivation, plantings, and the like) that mark the limits of the record monument.

STRAIGHT LINES. A line in a description is assumed to be the shortest horizontal distance between the points called for unless the contrary is indicated by the writings. To be absolutely correct, a straight line curves with the surface of the earth; but the curvature is so slight that it is not considered in legal descriptions. A line to be identified must have a definition of its direction and length. *Free lines* are not terminated by an adjoiner or monument as "beginning at a 2-inch iron pipe; thence N 60° 00′ W, 200.00 feet." If the same phrase were reworded "beginning at a 2-inch iron pipe; thence N 60° 00′ W, 200.00 feet to a blazed sycamore tree," the terminus of the line is fixed by the tree; the line is not free. Many of the lines described in deeds are dependent upon monuments and are not free lines.

A bearing quoted for a line defines it as a straight line. If a line is defined by monuments, without bearing or distance, the words "in a straight line" or "in a direct line" are often added to emphasize the presumed fact that the line is straight.

DIRECTION. As commonly practiced in this country, direction is defined by either a call for monuments or a bearing; but azimuth, deflection angle or coordinates may be used. If a deed is written "commencing at a blazed sycamore tree located approximately 100

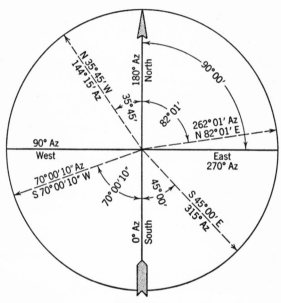

Figure 1-4.

feet west of Jones' well; thence to a blazed white oak, etc.," the direction is clearly defined. It is very desirable to quote the bearing of the line for plotting purposes, but it is not essential to the legality of the conveyance. Bearings are always read in degrees and minutes (plus seconds if fractions of a minute are involved) from the *north* point or from the *south* point. *Never* from the east or west points. See Fig. 1-4. The direction of a line is dependent upon which end of the line you are standing; thus, on a northwesterly line the direction would be SE if you were at the northerly terminus of a line, whereas it would be NW if you were at the southerly terminus of the same line. On a map it is immaterial which bearing you write since the drawing shows the relationship of one line to another; but in a written description the exact direction of travel of the bounds must be stated.

MAGNETIC BEARINGS. Most early boundary surveys within the United States were made utilizing the magnetic compass. Today, the transit or theodolite has superseded the compass, but, because of the numerous early magnetic compass surveys, it is necessary to understand the earth's magnetic field.

The north pole and the magnetic north pole are not in the same position. Within the United States magnetic north varies from 24 degrees east of north to 22 degrees west of north, a difference of 46 degrees. *Magnetic declination* or variation of the compass is the angle between true north and magnetic north. Declination changes with time. The amount of change within a one-year period is called the *annual change*. Unfortunately, the changes are not smooth, but are subject to *daily variations* of a more or less systematic pattern. Within any one day the daily fluctuations can be expected to be 7 minutes more or less, and in magnetic disturbances (called *magnetic storms*) the variation may be more than 1 degree.

Since surveyors compasses are graduated to half degrees, they can, at best, be read within 5 to 10 minutes' accuracy. This combined with daily fluctuations of the declination and potential magnetic storms illustrates the inaccuracy of compass surveys. An angular error equivalent to an error of 1 foot in 300 feet can be expected in most compass surveys.

DEFLECTION ANGLE. Most angles are turned by the deflection method, that of sighting on a given line and turning the angle to another line; normally the deflected angle is then converted into bearings. In some descriptions the deed author quotes the deflected angle rather than determining a basis of bearings and computing the bearings from the angles turned. A deed reading "commencing at the southwest corner of section 10; thence easterly 200 feet along the southerly line of said section; thence 20° 00′ to the right, 200.00 feet; thence . . ." means that the new line leaves the section line in a direction that is 20° 00′ to the right as you are looking in the direction of deed travel. To avoid possible ambiguity, the form "thence 20° 00′ to the right from the prolongation of the last course, 200.00 feet" is better.

AZIMUTH. Azimuth as used in surveying is the angle measured

clockwise from the meridian (either due north or due south) to the line being described. The armed services commonly use north as the line of origin, but in property line surveying the general custom has been to adopt south as the reference meridian as shown in Fig. 1-4. If south is used, 0° azimuth is S 0° E, 190° azimuth is N 10° E, and 280° azimuth is S 80° E. In a conveyance using such a system it is imperative that the assumed zero line be clearly defined, otherwise ambiguity results.

Strictly speaking any straight line other than a true north line has a changing azimuth or bearing as you travel along the line. This is caused by the fact that azimuth or bearing is determined by turning an angle from the described line to a true north line. Since all true north lines converge towards the north pole, the angle turned at each point along a line is being turned to a true north line which is not parallel with any other true north line at any other point on the line. The differences in bearings at the terminus of the ends of straight lines within a local area are insignificant, and all deeds are assumed to refer to one spot (usually the point of beginning) for their basis of bearings. On large geodetic maps and government triangulation maps, because of the vastness of the area surveyed, corrections are given so that the true bearing at the point considered is known. To avoid the confusion of changing bearings on any straight line, the *Lambert coordinate system* has been adopted wherein, within a definite zone, all bearings are referred to true north as defined at one point within the zone. Within any one legal description that uses azimuth or bearings, the assumption is that, unless the contrary can be proved, all bearings and azimuths are referred to the same basis at the same point and that the bearing of deed lines are constant.

COORDINATES. Any point can be defined with respect to any other fixed assumed point by stating the distances north, east, south, and west from the reference point. If the southwest corner of a section were assumed to be zero coordinates and the northeast corner of the section were found to be 5,281.62 feet north and 5,271.68 feet east of the assumed zero point, the coordinates of the northeast corner would be 5,281.62N, 5,271.68E. Likewise, if the southeast corner of the section were 3.17 feet south and 5,279.81 feet east of the zero point, its coordinates would be 3.17S, 5,279.81E. Coordinates given for any two points completely define the direction and distance between the two points and also define the direction and distance of each point from the assumed zero point. By adopting the same zero point for all surveys within a given region or zone, as in the *Lambert system,* all surveys can be related to one another, thus eliminating many mapping problems.

Coordinate calculations are based upon the assumption that the earth is flat. Within a limited area such an assumption introduces minor errors that do not exceed the limits of accuracy attained by ordinary measurements. A simple illustration will clarify the reason. An orange peel, a sphere, cannot be flattened without tearing, compressing, or folding the skin. Likewise, the surface of the earth cannot be represented on a flat plane surface, such as a

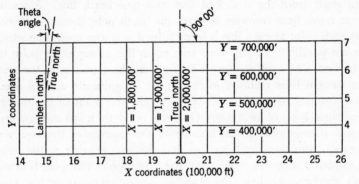

Figure 1-5. Lambert coordinate system

map, without distortion. A long narrow strip of orange peel can be flattened with a minimum of distortion. If coordinate systems are limited to long narrow strips of land, a minimum of error results.

LAMBERT AND MERCATOR GRIDS. Many states have established long narrow zones wherein a coordinate system is fixed by statute law. If the system is narrow in a north-south direction, it is called a *Lambert grid.* If it is narrow in an east-west direction, it is called a *transverse Mercator grid.* By limiting the width of the coordinate system to 158 miles, the limits of error due to curvature distortion can be confined to 1 in 10,000 or about 1 foot in 2 miles, well within the limits of accuracy of ordinary property surveys. The state of Tennessee has one Lambert zone; New York has three transverse Mercator zones and one Lambert zone (Long Island).

Illustrated in Fig. 1-5 is a Lambert coordinate system showing squares with 100,000 feet to a side. A network of parallel straight lines, intersecting at right angles, is called a *grid*. The *central meridian,* generally located in the middle of the area of the grid, is the true north-south line with which all grid lines are made parallel or to which all grid lines are at right angles. Since all true north lines converge towards the earth's poles, the central meridian is the *only true astronomic north line.* The central meridian forms the *Y axis* of the grid, and the line at 90° to the assumed zero point on the *Y* axis is called the *X* axis. To avoid negative numbers, the central meridian is assigned a large number such as 2,000,000 feet.

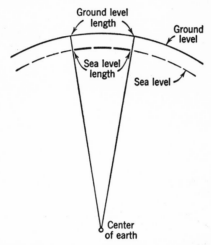

Figure 1-6. Lambert distances are reduced to sea level distances

Lambert bearings, except on the central meridian, are not relative to astronomic north. The difference between a true north line and the Lambert grid line is called the *theta* (θ) angle, see Fig. 1-5. On the transverse Mercator grid, the angle is called the delta alpha ($\Delta\alpha$) angle. As a survey extends farther and farther from the central meridian, the theta angle becomes greater. A deed description based upon a Lambert bearing must be clearly defined as such, otherwise true north may be implied.

In the Lambert or Mercator systems, horizontal distances are reduced to sea level. This correction, as shown in Fig. 1-6, is necessary because of the spherical nature of the surface of the earth.

CURVES. For the defining of a curve in a description, at least two elements of the curve must be stated and in addition (1) the relationship of the curve to the previous bound, (2) the direction of the curve, and (3) the direction of travel of the curve must also be stated.   Figure 1-2 shows common curves and their relationship to one another.   The direction of concavity of a curve is defined by the direction of a line drawn from the mid-point of the arc of a curve to the center point of the circle of the curve; it may be defined as easterly, southerly, southeasterly, etc.   The direction of travel along a curve can be stated to the right or left as indicated

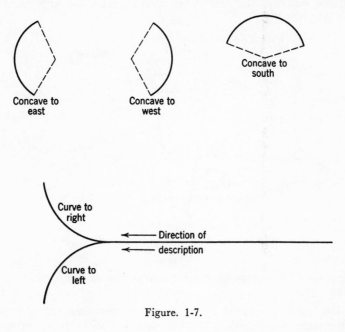

Concave to
east

Concave to
west

Concave to
south

Curve to
right

Direction of

description

Curve to
left

Figure. 1-7.

in Fig. 1-7, or by stating the direction as "southeasterly along the curve," or by stating a number of directions as "southeasterly, southerly, and southwesterly along the curve."   A statement that a line is tangent to a curve, i.e., it is 90° to the terminal radial line of a curve, or a definition of the bearing of a line and also a definition of the bearing of the radial line at the point of contact of the curve and the line, clearly indicates the relationship of the curve and the line.

In deeds only two curve elements need be given, but at least three are normally given: namely, radius, central angle (called delta), and length of curve (see Fig. 1-2).   Length of curve in most deeds is a computed quantity depending upon the given central angle and the radius. Rarely in metes and bounds descriptions are the middle ordinate, external, long chord and tangent used, but on plats they are more frequently seen. The *degree of curve,* often given on railroad right-of-way plats, is defined as the central angle of a curve subtended by a *100-foot chord* on the said curve. Along highways the degree of curve is usually, but not always, defined as the central angle subtended by a *100-foot arc* of said curve (see Fig. 1-2).

TABLE I

1 chain	= 66 feet
1 chain	= 100 links
40 chains	= ½ mile
80 chains	= 1 mile
1 chain	= 4 rods
1 chain	= 4 poles
1 chain	= 4 perches
1 link	= 0.66 foot
1 rod	= 16½ feet
4 rods	= 1 chain
1 mile	= 5,280 feet
1 mile	= 80 chains
1 acre	= 43,560 square feet
1 acre	= 10 square chains
1 vara av.	= 33.372 inches (Florida)
1 vara av.	= 33.333 inches (Texas)
1 arpent	= 0.8507 acres (Arkansas and Missoui)
1 arpent	= 0.84625 acres (Mississippi, Alabama, and Florida)
Side of a square arpent	= 192.50 feet (Arkansas and Missouri)
Side of a square arpent	= 191.994 feet (Mississippi, Alabama, and Florida)

PARALLEL LINES. Parallel lines are equal distances apart, said distance being measured at right angles to the lines or on radial lines of curves. Curves to be parallel are concentric (having the same center of a circle). In descriptions, parallel with a bound means parallel with all parts of the bound, be it curved, angular, or straight lines. A line parallel with a creek is parallel with all the bends and angles of the creek and is an equal distance from all the bends and angles unless otherwise indicated.

UNITS OF MEASUREMENT. Table I lists the common units used in deed description within the United States. The early colonial unit of linear measure was the 66-foot chain invented by Edmund Gunter, an English astronomer of the seventeenth century. Many of the early grants made by the English crown were in terms of "poles," four poles being equivalent to one chain. In later usage the term "pole" gradually assumed the name "perch" then "rod." Because of this early usage of the chain, the Continental Congress logically adopted the chain as the standard unit of land measure. One acre, being 10 square chains or 43,560 square feet, is used as the standard unit of area measurements.

A large portion of the public domain was made up of lands acquired from Spain, Mexico, and France by cession and purchase. Before the acquisition of those areas by the United States, many land grants using foreign measurements were made to private individuals, and such land grants, when duly authenticated and confirmed, were segregated from the lands subject to disposal. In the southwest and in Florida the Spanish and Mexican unit of length, called the *vara,* is equivalent to approximately 33 inches. The French crown grants prior to the Louisiana purchase were expressed in terms of the *"arpent"* which is an area unit equal to approximately 0.85 acre. The *arpent frontage* unit is the length of the side of 1 square arpent or approximately 192.5 feet. Owing to a lack of exact standards, the length of the vara and the arpent differed in various localities as can be noted from the average values shown in Table I.*

In modern subdivision maps and deeds the unit of a foot and decimal parts of a foot is used. Chains have become confined almost exclusively to sectionalized land.

6. Tax Deeds

TAX STATEMENTS. The purpose of a tax statement is to identify the land being taxed. Often the tax assessor shortens a lengthy metes and bounds description, thus avoids paper work, yet retains sufficient to identify the land. Since tax statements and tax deeds are not complete deeds, they should not be used as a basis for a survey or a legal document.

ABBREVIATED DESCRIPTIONS. Lengthy metes and bounds descriptions would occupy excessive space on tax bills if it were not for abbreviations devised for that purpose. See Table II. The following deed description illustrates the usefulness of this method:

Abbreviated: All that por of lot 40 of L M C acc map thrf #346 fld O of Rec of S D C Cal m p daf: beg at a pt on Nly li of lot 40 dist thon 140.84′ Ely fr N W Cor of sd lot th S 42° 44′ E 241.26′ th N 89°

* See page 465 of the *Manual of Surveying Instructions, 1947.*

TABLE II

According	acc	Continuing	contg
Account	acct	Convey	conv
Acre	ac	Corner	cor
Addition	add	County	co
Additional	addl	County and city	C & C
Adjacent	adjac	County Surveyor	Co Surv
Adjoining	adjn	Court	ct
Agreement	agmt	Cover or covering	cov
Along	alg	Curve	cur
Amount	amt		
Angle	ang	Decree	dec
Angle point	a/p	Dedicated	ded
Approved	appvd	Deed	d or dd
Arbitrary	arb	Deeds	dds
At	@	Degree	deg or °
Avenue	ave	Describe	desc
Azimuth	Az	Described as follows	daf
		Description	desct
Before	bef	Distant	dist
Begin or beginning	beg	District	dist
Beginning at a point	b a p	Division	div
Beginning of curve	B C	Document	doc
Between	bet		
Block	blk	Each	ea
Book	bk	Easement	eamt
Boulevard	blvd	East	E
Boundary	bdy	Easterly	Ely
Bounded	bded	Entitled	entld
		Escrow	esc
Center	cen	Establish	estab
Center angle	Δ or c/a	Except	exc
Center line	c/l	Exception	excpn
Certain	cert	Exceptions	excpns
Chains	chs	Excepting	excptg
City	cy	Extended	extd
Commence	com	Extension	extn
Commencing	comg	Egress	egr
Commencing at a point	cap		
Common	comm	Filed	fld
Company	co	Following	fol
Concave	conc	Foot, Feet	ft
Condition	cond	From	fr
Consideration	consid		
Contain or contained	contd	Government	govt
Contains	conts	Grant deed	gt dd
Containing	contg	Granted	gtd
Continue	contu	Grantee	gtee

TABLE II. (*Continued*)

Grantor	gtr	North	N
Guarantee	gtee	Northeast	NE
		Northeasterly	NELY
Having	hav	Northerly	NLY
Herein described	HD	Northwest	NW
Highway	hwy	Northwesterly	NWLY
Improvement	imp	Official	offcl
Include or including	incl	Official records	O R
Included	incld	Original	orig
Inclusive	incl	Other	oth
Information	info	Other property	OP
Instruction	instr		
Instrument	instr	Page	pg
Intersection	inter	Paid	pd
Intersection with	inter/w	Parallel	para
Ingress	ingr	Parallel with	p/w
		Parcel	par
Joint	jt	Part	pt
Jointly	jtly	Partial	ptl
Joint tenancy	J T	Particularly	part
Judgment	jdg	Parties	pties
		Partition	partn
Known	kn	Party	pty
Known as	kn as	Point	pt
		Point of beginning	pob
Land	ld	Point of commencement	poc
Lease	lse	Point compound curve	P C C
Lessee	lsee	Point of curve	P C
Licensed Surveyor	L S	Point of tangency	P T
Line	li	Point reverse curve	P R C
Lis pendens	l p	Portion	por
Long chord	L C	Possession	possn
Lying	lyg	Preliminary	prelim
		Premises	prem
Married man	m/m	Principal	prin
Married woman	m/w	Prolong	prol
Mean high tide line	m h t l	Prolongation	prol
Measured	meas	Property	prop
Mentioned	ment	Public	pub
Metes and bounds	M & B	Purpose	ppse
Miscellaneous	misc		
Month	mo		
More or less	m or l	Quarter	¼
More particularly	m p	Quarterly	¼ly
Memorandum	memo	Quiet title	Q T
Mortgage	mtg	Quit claim	Q C
Necessary	nec	Quit claim deed	Q C D

TABLE II. (*Continued*)

Radius	R or rad	State	st
Railroad	rr	Subdivision	sub
Railway	ry	Subject	subj
Rancho	rho	Successor	succ
Range	R	Survey	sur
Record	rec		
Record of survey	R of S	Tangent	tan
Regarding	re	Tax deed	tx dd
Regular	reg	Tax sale	tx s
Report	rep	Terminate	term
Reservation	resvn	Thence	th
Reserve	res	Thereof	thrf
Reserving	resvg	Thereon	thon
Resolution	resol	Therefore	thfre
Restrict	restr	Through	thru
Resubdivision	resub	Together	tog
Reversion	rev	Together with	tog/wi
Right	rt	Torrens	tor
Right angles	ra	Township	T or tp
Right of way	r/w	Tract	tr
Road	rd	True point of beginning	tpob
Road survey	R S	Trust deed	TD
Running	run		
		Under	und
Said	sd	Undivided	und
Second	" or 2nd		
Section	S or sec	Vacated	vac
Series	ser	Volume	vol
Signature	sig		
South	S	West	W
Southeast	SE	Westerly	WLY
Southeasterly	SELY	Which or whence	wh
Southerly	SLY	With	wi
Southwest	SW		
Southwesterly	SWLY		
Stamps	stps	Year	yr

01' E 37.5' th to the rt alg a tang cur whose rad is 87.03' a dist of 76.72' th N 47° 53' W 241.46' to a pt on the Nly li of sd lot 40 dist thon N 84° 14' 30" W 97.25' fr the NW Cor of lot 46 of D W Tr th Wly alg the Nly li of Lot 40 to p o b.

Translation: All that portion of lot 40 of La Mesa Colony according to the map thereof number 346 filed in the office of the Recorder of San Diego County California, more particularly described as follows:

Beginning at a point on the northerly line of lot 40, distant thereon 140.84 feet easterly from the northwest corner of said lot; thence S 42° 44' E a distance of 241.26 feet; thence N 89° 01' E a distance of 37.5

feet; thence to the right, along a tangent curve whose radius is 87.03 feet, a distance of 76.72 feet; thence N 47° 53' W a distance of 241.46 feet to a point on the northerly line of said lot 40 distant thereon N 84° 14' 30" W, 97.25 feet from the northwest corner of lot 46 of the De Witt Tract; thence westerly along the northerly line of lot 40 to the point of beginning.

An examination of the original document, from which the above was abbreviated, reveals that the assessor in shortening the deed changed the point of beginning and eliminated a number of courses from a distant starting point. If a surveyor were to use the above tax deed to locate the land, he would find the land in a different position from that found by a surveyor using the true deed.

SUBDIVISIONS

7. Subdivision Description Definition.

Within the limits of this book a discussion of subdivision descriptions will include all those descriptions which do not have senior rights between adjacent lots forming a part of the same platted map. Normally a subdivision is made by a subdivider or court who (1) causes a map or plat to be made showing the divisions of land and how they were monumented and (2) causes several lots to be created simultaneously at the moment of filing a map with or by the governing agency or court in compliance with existing laws.

Sectionalized land, subdivision maps, and court proceedings in partition fall within the above classifications. From the standpoint of the scrivener, subdivision maps offer the simplest means of describing land since they present the maximum of information and the minimum of words. "Lot 40 of La Mesa Colony, according to Map 346 as filed in the Office of the Recorder, San Diego County, Calif." or "Sec. 16, T15N, R20E, Principal Meridian" or "Lot 2 according to the partition map filed in Superior Court Case 17632" form complete descriptions of land that can be identified from all other parcels of land. Because of the simplicity of the title wording, it is not to be assumed that a lot and block description of a section of land is easier to survey than is a parcel of land described by a metes and bounds conveyance. Certainty and ease of location are totally unrelated to the length of the deed describing the land.

From the viewpoint of a surveyor or scrivener, the principal difference between a subdivision description (lot and block description) and a metes and bounds description lies in the second condition given above; i.e., all lots within a subdivision simultaneously exist at the moment of filing the map. Owing to this, each lot in a subdivision has a proportionate interest in any excess or deficiency within that subdivision. In metes and bounds descriptions lots are created in successive order so that a senior and junior deed exists with prior rights being granted to the senior or first-created deed.

Most subdivision laws require that, previous to filing a map, survey markers must be established on the land. Many older maps, made before the passage of such laws, were "office maps" made from the record without benefit of survey. In defining the word "subdivision," survey is not an essential consideration.

8. Federal Government Subdivisions. The partitioning of the public domain into townships and sections were true subdivisions made by a set of rules differing from those employed by the various states. All federal sectionalized land was surveyed and monumented in accordance with the rules imposed by Federal laws, state laws to the contrary being void. Sectionalized land did not provide for roads. For street location, a special problem not dealt with in the *United States Manual of Surveying Instructions,* common law and statutes as discussed in Chapter 3 must be relied upon.

With the exception of the original 13 states, Vermont, Maine, Kentucky, Tennessee, West Virginia, and Texas, most of the lands of the United States were owned by the Federal Government. The first prime subdivisions of government lands were made in about the year 1785 when the government divided parts of Ohio into townships and sections. As later surveys were made, the boundaries of former land grants, which were not vested in the government, were established. Land grants thus became dependent upon the Federal subdivisions records for evidence of boundary location.

9. Private Subdivisions under State Laws. Except federally owned land, subdivisions of parcels of land are regulated by state laws; but the laws have been changed from time to time. The title interest of a person owning a lot within a subdivision must be viewed with respect to the laws in force at the time the map was made.

Early subdivisions executed by private interests were poorly regulated by law, and any sheet of paper presented as a subdivision map to the land or recorder's office was filed upon payment of the filing fee. Occasionally, maps failed to show street widths, lot sizes, and what was being subdivided. The map of La Jolla Park was compiled with undimensioned lots and undimensioned curved streets laid out with a varying radius french curve.   On old maps, rarely was a statement made by the surveyor or engineer describing what monuments he found or set.   Being ignorant of what markers were originally set, how could a surveyor retrace a subdivision?   Most modern subdivisions are regulated by rigid laws which have corrected many of the conditions mentioned above.   Because of numerous problems arising from poorly made maps, many court decrees have been rendered outlining common laws.   These will be discussed in a later chapter.

10. Proceedings in Partition.   Tracts of land created by court decree in proceedings in partition are considered similar to subdivisions in that no junior or senior grant exists.

SECTIONALIZED LANDS

11. Scope of Work.   *The Manual of Instructions for the Survey of the Public Lands of the United States,** published by the Department of Interior, gives a complete discussion of the methods and instruments used in the survey of the public domain.   In addition a small pamphlet entitled "Restoration of Lost or Obliterated Corners and Subdivisions of Sections"† gives a brief discussion of restoration procedure.   Any publication covering the subject of deeds and their interpretation must of necessity include much of the material given in the above book and pamphlet.   This book does not include anything pertaining to the usage of instruments or the types of instruments used by the government, but it covers the original survey procedure sufficiently to enable correct restoration work and intelligent deed interpretation.

12. Summary of Present Procedure.   Not all government subdivisions were made in an identical manner, but the general features of rectangular surveys were followed as closely as possible.   Referring to Fig. 1–8 an *initial point* is established, a *base line* is extended east and west on a true parallel of latitude, and a *principal meridian* is extended due north and south.   The land, by present practice, is next subdivided into semirectangular blocks 24 miles on a side less convergence of the meridians or, by former practice, into semi-

* Hereinafter cited as *Manual.*

† Published by the Department of the Interior.   Hereinafter cited as "Restoration of Lost Corners."

rectangular blocks 30 miles, 36 miles or more to a side. Each rectangular block is next divided, checkerboard fashion, into smaller blocks, called townships, of 6 miles to a side less convergence. Townships are then subdivided into 36 squares, 1 mile to a side, with the northern and western tiers absorbing errors due to measurement and convergence.

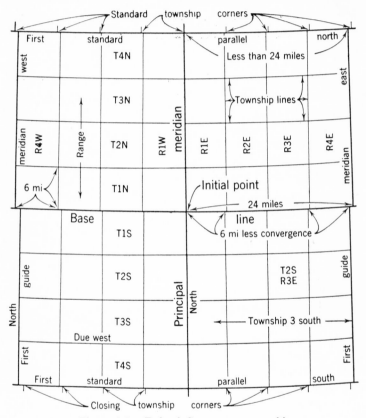

Figure 1-8.   Federal Government townships

13. Principal Meridian (See Fig. 1-8).   The principal meridian is a line extended from a selected *initial point* due north, due south, or both on a true meridian.   At half-mile intervals regular quarter corners and section corners are established alternately; at 6-mile intervals *township corners* are set; at intersections with meanderable bodies of water, *meander corners* are placed.

14. Base Line. (See Fig. 1-8). From the initial point the base line is run due east and due west on a true parallel of latitude and is marked by monuments set for quarter, section, township, and meander corners. The base line, being a true parallel of lattitude, is a curved line, and, when retracing it, the surveyor must re-run a curved line. In the early surveys where a compass was used to run the base lines, disregarding errors, the compass as used would result in a curved line. Present-day practice calls for surveying a straight line and then correcting to a curved line by the tangent offset or secant method or by using frequent observations with the solar transit to continually correct to a curved line.

15. Standard Parallels. (See Fig. 1-8). Standard parallels or correction lines are surveyed at intervals of 24 miles north or south from the initial point. As on the principal meridian, quarter, section, township, and meander corners are established at proper intervals along these curved lines. In older practice, intervals of 30, 36, or more miles between parallels were permitted, and, for any local area, the procedure used is determinable from the original field notes. Standard parallels are numbered and named in the following manner: the first standard parallel north, the second standard parallel north, the first standard parallel south, etc. Occasionally new standard parallels are necessary in older areas; and such parallels are given special names such as fifth auxiliary standard parallel north or Cedar Creek correction line.

16. Guide Meridians. Guide meridians are normally extended north from the base line, or standard parallel, at every fourth township line (24 miles) and are terminated by setting a closing corner at the intersection of the guide meridian with the next standard parallel or base line to the north. All meridians converge towards the north pole at a rate dependent upon the latitude of the particular township; thus, meridians in Alaska converge much more rapidly than do meridians in southern United States. Although guide meridians have identical bearings, i.e., due north, they are not parallel as can be seen in Fig. 1-8 where the first guide meridian east, initiated 24 miles east of the principal meridian and run due north, will intersect the base line at a point less than 24 miles east of the initial point. While guide meridians are being run, corners are set at intervals of half miles for quarter and section corners and at 6 miles for township corners; errors due to measurement are placed in the last half mile. To insure that closing corners are correctly set on the standard parallels, the parallels are re-run between the nearest standard corners located to the east and west. Measurements are recorded to the nearest corner.

Occasionally, when new surveys are initiated adjoining old surveys, especially where guide meridians were 30 or 36 miles apart by the older rules, auxiliary guide meridians must be run and a local name assigned, such as Grass Valley Guide Meridian.

With the establishment of the base line, principal meridian, standard parallels, and guide meridians and the setting of monuments on these lines, the controlling lines for a rectangular system inclosing an area of 24 miles north and south and 24 miles east and west, less convergence, are completed.

17. Township Exteriors within Guide Meridians and Standard Parallels. After the establishment of blocks of land 24 miles on a side, less convergence, townships or blocks of land 6 by 6 miles, less the convergence, are subdivided.

In the quadrangle southeasterly of the base line and principal meridian as shown in Fig. 1-8, the point of beginning of the regular survey would be at the township corner located on the first standard parallel south and 6 miles east of the principal meridian. From this point of beginning a true north line is run, setting corners at half-mile intervals and at meanderable bodies of water, for a distance of 6 miles, where a temporary township corner is established. Next a random line is run due west, with correction for curvature, and necessary temporary stakes are set at half-mile intervals. At the intersection with the principal meridian, the falling and closing distances to the township corner are noted. If errors are within acceptable limits, the true township line connecting township corners is computed and permanent corners are set on the true line opposite the temporary stakes. All the shortages caused by convergence of the meridians and errors of measurements are placed in the last half mile to the west. Next a line is run 6 miles north from the newly established township corner, then 6 miles west to the principal meridian, and corrected back on the true line. This procedure is followed until the closing 6 miles are run. Regular section and quarter corners are established on this last line at half-mile intervals until an intersection with the base line is established and a closing corner set. To assure the closing corner being on the base line, the base line is re-run from the nearest standard corner to the east and west of the line, and the falling distance to the nearest corner is noted.   All the errors due to measurement are placed in the last half mile.

The salient points for those primarily concerned with restoration surveys to note are: (1) Township corners between standard parallels and guide meridians are set by cross ties from four directions.   (2) Along the township line, quarter and section corners other than township corners are placed on a single line without

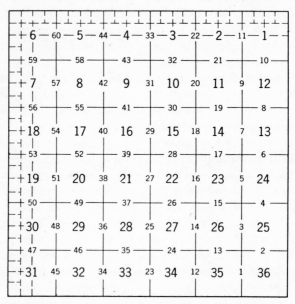

Figure 1-9.   Subdivision of townships.   Lines are surveyed in the numerical order indicated

cross ties.   (3) Errors due to measurements and convergence are placed in the western half mile of the township lines.   (4) Errors due to measurement are placed in the north half-mile closing upon the standard parallel or base line.

18. Subdivision of Townships.   Townships are normally subdivided into sections by surveying the lines in the numerical order indicated in Fig. 1-9.   Line 1, the west side of Section 36, is run by commencing at the previously set section corner common to sections 35 and 36 and running parallel with the east boundary of the township, setting a quarter-corner at one-half mile and a section corner at 1 mile.   Most section lines were established under the

older principle which stated that section lines are to be run due
north rather than parallel with the east township line.   Line 2 is
first run as a random line parallel with the south township line and
then corrected by running back on a true line between the two
section corners.   The measured length and corrected bearing of
line 2 is recorded, and a quarter corner is set at the mid-point on
the true straight line.   Lines 3, 4, and up to 10 are run in a similar
manner.   Line 11 is run parallel with the east township line by
planting a temporary quarter-corner at 40 chains, noting the falling
from the previously set section corner on the township line, correcting the line back, and planting a quarter corner on a true line
connecting the section corners.   All the error due to measurement
is placed in the last half mile with the amount noted in the field
book.   If the township is adjacent to and south of a standard
parallel, the closing section corner on the standard parallel must be
set.   This is done by re-running the standard parallel, placing the
closing corner at the intersection of the standard parallel with the
section line, and noting the falling to the nearest standard corner.
Rows of sections are successively surveyed westward in the above
manner until the last two rows are reached where random lines are
run both east and west.   Line 45 in Fig. 1-9 is run parallel with
the easterly boundary of the township, and corners are planted at
40 and 80 chains.   Line 46 is run east on a random line and back
on a true line planting the quarter-corner at the mid-point.   Line
47 is run west on a random line and corrected back on a true line.
The north quarter corner of section 31 is set 40 chains exactly from
the section corner common to sections 29, 30, 31, and 32, and all
errors due to measurement and closure are placed in the last westerly half mile.   Successive sections are surveyed in the last two
rows by continuing north, then east, then west, then east, then
north until all the sections are surveyed.   In the last line, 60, the
quarter corner is planted at 40 chains on a true line between section corners, and the errors due to measurements are placed in the
last half mile.   If, during the survey of the sections, meanderable
bodies of water are encountered, meander corners are set at the
points of intersection of the section lines with the shore of the water.
Meander lines are run around bodies of water to facilitate plotting.

Upon re-establishing sections of land, the surveyor is to follow
the footsteps of the original surveyor.   To aid in doing this the
following original instructions for *regularly surveyed* townships

should be carefully noted: (1) All section corners within a *regular* township are cross-tied from four directions. (2) Sections 1 to 5 inclusive have an irregular measurement in the northerly half mile. (3) Sections 7, 18, 19, 30, and 31 all have irregular measurements in the westerly half mile. (4) Section 6 has irregular measurements in the north and west half mile (see Fig. 1-10).

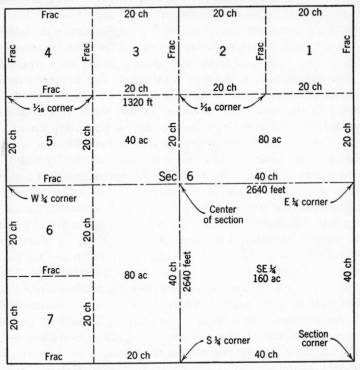

Figure 1-10. Section 6 has fractional measurements of more or less than 20 chains on lines marked "Frac"

(5) All quarter corners were set on a straight line connecting section corners. (6) Meander corners were set on all section lines at the edge of bodies of water. (7) Where the township closes on a standard parallel, the north quarter corners of sections 1 to 6 were normally not set.

From time to time in the past, parts of townships have been surveyed under special instructions in a manner differing from the regular procedure outlined above. An examination of the original field notes will reveal the exact methods used by the original surveyor.

19. Resurveys. Land owned by the government and once subdivided may be resubdivided by the government at any time in accordance with the manner prescribed by law. In the event of a resubdivision of a township two plats exist, one showing the original survey and the second showing the resurvey. Where an entryman patented a parcel of land by the original township plat, no resurvey or retracement is supposed to be executed so as to impair the bona fide rights or claims of the entryman. Usually the entryman's land is surveyed from the original markers and given a tract number, whereas the balance of the township, owned by the government, is resurveyed in accordance with the present rules of rectangular subdivisions. Unfortunately the government has not protected the bona fide rights of the patentee in every case. Frequently the tract designations do not correspond to the location shown on the original survey.

20. Defective Boundaries Encountered in Resurveys. Upon resurveying the boundaries of an older survey to initiate a new survey, defective conditions of the older survey are not incorporated into the new surveys. Defective conditions may be caused by alignment, measurement, or both. Where a new township is to be surveyed and it is found that the southerly line is defective in measurement only, new corners set at half-mile intervals will apply to the sections to the north and the old corners with irregular measurements will apply to the sections to the south. Double sets of corners may thus occur. Likewise double sets of corners may occur on the easterly, northerly, or westerly boundaries. Where the easterly or southerly boundary of a township is defective in its alignment, a new sectional guide meridian or sectional correction line is run as shown in Fig. 1-11.

21. Older Surveys and Irregular Procedure. In older surveys the procedure varied from the above, and the resurveys will vary accordingly. The old statute law "townships shall be subdivided into sections by running through the same, each way, parallel lines at the end of every two miles" is quite different from the present practice of running the lines every mile. As pointed out previously, standard parallels and guide meridians were run at 30-mile, 36-mile, or greater intervals, depending upon the instructions applying at the time. At one time two section corners were set where by present practice only one is allowed. Double corners existed on the west and north boundaries of the townships before about 1836 because of the rule that section lines were not required to meet the existing corners on the west and north side of the township. Such section corners set at the time when the original township lines were run would apply only to the sections north and west of the

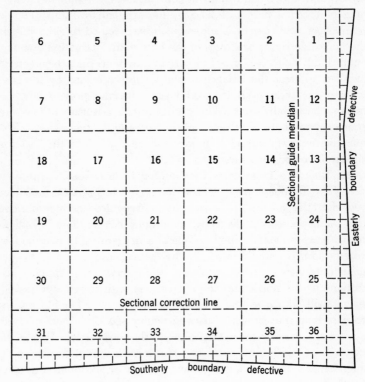

Figure 1-11.   Correction lines

township line. Examination of the original Federal Government notes predicates the proper procedure for retracing.

A review of all the special instructions issued for the survey of the public domain could not be given in a book of this type, nor is it necessary. Whenever a survey is made of a section of land, the surveyor must examine the original notes to determine the type and kinds of monuments set by the original surveyor. At such time the surveyor can note any irregular procedure and be governed accordingly in his resurvey work.

Occasional surveys were completed under the former law, "whenever, in the opinion of the President, a departure from the ordinary method of surveying any land on any river, lake, bayou, or watercourse would promote the public interest, he may direct the surveyor-general in whose district such land is situated, and where the change is intended to be made, to cause the lands thus situated to be surveyed in tracts of two acres in width, fronting on any river, bayou, lake, or water-course, and running back the depth of forty acres; which tracts of land so surveyed shall be offered for sale entire, instead of in half quarter-sections, and in the usual manner and on the same terms in all respects as the other public lands of the United States."* Before making resurveys of such parcels, the surveyor must obtain copies of all the special instructions that were given at the time and copies of the field notes.

Special statutes provided that in the State of California and the State of Nevada, departure from the rectangular system is permissible.†

22. Magnetic Compass. Until about 1902 the public land surveys were made with the magnetic compass; after that date surveys were made with instruments provided with the accessories necessary to determine the true meridian without reference to the magnetic needle (*Manual 1902*).

The magnetic compass is now recognized as an instrument of low precision and very unreliable under certain circumstances. Before the discontinuance of the compass, surveys were extended into the iron ore belt of Michigan. Many local areas are known to deflect the needle as much as 10 to 20 degrees with resultant distorted sections.

23. Field Notes. At the time the public domain was surveyed the original surveyors kept field notes which described the terrain, the monuments set, the lines run, and the general land features. These notes constitute the backbone for identification of the original lines.

24. Dedication of Roads. At the time the original surveys were made by the Federal Government, no provision was made for roads. To overcome this deficiency some states enacted laws requiring roads along section lines. Other states found this impractical because of the mountainous nature of the countryside. To dedicate

* Rev. Stat. 2407.

† U.S.C., Title 43, sec. 768 and sec. 770.

roads along section lines where the lines run up and down impossible grades would be of little benefit to the public.

25. Nomenclature for Sections. The nomenclature shown in Fig. 1-12 is used to designate separate parcels of sectionalized land. Reading descriptions of this type is simplified by following the description backwards, as for example: "the E½ of the SW¼ of

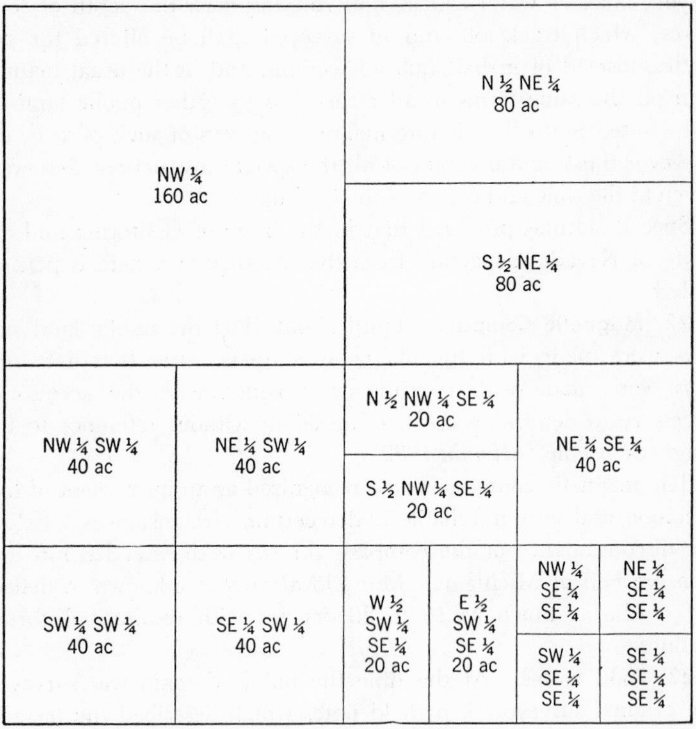

Figure 1-12.   Nomenclature for portions of sections

the SE¼" would be visualized as the SE quarter first, then the SW quarter of the SE quarter next, and then the east half of the last visualized parcel.

The smallest legal size recognized by Federal statute for homestead purposes was one-quarter of one-quarter; however, smaller parcels are commonly designated to identify portions of homesteaded holdings.   Since the government has authorized the disposal of 5-acre cabin sites in mountain and desert regions, the descriptions have been of the type: S½, SW¼, SE¼, SE¼ of Sec. 10, T 10 S, R 5 E, SBM.

SUBDIVISION SYSTEMS UNDER STATE LAWS

26. General. Subdivisions are the best systems developed to divide large tracts of land into smaller lots of marketable size. Lots sold in accordance with a properly made map, offers the simplest kind of deed description giving a maximum of information. Unlike subdividing the Federal lands into sections where the surveyor was instructed to follow a prescribed pattern and make his records public, private subdivisions were made in a variable manner without the field notes becoming public property. The deficiencies of early state subdivision laws were many, and numerous examples of poor subdivision maps are available. Subdivision laws developed in steps, each step being brought about to correct the deficiencies of earlier laws. As more and more trouble arose from incomplete subdivision maps, modern laws incorporating modern methods were enacted.

27. Maps. Maps are shorthand notations devised by man to avoid lengthy written instructions and, at the same time, give a visual picture of the land in question. A filed map is not necessarily proof of a survey. Many early maps were "office maps" made from the record only.

28. Minimum Requirements of Good Subdivisions. Modern subdivision laws require the subdivider to make a permanent record of his subdivision both upon the ground and in the recorder's office. As a condition of permitting a subdivision, each of the following steps should be required by the governing body:

FILING OF TENTATIVE MAP. An improperly planned addition to a city is economically unchangeable after the addition is built upon. The public agency that is burdened with the future flow of traffic and the maintenance of dedicated streets must have an early opportunity to declare whether the subdivision meets the requirements of the public. Numerous examples of poor planning, as out of date as the horse and buggy, are observable in our cities today. Such conditions can only be avoided by proper control of planning.

INSTALLING IMPROVEMENTS. As a condition of permitting a subdivision, improvements such as sewers, water, paving, and sidewalks may be required. Before approval of a final map the sub-

divider must either install the improvements or post bond sufficient
to pay the cost of the improvements.

FEATURES OF THE FINAL MAP. Every final map should incor-
porate all the following features: (1) on the face of the map the
legal title of the property being subdivided; (2) a certificate of
title insurance guaranteeing that the subdivider has a clear title,
free of all incumbrances, including taxes and bonds; (3) the
bearings and distances or curve data of every property line on the
map; (4) the relationship of the instant subdivision with all adjoining properties and adjoining public rights of way; (5) the
character and place of all monuments found or set; (6) a certificate of survey by a licensed surveyor; (7) which streets and easements are to be dedicated; (8) approval of the names of the streets
and acceptance of the dedication; and (9) approval by the county
or city surveyor or engineer.

MONUMENTING. The most serious defect of older subdivisions
was failure to require monumentation by a surveyor. The principle, "the original monuments set by the original surveyor to mark
a property, are unalterable," is the universal rule for retracement
work; yet many maps fail to state what was set.

All lot corners, angle points, point of curves, and tie points at
proper offsets should be set by the surveyor and clearly indicated
on the filed map. A few states are permitting delayed staking;
i.e., allowing monuments to be set after the map is filed and all
improvements are in. If delayed staking is permitted, the surveyor
must place a certificate on the map stating that he will set the
monuments indicated on the map within 60 days after the installa-
tion of all improvements.

The practice of setting only block corners, as permitted in a
number of states, should be discouraged. The best way to stop an
argument between neighbors is to prevent it in the first place. All
property should be marked prior to occupancy, thus avoiding any
misunderstanding before it occurs. From the point of view of
costs, it is more economical to set all markers before the erection of
fences and other obstructions. From the point of view of equity,
it is better to have the subdivider add a small cost for the staking
of each lot than it is to have some of the lot owners pay a high
price for the survey of their lots and then have adjoiners benefit by
their survey.

INSPECTION. No subdivision should be approved by the governing body before an inspection by the city or county surveyor or before a certification on the map by the city or county surveyor that all the monuments indicated on the map are in their proper position.

SALE OF LOTS. To maintain control over subdivisions, there must be a law prohibiting the sale of any one lot before the filing of the map.

FILING OF THE MAP. The purpose of filing a map is to insure that it is not altered after property is sold. Without a place to file subdivision maps and without assurance that a filed map cannot be altered, the method of selling lots by subdivision maps would fail.

29. Summary. Written deeds are the means by which particular parcels of land are described, and monuments placed upon the ground are the means by which land is located. A deed must explain how a person can find a monument or monuments on the ground and, from these monuments, explain how the land is to be located relative to the monuments.

Land may be described by metes and bounds descriptions or by lots on a map. Metes and bounds descriptions are often long and lack a visual picture of the land itself. Subdivision maps present a means whereby land can be visualized and can be described on a deed with a minimum number of words and a maximum amount of information. A subdivision map shows the relationship of the described property to its neighbors and often distant properties; thus lost monuments can be readily replaced. But there are economic disadvantages. A subdivision map must be filed with a governing agency to insure that it is not tampered with. As a condition of filing the map numerous restrictions are imposed by law. Streets must be dedicated; title insurance must be purchased; improvements must be installed; five to twenty governing departments must approve the map; and considerable time is consumed. But once a subdivision map is filed, the cost of recording deeds and the cost of sending out tax bills is reduced from then on.

The initial rights to land must be acquired by written conveyances. But after land is once acquired, the size and shape may be added to or subtracted from by the acts and conduct of adjoining neighbors. In the following chapter the means by which land may be transferred by unwritten considerations is discussed.

CHAPTER 2

Transfer
of Real Property

REAL PROPERTY DEFINED

30. Real Property Interests. In the preceding chapter systems for describing and locating the boundaries of real property have been enumerated and explained. The professional function of the surveyor is limited to the describing and locating of boundaries; but in carrying out that function it is necessary for the surveyor to have a general knowledge of real property law. In practical effect the surveyor is invariably employed by those who have some legal rights in land and who desire to protect them or by those who desire to acquire such legal rights. In ascertaining the physical location of the land in which the legal rights exist the surveyor must be able to work with and understand those whose function it is to describe or define or ascertain the extent of the legal rights in or to the land.

31. Definition of Real Property. *Real property* has been legally defined as "the interest that a man has in lands, tenements, or hereditaments, and also in such things as are permanent, fixed and immovable and which cannot be carried out of their places, as lands and tenements." The authority in which the definition is found states an explanation of it. These terms designate both things that are permanent, fixed, and immovable, such as land, and rights arising out of or connected with lands, and they include land and whatever is erected or growing thereon, or affixed thereto, and also rights arising out of, or annexed to, or exercisable within or about, the land. Under the old common law the three terms, lands, tenements, and hereditaments had distinct meanings, but those meanings have become more or less obscure in present-day definitions of the three terms. All three terms are now commonly used in reference to the solid material of the earth, the structures or things attached to it, the things growing out of it, and the rights to the usage or benefit from them. *Land* has been defined as that species of property which, by its fixed situation and qualities, has engrossed the term "real" as its peculiar descriptive. Land includes the solid material of the earth but it also has been held by courts to include the structures annexed to it and the crops, trees, and other growth arising out of that solid material. Tenement is an even more inclusive word than land according to court interpretations. The term *tenements* can be defined to include every species of realty corporeal and incorporeal that has permanence. The term *hereditaments* is the most comprehensive term by court definition of the three used in the definition that is given of real property. It not only includes land and tenements but also all the legal rights tangible or intangible and corporeal or incorporeal that arise out of the solid material of the earth and are capable under the law of being inherited.

It is of interest to note, however, that both the materials and the rights to those materials that are included in the term "real property" are determined by the location of the jurisdiction in which the property is situated or it sites. Both materials and rights to use materials according to interpretations of various states may be changed from real property to personal property and may even, according to the law of one state, be real property but by the law of another be personal property. As an example, a house or other structure that is in condition to be removed from a parcel of land without injury to the land may have assumed the character of personal property. Another example is building material left after the destruction of a structure and sand, gravel, or top soil in condition to be removed from its natural site.

32. Historical Background. Historically, all real property was owned by the sovereign or government. As settlers or colonists arrived, they acquired rights in the real property either by express grant from the soverign or by possession, occupation, and use of the land with a subsequent acquiescence and acknowledgment of interest in the settler by the soverign. The first owners almost invariably had the entire beneficial interest in the parcels that they acquired. As time passed and as the economic life in the colonies grew more and more complex, so did the ownership in many parcels of land. By various kinds of transfer including descent, inheritance, sale, and adverse possession, ownership of various interests in individual parcels of land came to be acquired by more than one owner. As an example, an owner of a parcel of land might transfer to one person the right or easement to use a path or road across that land; to another he might transfer a right to dig coal on the land; and to a third the right known as a remainder after a life estate to ownership of his residual interest in the land after his death, reserving in himself only the limited right of enjoyment for his lifetime of the land from which had been subtracted the right to dig coal and the right to exclusive use of the path or roadway across the land. Such transferred rights in land or real property interests were and are in turn subject to transfer by and from their original owners. Today there are few parcels of land owned in their entirety by individuals from which one or more than one real property interest has not been subtracted and transferred. Even the ownership of most small residential lots is limited by prior transfers to public utilities of rights to string power or telephone lines over the lots and transfers of rights to pipelines beneath the surface of the lots.

33. Specific Interests. Courts generally agree that an estate or interest in real property or real estate includes all freehold estates, whether corporeal or incorporeal, and whether in possession, reversion, or remainder. Thus the terms include absolute or entire fees, fee simple titles, life estates, estates in remainder, ground rents, a mortgagor's equity of redemption, until barred by foreclosure or otherwise, mining claims, and partnership property. The terms also include hereditaments, whether corporeal or incorporeal, such as easements.

Such is the complexity of real property law and the number and kinds of interests that may exist in land, that it is difficult to classify and enumerate all of them in any summary of the law such as this. It is the policy of law to prohibit any restrictions on alienation or transfer of property. Legislatures and courts in furtherance of that policy have allowed the transfer of nearly every conceivable benefit or right and combination of such benefits or rights that can exist in land. Real property interests are created by transfers or conveyances which may be either voluntary or involuntary. Except for statutory limitations on transfer of real property enacted in the exercise of police power, such as zoning ordinances and subdivision laws, and other legal restrictions designed to prevent the creation of real property interests that will by their own nature restrict further transfer, every owner of a real property interest may create new and different interests by transferring part of what he owns. Not only may an owner transfer his total interest in part of the land in which his right lies, but he may also transfer part of his interest in a given area of land and own a lesser interest in that given area. Real property interests can be and have been transferred from their owner or owners to one or more other owner or owners for periods of time that range from those limited to the will of the transferor to specified periods of days, months, years, lifetimes, or perpetuity. The duration of such transfers can be and often are also limited by the terms of the transfer as to some condition such as the type of use to be made of the transferred interest. It is also possible that the enjoyment of rights transferred may be deferred by the terms of the transfer.

34. Classification of Real Property Interests. In legal phraseology the owner of an interest in real property is said to have an estate in real property. In law generally estates are classified according to duration, according to whether they include rights of present or future enjoyment, according to whether they are owned by one or more persons, and according to the nature of the rights of several owners. The *Cyclopedic Law Dictionary* in its definition of Estates sets up the following classification:

The various estates classified with reference to their quantum or duration may be tabulated as follows:

I. Freehold estates
  A. Estates of inheritance
    (1) Fee simple
    (2) Fee tail
  B. Estates not of inheritance (life estates)
    (1) Conventional Life estates
      (a) Estates for life of the tenant
      (b) Estates *pur autre vie.*
    (2) Legal life estates
      (a) Tenancy in tail after possibility of issue extinct
      (b) Dower
      (c) Curtesy
      (d) Estate during coventure.
II. Estates less than freehold (leasehold estates, chattels real)
  A. Estates for years
  B. Tenancy at will
  C. Tenancy from year to year
  D. Tenancy by sufferance.

Estates classified according as they give rights of present or future enjoyment are:

I. Present Estates
II. Future Estates
   A. Reversions
   B. Remainders
   C. Contingent Uses
   D. Springing Uses
   E. Shifting Uses
   F. Executory Devises.

Classified according as they are owned by one or more persons, and according to the nature of the rights of several owners, they are:

I. Estates in severalty
II. Joint Estates
   A. Joint tenancy
   B. Tenancy in common
   C. Tenancy in coparcenary
   D. Tenants in entirety.

The outline of methods of real property classification which has just been stated makes no attempt to include a method of classification of the beneficial use or uses which may be included in any of the estates listed. It should be obvious that such an infinite number of benefits or rights and combinations of benefits and rights can arise out of land that such classification is well nigh impossible. Under our system of law it can be generally stated that the complete ownership in a given parcel of land includes not only all rights to the surface of the land but to the area to the heavens above and to the center of the earth below that surface.

35. Freeholds or Fees. Of all the estates that are classified, the freehold estates or fees are the most substantial or important because of their permanent duration, although their existence may be made conditional at the time of and by the instrument in which they are created. The *fee simple* or *fee simple absolute* is an estate where a right or rights in land exist without duration and/or limit. All other fees while indefinite in duration are subject to some condition. The *fee tail,* now nearly extinct as far as usage is concerned, is an estate limited in duration to the period of use by the person for whom it is created and his male descendants. Other conditional fees which are not listed in the classification given but which are still in common use are the fee simple determinable and the fee simple subject to a condition subsequent. The *fee simple determinable* is an estate in which the creator or grantor retains a right or reversion interest which is a power to terminate the estate and recover it if any subsequent owner of the fee that is granted violates the condition set out in the instrument by which it is created. The *fee simple subject to a condition subsequent,* on the other hand, terminates automatically on violation of the condition that is set out in the instrument that creates it, thereby activating an automatic reversion of the beneficial rights included in the fee.

36. Life Estates. Conventional life estates are those created for the duration of the life of an individual or in some cases of joint lives of more than one person. Generally they are created for the life of the person who is given a right of possession or who is the life tenant. Occasionally, however, life estates are *pur autre vie* or for the life of one other than the one given the possessory interest.

Legal life estates are life estates that are created by operation of law rather than by voluntary act of the grantor. In many non-community property states surviving wives and husbands of persons who own real property may elect on the death of their spouse to take either life estates for their lives in the real property of the decedent spouse or to take a fee estate in that real property as tenants in common with other heirs. This right for a surviving wife is called a *dower interest* and for a husband a *curtesy interest.*

37. Leases. Estates less than freehold estates (lease estates, chattels real) technically are not real property but are personal property. This distinction, however, is not important in any general summary of real property interests. Such interests are rights arising out of contracts called *leases* and may and often do give possessory rights for periods longer than any life expectancy. The most common form of lease is an estate for years or for a specified period of years. A *tenancy at will* arises out of a contract usually oral by which the owner of a more substantial estate gives a right to a tenant to possess real property at the will of such owner. A *tenancy from year to year* is as the name implies simply a lease for one year. A *tenancy at sufferance* is one arising out of an implied agreement where the so-called tenant occupied land without any permission from the person who has the right of possession.

38. Future Interest. The most common of the estates that are known as future interests because they consist of rights of enjoyment to commence in the future are *remainders* and *reversions.* *Remainders* are rights of enjoyment of real property interests subject to life estates. Although their duration is indefinite they are, of course, certain of enjoyment. A *reversionary interest,* on the other hand, is a right to future enjoyment of real property which can only be achieved by termination of a conditional fee which may be a fee tail, a fee simple determinable, or a fee simple subject to condition subsequent. A common example of a reversionary interest is that of an owner of real property who has conveyed a right of way or easement for road purposes across the land in which his real property interests lie. In the event that the roadway across the land should ever be abandoned by the public agency that has acquired the easement, the rights of that public agency will revert to the grantor or his successors in interest.

The future interests or estates in real property known as *uses* either *contingent, springing,* or *shifting* are the rights of future enjoyment in those called the *cequi que use* of the profits of land to which another has the legal title and possession together with the duty of defending the same and of making estates thereof according to the direction of the *cequi que use* whose rights of enjoyment have accrued on happening of the events enumerated in the instruments that created them. In practical application of real property law, future interests of this class are seldom created. The last class of future interest that is mentioned in the classification given is an *executory devise.* This type of estate is created by a devise in a will of a substantial estate in real property to take effect upon some contingency subsequent to the testator's death.

39. Estates by Severalty and Joint Estates. Of the estates classified according as they are owned by one or more persons, and according to the nature of the rights of the several owners, the *estate by severalty* is one held by a person in his own right, without any other person being joined or connected with him in point of interest during his estate. All estates not estates by severalty are, of course, *joint estates.* Perhaps the most common form of joint estates is the joint tenancy. A *joint tenancy* is an estate owned in equal shares by two or more persons who acquired it by one conveyance, who have equal right of possession, and who have right of ownership. The reason for the popularity of this form of estate is that the title of a decedent joint tenant passes on his death automatically and without probate to the survivor or survivors. Another form of joint estate by which real property is often owned by two or more persons is the *tenancy in common.* An estate in common is one held by two or more persons in joint possession at the same time by several and distinct titles. An estate or *tenancy in* *copancenary* is another form of joint estate. In this form is found unity of time of creation, unity of title or conveyance by which it is created, and unity of or joint possession. But in this form of estate the percentage of the interest of the several tenants or owners differs. The last form of joint estate is that known as a *tenancy by entirety* which estate arises on a conveyance to a man and wife jointly. In this form of estate the interests of the two tenants are considered by the law as one entity or entirety.

40. Summation. The reader should now be aware of the complexity of the subject of real property. The importance of locating and describing the physical boundaries of the area of land in which the real property interest lies is equaled by the importance of identifying and describing the extent of the rights, estates, titles, interests, or benefits in the land located and described. The legal concepts of real property interests in the United States are not uniform in the states. Generally, real property law in the United States is based on the English Common law as it was brought to America by the early colonists who settled here. Real property law is, however, usually state law rather than Federal law, and the common law has been modified through the years by statutes enacted by State legislative bodies, as well as by the different interpretations of the law determined by the courts of the various states. No summary of real property law can do more than generalize about that law. The commonly accepted means of classifying real property estates or interests are given, but even these classifications and the estates therein enumerated are not uniformly accepted by the laws of the several states. Some of the states were formerly possessions of countries such as Spain, France, and Mexico, and the real property law of those states has been influenced to varying extents by the laws used by their early settlers. The only generalization that can safely be made is that real property interests vary as to the extent of the benefit, as to the type of benefit offered, as to the duration of the benefit, as to whether the enjoyment of the benefit is in the present or the future, and in the number of owners who may share in the benefit.

WRITTEN TRANSFERS OF REAL PROPERTY

41. Transfers in General. In the preceding pages emphasis has been given to the nature of real property and to the rights, interests, and/or estates created by transfers which are either voluntary or involuntary.   In any transfer of real property it is essential that it be determined who is acquiring the interest, from whom the interest is being transferred, the extent of the interest including what rights of enjoyment or benefits from the land are being transferred; when such rights or benefits are to commence; how long they are to continue; and on what conditions, if any, they are to be terminated; and, last but not least, in what particular area of land the right or rights exist.   In general there are only two methods of acquiring or losing title or interest in real property; they are *descent and purchase*.   *Descent* is, of course, the passing of an interest in real property by the death of an intestate owner, or one who leaves no will, to his heirs or heirs at law.   The term *purchase,* on the other hand, includes every method by which an interest in real property may be acquired other than acquisition by right of blood or relationship. It includes escheat, occupancy, prescription, adverse possession, prefecture, and *alienation,* which is the voluntary transfer of ownership or title usually by written conveyance or by a devise as set out in the last will of a decedent transferor.

42. Historical Background.   This chapter attempts to outline briefly the methods by which real property interests are alienated or voluntarily transferred or conveyed.   But, in order to better understand the methods used in the voluntary transfer of real property, it is necessary to have a glimpse at the history of real property transferring.   In the early stages of the common law in England while the feudal system was in existence, all land was owned by the sovereign who rewarded his lieutenants or lords by grants of possession and use of lands including the right to pass such possessory rights on their deaths to their oldest sons.   Gradually with passage of time the rights of the holders of possessory interests in the land were increased to permit them more and more freedom in disposing of their rights by purchase.   Until fairly recent times, however, any transfer in ownership of an estate in real property entailed an actual or symbolic transfer of possession of the land known as a livery of seisen.   With growing literacy in England and/or perhaps an improvement in the science of surveying, it became more and more common to accompany livery of seisen with a written conveyance in which was expressed the intent of the parties to the transfer.   Such was the advantage in transferring real property by written conveyance in preserving a record of such transfers that in 1677 the English Parliament passed an act commonly known as the Statute of Frauds but more properly entitled "An Act for the Prevention of Frauds and Perjuries."* This act required, among other things, that all conveyances of real property be evidenced by written memoranda and subscribed or signed by grantors of such real property. The Statute of Frauds was in turn adopted into the law of the various British colonies and by the states of the United States from its inception. From the time of the adoption of the Statute of Frauds in Britain and from the time of the first transfers of real property interests in what are now the states of our Union, nearly all such transfers have been evidenced by a written document properly executed. As in nearly every other rule of law, however, there are exceptions to the requirements of the Statute of Frauds. Those exceptions are based on the rule that equity will not permit a statute or law designed to prevent injustice or fraud to make the occurrence of injustice or fraud possible, and it sometimes happens that real injustice can occur because of requirements that conveyances be in writing.

43. General Requirements of Conveyances. In addition to the requirement that conveyances be in writing, legislatures and courts have adopted other requirements to safeguard or protect rights in real property and to maintain an orderly system for the creation or transfer of such interests or titles. The requirements common to all conveyances are that they be by written instrument; that the documents identify grantors and grantees; that they identify the physical location of the land in which the real property interests being conveyed are situated; that they identify the real property interests being conveyed; and that they express the intent to convey those interests.

44. Conveyance Defined. The term *conveyance* not only means a mode of voluntarily transferring real property but also it is often used to signify the instrument or document by which title is passed. The term has been defined by statute as signifying every instrument in writing by which any estate or interest in real estate is created, aliened, mortgaged, or assigned or by which the title to any real estate may be affected in law or in equity except wills and testaments, leases for a term not exceeding three years and executory contracts for the sale and purchase of land.†

* St. 29 Car. 11c 3.
† 1 Rev. St. N. Y. p. 762 S 38.

45. Deeds—Requirements. The most common method of conveying real property interests is by conveyances known as deeds. Historically and under the old common law a *deed* was broadly defined as a written instrument under seal. In modern times, however, a deed is often defined as and usually thought to be a sealed writing, signed by the party to be charged, which evidences the terms of the contract between the parties, whereby the title to real property is transferred from one to the other *intervivos* or during their lifetimes. In general the requisites or essentials of a deed are: (1) competent or proper parties; (2) a proper subject matter; (3) in at least some classes of deeds, a valid consideration; (4) a written or printed form; (5) sufficient and legal words; (6) reading, if desired, before the execution; (7) execution, signing, sealing, attestation; and (8) delivery.

Whether a deed contains the essentials or requisites that constitute it a valid conveyance of real property depends on the law of the place in which the real property which is its subject matter is situated. And just as the laws of the several states may vary in their requirements as to what may or may not constitute a sufficient description of the boundary of the parcel in which an interest is sought to be conveyed by a deed, so they may vary in their requirements as to other essentials of the conveyance. The rule that the deeding of real property interests is governed by the laws of the jurisdiction in which the real property is situated has been modified by most states to allow the law of the place where a deed is executed to control its manner of execution and the validity of personal covenants or agreements contained in the deed.

46. Parties. Competent parties to a deed or in fact to any other contract are persons who at the time they execute the deed or contract know what they are doing and the nature of their act. There must, of course, be at least one grantor and at least one grantee, and execpt in conveyance transferring future interests the grantee or grantees must be in existence at the time of execution. As an example, a deed by a father to his unborn child can pass no possessory interest to the child and a deed that purports to do so is invalid for lack of a competent party. It is also generally true that a deed by which a person purports to convey an interest in real property to himself has no legal effect.

In addition to requirements that there be two parties who know what they are doing when the deed is executed, it is also true that the person who is grantor must have a real property interest or must represent someone who has to deed such an interest to a grantee. Without such an interest a person cannot be a grantor and his deed can have no legal effect in transferring title. A person who has a power of appointment or who acts under a power of attorney may properly act as grantor but unless a grantor has such a power or has himself an ownership in real estate he is not a proper party to a deed.

47. After Rights. It is interesting to note, however, that, whereas a deed of a grantor, who has no ownership in the real property that is the subject of the deed, passes nothing at that time to the grantee, in many states if the grantor ever acquires the subject matter of his deed the old deed then becomes effective. This rule which sometimes gives retroactive effect to an invalid deed does not apply to deeds known as *releases and quitclaims.* A *release or a quitclaim deed* merely conveys whatever interest a grantor may have in its subject matter and contains no warranty or representation that a grantor owns any interest in the subject matter of his deed. Under the common law a grantor was required to be in possession of the real property which was the subject matter of his conveyance as well as own an interest in that real property; modern statutes generally now allow interests in real property to be conveyed by deed of a grantor who is not in possession of that subject matter.

48. Subject Matter. In general the subject matter of a deed may consist of any interest or right in land. This rule too, like nearly every other rule of law, is subject to several exceptions. Mere uncertain possibilities of interests and mere possibilities of interests in real property are not grantable by deed. Thus such executory and contingent interests in real property as that which an only son may have in the land of his elderly infirm and widowed father are not subject to conveyance by deed. Nor is the executory interest of the owner of an option to buy land even though the option may be binding as between the owner and the owner of the real property which is the subject matter of the option. In order to be conveyable by deed, interests in real property must be present interests or, in other words, be owned by the grantor at the time of execution of the deed of conveyance. Legalistically, the rule is that interest to be conveyed by deed must exist in possession, reversion, or remainder, or by executory devise, or contingent remainder.

49. Consideration. As the third requisite or essential of a deed the statement was made that in at least some classes of deeds a valid consideration was required to pass between the parties. *Considera-tion* itself is often defined as a benefit or advantage to the grantor and for a detriment to the grantee. Under modern common law and the statutes of most states the various requirements which still exist that consideration pass between the parties are in practical effect only requirements that conveyances represented by deeds be without fraud or misrepresentation or the taking of unfair ad-vantage by one of the parties over the other. In cases involving fraud or misrepresentation or undue influence of a grantee, equity in determining whether to allow recision will take into considera-tion the adequacy of consideration, but in modern practice it is generally true that a failure of consideration in itself will not make a deed invalid.

50. In Writing. The fourth requisite of a valid deed is that it be in written or printed form. The writing also is generally required to be on either paper or parchment in order to give greater security against alterations and erasures. The requirement that conveyances including deeds be in writing is, as has been previously mentioned, found in the Statute of Frauds which has been uni-versally adopted into statutory law by American jurisdictions. In-terests in real property still exist however in states that were form-erly governed by nations other than Britain which originated by unwritten or parole conveyances under system of law not requiring that conveyances of real property interests be effected by written instruments.

51. Legal Words. The fifth and perhaps most essential require-ment of a deed is that it be expressed in sufficient and legal words. Every agreement or contract including a deed must, of course, be definite and certain in order to be enforceable, but in case of am-biguities the courts generally allow the parties to produce other evidence to show the intentions that should have been expressed with certainty in their agreement. A deed, however, once executed may and invariably does become a permanent link in a chain of title. The effect of other types of agreements, however, is com-pleted once their purpose has been carried out, which is usually in a relatively short space of time. The effect of a deed or con-veyance may continue to exist permanently and long after the parties to the transfer of title are dead and gone; certainly long after any evidence of their intent in a transaction other than that expressed in their written instrument has become possible to produce in court.

Words used in deeds need not be technical words but they must clearly express the intention of the parties, and obviously in legal terminology certain so-called technical expressions which are not commonly used by the public can best express this intention. Whatever the words used, however, they must, to constitute a valid deed, always clearly identify the grantor and grantee; contain operative words either in the past or present tense showing the intention of the grantor to make a present grant; contain some description or designation of the land from which an interest is deeded, which words may either describe the parcel with particularity or state a reference to some other document from which the location of the parcel may be determined with particularity; contain words that define and limit the estate being conveyed; and contain words in conclusion that state the execution and date of the execution.

In addition to words that state the facts mentioned above which are always considered essential, in some jurisdictions some types of deeds require words that state the fact that consideration was paid for the transfer by the grantee to the grantor. Where this requirement is found however, it is sufficient to state that a "valuable consideration" was paid without stating the amount or kind of consideration.

The portion of a deed that contains words that identify the parties, the so-called operative words of grant, the fact of consideration, and the description of the land is called the *premises*. The part of the deed that contains words that define and limit the estate or interest conveyed is called the *habendum*. And the words that complete a deed are known as a *tenendum* which under old common law contained a required statement of the lord to whom the grantee of an estate should be beholden is obsolete in the United States, although it was used in deeds made in pre-Revolutionary times in Colonial America.

52. Opportunity to Read. The sixth essential of a valid deed is the requirement that the participating parties who execute the deed read it or have an opportunity to read it before its execution. This requirement should, of course, require no explanation, considering the nature of the deed to be an expressed intention by one party to convey and of another party to accept an interest in real property. Certainly the law protects the rights of parties not to be bound by an agreement that they do not intend to contract.

53. Execution, etc. The seventh essential of a valid deed includes the requirements that the deed be executed, signed, sealed, and attested. *Execution* is defined by the *Cyclopedic Law Dictionary* as "the accomplishment of a thing, the completion of an act or instrument, the fulfillment of an undertaking . . . ." Generally, by the execution of an agreement the intentions of the parties agreed to are fulfilled. A deed that is an agreement to make a present conveyance is executed by its completion by the parties, or more specifically when the formalities required by law are completed. Under modern statutory law, generally, the formalities required are only that the deed be signed by the grantor; that a notary or other person authorized by law witness the signing by the grantor at the request of the grantor and sign it as an attesting witness; and that the deed be delivered to the grantee, which is the eighth and last essential of a valid deed. Both the statutory law and the common law as interpreted by the courts of the various states differ widely as to the required details of execution of deeds; however, the present tendency of nearly all states has been to simplify those requirements. Although under common law a deed is defined as an instrument under seal, many American jurisdictions have completely eliminated the requirement that such conveyance be under seal and the law of the jurisdictions that still require a seal is satisfied by nearly any mark, even including the typewritten word "seal" which a grantor may use or adopt as his seal.

54. Delivery. Delivery of deed which is the last act required to execute the conveyance that it represents is invariably required by all jurisdictions; however, usually it is held to take place when the words and acts of the grantor are such that it is clear that it is his intention to treat the deed as his own and to make a delivery of it to the grantee. An actual manual delivery by the grantor to the grantee is not required, and a delivery by an attorney or agent of the grantor is usually sufficient. Even a retention of physical possession of the deed by a grantor has been held not inconsistent with delivery when evidence of his intent that the conveyance has been consummated is clear. It is, however, necessary in any delivery that the grantee have knowledge of such delivery and that delivery be accepted by the grantee. The intent to accept by the grantee may be inferred by his conduct just as the delivery by the grantor may be inferred. And in many jurisdictions acceptance by the grantee is presumed when the deed confers a benefit on the grantee.

The effective date of a deed is the date of delivery and not the date of signing, recordation, or attestation, and the transfer of the property is consummated at that time. The date of delivery is also, of course, the date upon which the grantor and grantee become bound by whatever stipulations, recitals, conditions, and limitations are contained in the deed.

55. Executory Contracts. The vast majority of voluntary conveyances of real property transfers of interests or estates have been consummated by use of deeds, but another common method of conveying such interest is through use of executory contracts of sale. Deeds, of course, are contracts that are executed upon delivery, and the transfers of title that they represent are completed on delivery. *Executory contracts,* on the other hand, are agreements by grantors to pass title or transfer estates or interests upon future fulfillment of promises or condition precedent by grantees. Usually, the conditions to be fulfilled by grantees entail the payment of money but promised consideration to be given by a grantee may consist of the doing of any other act that may benefit the grantor and/or cause a detriment to the grantee. Executory contracts for the sale of land are based on the general law of contracts even though they relate to the transfer of estates in land and, upon execution or fulfillment by grantees of promises made by them, may have the force and effect of executed or completed conveyances. Generally executory contracts for the sale of real estate interests by their terms require the grantor to deed those interests to the grantees upon fulfillment by them of their promises, but the contract becomes enforceable usually when grantees can prove the fulfillment of the promises made by them. No special formality need be observed in the preparation or signing of an executory contract for the sale of estates in real property except that such contracts must, pursuant to the Statute of Frauds, be in writing and must be signed by both parties to bind them, which last requirement is not generally true of deeds although in that form of a deed known as an indenture the signatures of both parties are used. Among the most commonly used executory contracts for transfer of real estate are installment contracts, escrow agreements, and offers to purchase which are accepted by grantors containing conditions to be fulfilled

by the parties.   The form of agreement known as an *option* is also
an executory contract often used in the sale of real estate.   Options
are simply agreements by which one person purchases from another
the right to demand and receive or to deliver property either at a
specified time or within a specified time limit for or at a stated
price.   Thus options are peculiar in that the purchaser in return
for his consideration acquires a right or election which he may or
may not decide to exercise.   As in other types of executory contracts for the sale of real estate, options usually provide for the
deeding of property upon the meeting of a condition or conditions
which is or are the consideration for the transfer; however, they
also are enforceable by court decree upon a showing that the conditions have been met or tendered.

56. Wills.   Although from a very technical standpoint wills are
not themselves conveyances, they are often included in the definition
of conveyances and many real estate conveyances are consummated
or executed in accordance with the intentions expressed in them.
A *will* is defined as a "legal declaration of a man's intention respect-
ing the distribution of his property which he wills to be performed
after his death" (*Cyclopedic Law Dictionary*).   The intention of a
decedent testator or person who makes a will is actually effected
or executed by a decree or order of a probate court known as a
decree of distribution by which transfer of the testator's property
is conveyed in accordance with his expressed intention, or as nearly
so as may be possible.   An intention to dispose of real property as
distinguished from personal property is known as a *devise,* whereas
an expressed intention for the disposition of personal property is
referred to as a bequest.   A *specific devise* is an expressed intention
for the disposition of a specific real property interest; a *general
devise* covers all real property; and a *residual devise* covers all real
property interest not specifically devised.   Wills once made are, of
course, always thereafter during the lives of the persons who make
them subject to change or revocation in part or in their entireties.
Furthermore, it often happens that property specifically devised by
a will is transferred from the ownership of the testator after the will
is made but prior to the death of the testator, in which case the
devise will lapse and the *devisee* or person intended to receive the
property will get nothing.   Or, as sometimes happens, the testator
may be insolvent at the time of his death and all property included
in his estate may be required to be sold in order that his creditors

may be paid. Other factors that may prevent the intention of a testator from being carried out are his failure to consider the dower or curtesy or community property interest that his spouse may have in his estate, or the right of a *predemitted* heir, that is, a spouse or children whom the law presumes the testator intended to benefit if he fails to mention them in his will and who takes a statutory share of his estate unless mentioned in the will.

As has been previously mentioned, the distribution of an estate intended by a person before his death as expressed in his last will is carried out by a probate court after his death as nearly as possible in accordance with the decedent's expressed intent. In fact, whether or not a person dies leaving a will, if he leaves any real property, not including that which he may hold in joint tenancy, his real estate will be distributed in accordance with the decree of a probate court. If he dies without a will, however, the court instead of distributing the property in accordance with any intention expressed by the decedent will distribute the property in accordance with the law of intestate succession of the jurisdiction in which the property is situated if it is real property, or in accordance with the law of the domicile of the decedent if the property is personal property. Laws of intestate succession which determine heirship invariably favor persons related to the decedent in accordance with the degree of relationship. Thus widows and children usually inherit, and, if there are none, then blood kin inherit in accordance with the decree of kinship. Generally, if a person dies intestate leaving no relations, his estate will be distributed to the state.

The legal proceedings by which the affairs of decedents are wound up and their estates including their real property distributed are called *probate proceedings.* Briefly, the important steps required in probating estates are: (1) admission of the will to probate and appointment of an executor if there is a will, and if not, then admitting the estate to probate and appointment of an administrator; (2) filing of the inventory of the estate; (3) notice to creditors of the decedent; (4) appraisal of the estate and determination of the tax, if any; (5) rendering of an accounting by the executor or administrator to the court and payment of approved claims; (6) closing of the estate including distributing in accordance with the will as interpreted by the court or in accordance with the law of intestate succession and the discharge of the executor or administrator. The time required by the probate proceeding will depend on statutory requirements, disputes among heirs, whether or not sale of estate property may be required to pay claims or to facilitate distribution, and other factors. Normally, at least six months are required for probating an estate; however, some probate proceedings last for many years. In the probate proceeding, the executor or administrator acts as representative of the estate and it is his duty to wind up the affairs of the decedent and procure the distribution of the estate. If the situation requires it, the administrator may sell or even buy property, borrow money, sue or be sued in any type of civil action as may any property owner or business man. It is, of course, the particular duty of the representative of an estate to marshal and protect its assets, and in the carrying out of his duty he often has occasion to employ surveyors.

Probate courts in interpreting and carrying out intentions expressed in wills for the distribution of real property interests generally have less discretion under the laws of the various jurisdictions than courts concerned with disputes between parties to a deed, executory contract for the sale of land, or two adjoining owners involved in a boundary dispute. In every case the court will seek to carry out the intentions of the parties and do justice under the law; however, in the determination of the intention of a decedent's property the court is limited in admitting evidence of the decedent's intent not expressed in a will.

TRANSFERS NOT IN WRITING

57. Unwritten Conveyances. Most conveyances of real property interests are made by deed, by executory contracts, and by decrees of distribution which are written instruments as required by the Statute of Frauds. Both under common law and statutory law all jurisdictions authorize other methods of conveyances and transferring which need not be evidenced by any written instrument. Surveyors are often employed to survey land interests that have been so transferred not only without being evidenced by any written instrument but also without any public record having been made of the transfer. In every case of such transfer without formality of a written instrument of record, title passes either through an executed oral agreement or through use by the transferee or by the transferee and those who use the land with the consent of the transferee.

Transfers of title or interests in real property in which written conveyances are not required can be divided into two classes. The first of those are transfers in which there is either an actual oral agreement to transfer or in which the law implies an actual agreement from the conduct of the parties; in the second of these classes of transfers the transfers are involuntary on the part of the transferors and arise out of adverse user on the part of transferees without disturbance by owners for long periods of time.

Transfer of real property interests not required to be evidenced by written conveyances which are by agreement either actual or implied are dedications to public use and boundary line establishments. Where real property is transferred for public use or to establish a boundary line by actual agreement and the agreements can be proved either by written record or by testimony of conversations, showing acquiescence of the parties, the courts of nearly all jurisdictions will enforce such agreements without any further proof. Problems that arise in these transfers are those which are related to conduct of the parties from which, if proved, courts will imply agreements to transfer real property. Requirements of the courts of the various jurisdictions are at considerable variance but as a very general rule all courts rely on a legal principle known as *estoppel by facts in pais* in implying agreements from conduct. *Estoppel by facts in pais* is defined as "the preclusion of one to deny that which, by his conduct, he may have induced another to believe and act on to his prejudice."

58. Dedication to Public Use. The laws of all jurisdictions recognize and accept the type of transfer known as a dedication to public use. *Dedication* is defined as "an appropriation of land to some public use, made by the owner, and accepted for such use by or on behalf of the public." Among the public uses for which land may be legally dedicated are religious and pious uses, cemeteries, highways, streets and alleys, squares, parks and public commons, schools and education uses, wharves and landing places, and bridges. Dedications are broadly classified either as *statutory or common law, statutory dedications* being those in or pursuant to a statute and *common law dedications being those in which the law* implies a dedication from acquiescense on the part of an owner in public user of his land; and common law dedication operates by estoppel rather than by any express grant whereas a statutory dedication invariably operates by an express grant of an owner to the public as represented by some public agency, public utility, or religious or charitable organization. Incidentally, jurisdictions whose legislatures have enacted statutes that provide for a method or methods by which property may be dedicated to a public use also generally authorize dedications to be made pursuant to the common law, and in some cases have even enacted statutes providing for the latter method of dedications.

59. Statutory Dedication. Generally, statutes that create modes of dedication not known to common law set out a method of conveying lands by deed or some other conveyance. Usually such statutes provide that where an owner has had his land surveyed and platted on a map or plat which designates certain areas as streets, parks, and/or other areas intended for public use, and records the map or plat, that owner has irrevocably dedicated such area so designated for public use.

60. Common Law Dedication. Under common law dedication is accomplished either by an express, oral or written, declaration by the owner or dedicator or by conduct by such owner from which his intent to dedicate land for a public user may be implied. In either case the common law requires that the owner's intention to dedicate be clearly and irrevocably manifested. Where the intention to dedicate is implied from the conduct of the owner, the duration of that conduct which might be required to show the intent to dedicate depends, of course, on the type of conduct. Whether conduct implies an intent to dedicate, of course, is a question of fact not of law. That fact may be proved by indirect evidence as no formalities in making such a dedication are required by law. The most common conduct on a part of an owner for which an intent to dedicate may be proved is a long acquiescence on his part to a public user.

In either a statutory or common law dedication, the dedicator may impose such conditions and restrictions as he desires although, as must be obvious in a dedication implied from acquiescence to public user, conditions and restrictions of use are usually not specific.

61. Acceptance of Dedication. As in a grant of land or real property made by deed, a dedication is not concluded without an acceptance either by the public or by some public or religious organization authorized by law to accept on behalf of the public. Some jurisdictions, however, have provided in the statutes that provide for the manner of dedication that, if the dedication or offer of dedication is made in accordance with the statute, it is accepted or completed without any action by any public agency. In any event an offer of dedication either express or implied may be accepted by the public by its entering on the land and enjoying the privileges offered or simply by public user.

Many examples of common law dedication of private property to a public use can be found. Probably one of the most usual examples of such dedication occurs when a private property owner allows the public to use a pathway or roadway across his land for a long period of time without any effort to restrict such use or to warn the users of his continued claim of unrestricted ownership in the area used. All readers will recall instances of pathways across campus and other such areas that are from time to time chained or otherwise blocked to public use or which are posted with signs warning the users that the area used is private property and that permission to use the path may be revoked at any time. Such devices are often utilized by property owners in an effort to avoid claims that their property has become dedicated to public use by long-continued acquiescence to the use.

62. Boundary Line Establishment. As has been previously stated, another method by which transfer of real property interests are in fact effected without written conveyance or public record is in establishment of boundary lines. This method of transfer requires an express or implied agreement of the parties who are the owners of adjacent or contiguous land. A *boundary* is, of course, defined as "any separation, natural or artificial, which marks the confines or line of two contiguous estates." The definition also states, "The term is applied to include the objects placed or existing at the angles of the boundary lines of separation" and "A *natural boundary* is a natural object remaining where it was placed by nature" and "An *Artificial boundary* is one created by man."

Where a boundary line is established by the express or implied agreement of contiguous owners and without use of a written conveyance, the agreement relied on in order to bind the parties must effect a settlement of an uncertain boundary and in some jurisdictions the further requirement is made that the agreement effect a settlement of an actual existing dispute. A further requirement is usually made that the parties or at least one of them take some action in reliance on the agreement usually through making improvements in the area up to the agreed line. In any event, all jurisdictions seem to require that there must be an acquiescence and possession of land by the respective owners in reliance on the agreement.

A typical factual situation in which a California court confirmed the establishment of a boundary line in a case in which the author represented one of the parties arose as follows: A, the owner of a large residential lot, built two single-family residences on his lot with a two-car garage between and to the rear of the houses. An unpaved driveway was graded from the front of the lot to serve the garage. A then conveyed one house and half of his lot to B and the other house and the other half of his lot to C. C not having a car partitioned the garage and used the half of it closer to his house for storage. B who had a car paved the driveway and built a fence between the driveway and C's house. Neither B nor C ever had their property surveyed. Both were in doubt as to the location of the boundary line shown by their respective conveyances, and both accepted B's fence line as the true boundary between their respective parcels for a number of years. C then sold his parcel to D who immediately had his parcel surveyed and discovered that C's fence and part of the driveway encroached on the parcel to which D had become the recorded owner. The court held that the elements necessary to establish a boundary line by acquiescence were established and quieted title in B to the area occupied by his fence and driveway.

63. Adverse Possession. The various methods of transferring real property interests which have been mentioned in preceding pages have all been transfers in which the agreements of the parties to the transfers were required. Although it is true that in common law dedications and in boundary line agreements the laws of all jurisdiction allow such agreements to be implied from conduct of parties to transfers, still, even in these methods of transferring real property interests, findings of actual acquiescence are required to make such transfers enforceable. Laws of all jurisdictions do recognize one type of transfer of real property interests without any agreement by the party from whose ownership the transfer is made and without any compensation. Such involuntary transfer takes place when real property interests pass by adverse possession or prescription.

Adverse possession is defined as possession of another's land which when accompanied by certain acts and circumstances will vest title in the possessor. Another and more comprehensive definition defines *adverse possession* as "the enjoyment of land or such estate as lies in grant, under such circumstances as has been commenced and continued under an assertion or color of right on the part of the possessor. There must be actual possession. The possession must be open and notorious, distinct and exclusive, hostile and continuous in the occupant or those claiming under him for the period prescribed by statute." The term *prescription* is included in the term "adverse possession" and is simply the limited possession or use of another's land which vests title in the user of the land of incorporeal hereditaments such as an easement.

64. Requirements. The requirements imposed by laws of the various jurisdictions for transfer of title by adverse possession or user vary considerably as do laws governing other methods for transferring titles to real property. Decisions of all jurisdictions are unanimous in requiring possession to be actual, visible, exclusive, hostile, and continued during the time necessary to create a bar under the statute of limitations. In addition to the requirements stated, some jurisdictions also require one or more additional facts to be proved in order to enforce transfer of title by adverse possession or user. The additional requirements are that the claimant possess adversely under some color of title; that he pay taxes on the land during the period of possession; that the possession of the claimant be lawful and peaceful; and that the claimant possess in good faith; that he reside on the land; and that he make improvements. Statutes of limitation of various jurisdictions that limit the periods in which owners may evict from their land persons who are in adverse possession of the land or using the land vary greatly. The periods of limitation range from one to thirty years in the various states.

65. Actual Possession. Actual possession as distinguished from constructive possession of land which is an incident of ownership consists of exercising acts of dominion over it, of making the ordinary use of it, and of taking the profits of which it is susceptible. Whether actual possession exists is a mixed question of law and fact. The solution of the question depends upon the situation of the parties, the nature of a claimant's title, the character of the land, the quantity of the land, and the purpose to which it is adapted and for which it has been used. In any event, it is generally required that acts that constitute actual possession be exercised with sufficient continuity to acquaint the owner with the adverse possession of the claimant should the owner visit the land prior to the end of the period prescribed by the Statute of Limitations. Such acts of domination as residing on the land, farming the land, improving the land, building structures on the land are, of course, only a few of the acts that may be used to prove the actual possession of land by a claimant. Acts of domination according to the rule generally followed need not be performed by the claimant personally but may be performed by his tenant or agent, and the period of possession required may possibly consist almost entirely of time in which the claimant himself is not even in the state in which the land is situated.

66. Open and Notorious. For possession to be *open and notorious* as is generally required for a claimant to clear or quiet a title arising out of an adverse possession, the owner must either have actual knowledge of the adverse holding or such possession must be so open, visible, and notorious as to raise the presumption of notice to the world that the right of the true owner is invaded intentionally and with a purpose to assert a claim of title adversely to his. Such adverse possession must in fact be so patent that the true owner could not be deceived.

67. Continuous. Possession in addition to being actual, open and notorious must be continuous for the whole period required by the applicable statute of limitations. This has been held to mean that the true owner of the land adversely possessed has sufficient cause during each day of the possession to legally procure the eviction of the claimant from the land as a person occupying the land without authority or right. The requirement that possession be continuous for the statutory period does not mean that successive periods of adverse possession by more than one person each of whom are in pivity can not be added or tacked together to make up the entire statutory period required. The privity between such adverse possessors may arise out of either a contractual relationship or operation of law, an example of which would be inheritance; *continuity in possession* for the statutory period, of course, means continuity of adverse possession for that period. If during a period of possession a claimant recognizes the title of owner by such an act as offering to lease or accepting a lease to the land, the continuity of adverse possession is interrupted and a subsequent claim by the possessor cannot be based on any period prior to the interruption. So too such continuity is interrupted by a judgment of eviction against the possessor and even by the filing of an eviction action against him according to some court decisions.

68. Exclusive. As has been stated, adverse possession is required to be exclusive in a claimant, which means generally in legal effect that, although it is not necessary for a claimant to exclude all other persons from entering on the land, such other use must be with his permission unless the others possess the land with him as co-tenants. Certainly any joint possession by the claimant with the owner or the public cannot meet the requirement that possession be exclusive.

69. Hostile. For possession of a claimant to be hostile, which it must be in order for it to ripen into ownership, the claimant must be in possession as an owner. Certainly a recognition of or a holding by him in subordination to the title of the owner cannot be construed to give the claimant's possession the hostile character that it must have to ripen into ownership. That the claimant or occupant openly or tacitly disavow the right of the owner is generally required. Actual possession without claim of right is not adverse possession no matter how long continued. Note should be made of the requirement that a claim of right asserted must be to the fee estate for the possession to ripen into ownership of that fee estate because possession under a claim of right to a lessor estate can only ripen into the lessor estate.

70. Boundaries of Land Adversely Possessed. The question about an ownership acquired through adverse possession that every student of surveying will naturally ask himself is what principle can be followed in determining the boundaries of the land in which rights are acquired? The answer to this question is that the law followed by most jurisdictions is that the adverse possessor who takes land under a color of title acquires title to the real property interests in land described in that conveyance whereas the adverse possessor who acquired land under an assertion of title but without any color of title takes title to real property interests only in the land that he has occupied, used, or actually possessed. Statutes and court decisions in some states make an exception to the principle stated above where an adverse possessor actually occupies a part of a parcel having well-defined boundaries though he is without color of title, in which event he has been held to take title to the entire bounded parcels. Whether or not the adverse possessor possesses land under color of title, no exception is made to the principle that there must be some actual possession. Color of title in itself confers no benefit no matter how long held and no matter how open and notorious and hostile its holding.

3

Locating Metes
and Bounds Conveyances

71. Contents. In a previous chapter unwritten means of transferring land, either voluntary or involuntary, were discussed. In this chapter and in the following chapters, methods of locating land based exclusively upon written title are presented. The principles given in this chapter define paper title rights of the landowner, but do not define the true ownership lines if title has been transferred by estoppel, adverse rights, or any other oral means. Transference of title by oral means, as given in Chapter 2, is an exception to the following principles for locating land based upon a written title.

72. Limitations on Principles. Within the following pages are many principles to be used as an aid in locating the position of real property. Unfortunately, most principles have exceptions and are not 100% applicable. The principle that monuments when called for are controlling over distance, bearing, and area, though usually true, has not been adhered to in every court case.

When deciding on the proper location of land as described in a written document, the attorney or surveyor bases his opinion upon past court decisions, statute laws, and the common customs of former surveyors. Given the same set of circumstances and facts, two judges have been known to render opposite decisions. If those who are to interpret the laws are not always in agreement, it can be expected that those who locate real property will at times be in disagreement, but such disagreement should be reduced to a minimum.

By reading numerous court cases and studying statute laws, principles can be stated that are nearly 100% true. The surveyor positions boundaries and the insuring agency insure boundaries in the place that they believe the court will uphold. By following principles that the majority of courts accept as true, the surveyor and title examiners are doing their best within their ability. These principles, as presented in the following pages, were formulated after abstracting numerous court cases, legal books, and literature on the subject. Each principle is followed by a statement of the limitations and exceptions to the principle and of selected court cases illustrating the principle.

The viewpoint of a surveyor, attorney, and title examiner are somewhat different. The surveyor's tool, mathematics, is an exact science giving only one answer for a given set of data. Trigonometric solutions lead to the same result no matter who calculates them. The attorney's answer to a legal problem is often clothed with numerous exceptions and possibilities depending upon the circumstances of the particular case. Thus, in deciding upon the meaning of the terms in a legal description, the judge holds to the principle that whatever most clearly shows the intent of the parties to the deed is the meaning. Numerous solutions for similar circumstances are thus possible, depending upon the person who is doing the interpreting and upon the peculiar conditions. As contrasted with the surveyor and the attorney, the title examiner's problem is limited to one side of a boundary problem. He is insuring that the description that he is guaranteeing does not encroach on another. If there is an overlap or a possibility of an overlap, he merely excludes the overlap from his insured area by an exception in the title policy. He does not arrive at a solution; he merely makes sure that the portion of the deed that he insures is free of defects.

Setting up rules or principles as is being done in the following pages, is subject to two criticisms. First, those accustomed to dealing in generalities and deciding each case on its own merits, will say that rules are too rigid. On the other hand, those who have a mathematical mind are apt to say that principles are too flexible since several answers may be possible.

73. Statute and Common Law. A statute law takes precedence over common law. The east one-half of a parcel of land is normally the east one-half of the area; but a Federal law declaring that one-half of a section is determined by a straight line drawn between quarter corners overcomes the common law. Passage of a statute law does not alter a property line previously established by a different law. Thus, in New York, under the Dutch rule, streets belonged in fee to the crown. Adoption of the English law did not vest title to the street bed in the adjacent owners. The rules presented herein may be altered in a jurisdiction by the particular statute law wherein the land is located.

The common and statute laws of the different states are usually in agreement, but this is not always true, as in the case of rights along navigable rivers where in some states ownership extends to ordinary high-water mark, whereas in others to low-water mark. Variations in laws between different states will be noted.

74. Presumptions at Law. A principle or policy of law requiring that from a given set of facts certain deductions are to be made from the particular facts is the foundation of presumptions at law. Thus, if a particular person has not been seen or heard from for an extended length of time, the presumption is that he is dead.   This is a *rebuttable presumption* that may be rebutted by other evidence. Certain presumptions, called *irrebuttable presumptions,* are declared by law to be conclusive, i.e., a child under seven cannot commit a crime and everyone is presumed to know the law.   A presumption (unless declared by the law to be conclusive) may be overcome by other evidence, but unless the presumption is controverted the jury is bound to find according to the presumption.   The burden of proof resides in the person attempting to prove that the presumption is incorrect.

A majority of surveying legal principles, such as monuments control over distance, bearing, and area, are rebuttable presumptions which may be overcome by evidence of a contrary intent as gathered from the entire deed and the surrounding circumstances. Whether a rule is rebuttable may be deduced from the usage of such words as "the contrary may be shown," "except," and "it is presumed."   Many of the rebuttable presumptions are so seldom rebutted that the principles may have few exceptions.   Area being subordinate to other considerations in a deed is recognized so frequently that many erroneously assume it to be an exact rule.

75. Definition. *Metes and bounds descriptions as discussed herein are those written deeds in which junior and senior titles exist.* The reason for this definition, as adopted, is to eliminate excess and deficiency proration as a consideration in discussing the location of parcels according to a metes and bounds description.   In a lot and block description, where several lots are created as a group at the same time, it is implied that the lots being surveyed are to share any excess or deficiency that may exist between found monuments.   In a metes and bounds description, where senior rights exist, the instructions are followed exactly as written, each course being fixed at a definite amount by the superior call for the course. Excess or deficiency does not exist except in so far as it is necessary to use excess and deficiency to establish the subdivision lot lines referred to or called for in the metes and bounds description; thus, the westerly 50 feet of lot 2 conveys exactly 50 feet, no more nor no less, but to establish the line of lot 2 proration might be used. In a metes and bounds description there may be conflicting elements such as: "321.02 feet to Olive Street" where it is only 310 feet to Olive Street. Both calls are exact and definite; the deficiency of 11.02 feet is not prorated but must yield to the superior call (in this case the street line).

76. Deeds Must Be in Writing and Deemed to Be the Whole

Principle. *When establishing the boundaries of a property in accordance with a written deed, the boundaries must be established in accordance with the written terms of the deed. Parole evidence may not be taken to determine the terms of a deed, but may be taken to explain ambiguous terms of a deed.*

To allow an owner to express an opinion as to what the terms of a deed were is equivalent to permitting land to be transferred by parole means. Explanations of deed terms are sometimes necessary and proper as in the following deed: "Beginning at the southwest corner of Love's intersection; thence, etc." An oral explanation that a Mr. Love formerly lived at the intersection of the present Tavern and South Grade Roads and the intersection was then known as Love's intersection is proper; but to dispute the fact that the point of beginning was at Love's intersection is improper.

Words may not be added to a deed or varied. The attorney who drew up a deed would not be permitted to claim that additional land was to be included in the deed. A deed that is applicable to either of two properties is void and may not be identified by verbal means. But a word existing may be explained. "My house and lot" is a valid deed if it can be explained that "my house" can apply to only one house. But such a deed is void if verbal explanation is necessary to distinguish between two houses that might be "my house." In other words, the addition of a term to differentiate between the two houses is not permitted.

Parole evidence may be resorted to for the purpose of applying the description contained in a writing to a definite piece of property and to ascertain its location on the ground, but never for the purpose of supplying deficiencies in a description otherwise so incomplete as not to definitely describe any land. The description must be in itself capable of application to something definite before parole testimony can be admitted to identify any property as the thing described.*

When the terms of an agreement have been reduced to writing by the parties, it is to be considered as containing all those terms, and therefore there can be, between the parties and their representatives, no evidence of the terms of the agreement other than the contents of the writing. But this does not exclude other evidence of the circumstances under which the agreement was made to explain an extrinsic ambiguity, or to establish illegality or fraud. For the proper construction of an instrument the circumstances under which it was made, including the situation of the subject of the instrument, and of the parties to it, may also be shown, so that the judge may be placed in the position of those whose language he is to interpret.

LIMITATIONS ON THE PRINCIPLE. Although in all states deeds must be in writing to be valid, there are exceptions in a few states as to the necessity of all the terms of the deed being in writing. In North Carolina the court held that where the parties to a deed have gone upon the land and made a physical survey of the same, giving it a boundary that is actually run and marked, and the deed is thereupon made, intending to convey the land that they have surveyed, such land will pass, though a different and erroneous description may appear on the face of the deed.† It was further observed, "This is regarded as an exception to the rule, otherwise universally prevailing, that in the case of written deeds the land must pass according to the written description as it appears in the instrument."

77. Direction of Survey. In surveying a lot within a subdivision any of several found original stakes can have equal standing as a starting point. If four corners of a block are found, each corner has an influence upon the location of a lot within the block, and no definite direction of survey is called for. Most metes and bounds surveys are written so that the survey proceeds in a definite direction from one point of beginning.

* Cushing v. Monarch Timber Co., 75 Wash 678.
† 162 NC 326.

78. Terms of the Deed

Principle. *When a conveyance is reduced to writing it is assumed to contain all the terms intended and is construed, if possible, to give effect to all the terms.*

Deeds to be valid must be in writing; to permit the addition of terms to a deed or the omission of terms in a deed would defeat the purpose of requiring a deed to be in writing.   California, being one of the later states admitted to the Union, enacted many of the common laws of the older states, as in the following example,* into statute laws.

In the construction of an instrument, the office of the judge is simply to ascertain and declare what is in terms or in substance contained therein, not to insert what has been omitted, or to omit what has been inserted; and where there are several provisions or particulars, such a construction is, if possible, to be adopted as will give effect to all.

79. Call for a Plat

Principle. *Where a property description calls for a plat or map and the parties acted with reference to the map, the plat or map becomes a part of the description as much as if it were expressly recited in the deed itself.*

Whenever a map or plat is called for, the monuments, distances, bearings, and data of the plat become a part of the description. According to Map 1205, as shown on Record of Survey No. 1272, or according to Road Survey No. 1020 are terms that include a map or plat as part of a deed.   It makes no difference whether the map was legally recorded or not provided the map or plat was referred to and is identifiable as the one referred to.   A call for an adjoiner often includes a call for a map or plat not mentioned in the deed; thus, "to Smith's west line" includes any plat in Smith's deed which determines Smith's west line.   Private survey notes, where properly identified as part of an original survey of the original parties, are also called for.

A map, referred to in a grant for the purpose of identifying the land, is to be regarded as a part of the grant itself, as much as if incorporated into it.†

* CCP Sec. 1858.
† Ferris v. Coover, 10 C 590

LIMITATIONS ON THE PRINCIPLE. The importance of a plat is dependent upon whether the parties acted with reference to the map and also upon the data given on the plat. If there is a clear error in the call for a map, or if it is apparent that the parties did not act with reference to the map, the map will be treated as surplusage. Where there is a call for a plat, it is presumed that the parties did act with reference to the plat; the contrary must be proved, not surmised. The data on the map determines its importance. If the plat shows an accurate survey with calls for monuments, much greater control is afforded the map than would be given to a picture drawing with little or no information on it.

80. Informative and Controlling Terms. An informative term in a deed is one that adds information about the terms of the deed, but, if the informative term is in conflict with the term that it modifies, it yields. Informative terms act as aids to distinguish the controlling term in a manner similar to adjectives that assist in distinguishing like objects or nouns from one another. "A house," "a red house," "a red house with a green roof" may all refer to the same house, but in the last-described house there is more certainty of its being correctly located because of the additional descriptive terms. "Beginning at the southeast corner of lot 2; thence N 12° 10′ E, 200.00 feet to a concrete monument" contains two informative terms "N 12° 10′ E, 200.00 feet" and a controlling term "a concrete monument." The "N 12° 10′ E, 200.00 feet" as given above is an aid to distinguish the concrete monument from similar monuments, and acts as a modifier of the term "a concrete monument." In a deed in which the controlling term cannot be distinguished or located, the informative term may then become the controlling term, as in the above "N 12° 10′ E 200.00" would become exact if the monument were lost.

In determining the title interest of a client, conflict may occur between the written instrument, the subdivision map, the measurements on the ground, or within the written instrument itself. When a conflict occurs, the surveyor, title engineer, or attorney should be able to recognize the deed term that is controlling and the one that is informational but not controlling. Court precedence and statutes, that must be relied upon to determine which conflicting term shall be followed, are discussed in their normal order of importance under the following heading.

ORDER OF IMPORTANCE OF CONFLICTING ELEMENTS

81. Junior and Senior Rights

Principle. *A junior grant, in conflict with a senior grant, yields to the senior grant.*

"First deed and last will" is the often-quoted principle. He who conveys an interest in land to one person cannot at a later date sell the same interest to another. For every title policy, abstract, or boundary location of a junior deed the title examiner or surveyor should find out what the rights of the senior deed are.

The availability of records to prove seniority of deeds varies considerably throughout the United States. In those states in which title insurance policies are issued on land, the problem is simplified since the facts of seniority are disclosed by the title policy. The surveyor who is locating land from a title policy description need not devote research time to title matters other than that described or called for by the policy. The title company is assuming responsibility for the correctness of the title as written.

Where the abstract system is used the facts of seniority are sometimes difficult to determine. In some localities, deed records are meager. In Massachusetts, two fires played havoc with the recording system.

The date and time of recording or registering a deed are not the sole determining factor in proving seniority. Thus, land sold to Jones on 2/6/56 may not be recorded until 3/6/56 whereas that sold to Brown on 2/20/56 may be recorded on 2/20/56. A court decree may eliminate former seniority since the line decreed by the court becomes the true line regardless of former seniority.

82. Intentions of the Parties to the Deed

Principle. *Excepting senior rights of others, the intentions of the parties to a deed, as expressed by the writings, are the paramount considerations in determining the order of importance of conflicting elements.*

The primary and fundamental principle to which all others relate and must yield is that the intentions of the parties gathered from the whole instrument, taken in connection with the surrounding circumstances, must control.*

* Cates v. Reynolds, 228 SW 695, 143 Tenn 667.

Principles given to determine the order of importance of conflicting elements are not conclusive but are principles of evidence or principles of construction adaptable to surrounding circumstances. A call that would defeat the parties intentions is rejected regardless of its comparative dignity.*

The following principles of construction, given to determine the control between conflicting elements within a deed, are rebuttable presumptions subordinate to the above principle. Like all principles based upon rebuttable presumptions, when the contrary is shown, the presumption is overcome and the principle does not apply. In court cases involving land boundary disputes the intentions of the parties who were a part of the original transaction are the paramount considerations; the intentions control all other points.

Land, excepting by the means given in Chapter 2, cannot be transferred by parole means; only a properly written and signed document can be used. To determine the intent of an instrument from the parties of the transaction by oral statements is tantamount to permitting transfer of titles by parole means. The intent must be determined from the written instrument itself; not from the mistaken ideas of one of the parties. Where a party believes he has a right to a disputed parcel of land and that right is not based upon a written deed, only a court or a true title owner can transfer paper title. In such cases, the surveyor should advise the client to see his attorney.

If two facts in a deed are in conflict, it becomes necessary to decide which fact was intended and which was informational before a proper location can be made. A deed written "N 20° W a distance of 310 feet to the Atlantic Ocean" presents a problem of conflict where the Atlantic Ocean is in fact 410 feet away. What was intended? Here the courts rule that the natural monument, the Atlantic Ocean, more clearly shows the intent than does the informative distance of 310 feet. In this case it would not be proper to ask the buyer or seller what his intentions were; the document as signed is the best evidence of intentions. The surveyor, attorney, or title engineer must decide what the intentions were, based upon the written instructions and the surrounding circumstances.

To determine the intent of a deed, sometimes an explanation of the terms of a deed or an understanding of the surrounding circum-

* Miller v. Southland Life Ins. Co., 68 SW 2nd 558.

stance existing when the deed was written is necessary. Thus a deed commencing "at a well-known sycamore tree in Alpine" must be investigated and parole evidence taken to explain where the tree is. A deed stating "starting at a blazed pine tree; thence running a line through a second blazed pine tree to the Cuyamaca Park line" is indefinite without extrinsic evidence. Here terms are not being added to or subtracted from a deed; an explanation of the terms existing in the deed is being sought.

In no section of the law is a statement made that any particular element written in a deed is controlling; the element most effectually expressing the intent of the parties is to be adopted. As early as 1858 it is stated,

The rules adopted in the construction of boundaries are those which will best enable the courts to ascertain the intentions of the parties. Preference is given to monuments, because they are least liable to mistake; and the degree of importance given to natural or artificial monuments, course and distances, is just in proportion to the liability of the parties to err in reference to them. But they do not occupy an inflexible position in regards to each other. It may sometimes happen, in case of a clear mistake, that an inferior means of location will control a higher.*

The intentions of the parties to the deed must be gathered from all the terms of the deed, each term taken in the light of all other terms. A call for a monument, though normally controlling, may be rejected where all the other terms in the deed indicate that the call for the monument was inserted in error. The following principles of construction are presented to define what the courts have declared as normally expressing the intent, but where all the other terms of the deed indicate that the principle does not express the intent, the reason for the principle ceases.

83. Aids to Interpret the Intent of a Deed. The following *maxims of jurisprudence* are frequently quoted in cases involving land disputes: When the reason for the principle ceases, so should the principle itself. Where the reason is the same, the principle should be the same. One who grants a thing is presumed to grant also whatever is essential to its use. Between rights otherwise equal, the earliest is preferred. Particular expressions qualify those which are general. An interpretation that gives effect is preferred to one that makes void.

* Ferris v. Cooper in the syllabus of 10 C 590.

GENERAL ACCEPTATION OF TERMS. The terms of a writing are presumed to have been used in their primary and general acceptation, but a local, technical, or otherwise peculiar signification may be shown to be the intent, in which case the agreement must be construed accordingly.

LEAST LIKELY MISTAKE.

If a deed contains conflicting descriptions, that description is to be adopted which is the least likely to be affected by mistakes.*

DATE OF EXECUTION. Unless there is something in the instrument to the contrary, a conveyance referring to natural objects and boundaries speak as of the date of its execution.

84. Control of Unwritten Title Lines

Principle. *Title lines established by estoppel, agreement, prescription, or other unwritten means are local in character and cannot be used to establish lines of the written deed.*

Any property line determined by unwritten means can only be considered local in character. An agreement with a neighbor to fix a disputed unknown line cannot be used as a basis to establish lines of the written deed.

85. Lines Marked and Surveyed

Principle. *Where lines are actually located and marked upon the ground by the parties of the transaction and at the time of the transaction and called for by the deed, the lines so marked most clearly show the intentions of the parties and are presumed paramount to other considerations, senior rights and clearly expressed contrary intentions being excepted.*

LIMITATIONS OF THE PRINCIPLE. The lines marked and surveyed have force only where (1) the lines were established prior to, or simultaneously with, execution of the deed; (2) the lines as run were considered as the lines of the transaction; (3) the lines are identified; (4) the lines run do not encroach on a senior right; (5) the lines run are not for the purpose of meandering a body of water; and (6) in most states, but not all, the lines run are called for in the deed.

* Vance v. Fore, 24 C 436.

If an owner incurs the expense of a survey and then describes lands in accordance with the lines laid out, it can only be presumed that he intended to convey to the lines delineated upon the ground and not to erroneous informative calls for bearings and distances. Measurements taken upon the ground are aids to locate where the lines are, if lost; but the lines themselves, when found upon the ground, represent the original position of the lines intended and are controlling.

All of the rules of law that have been adopted for guidance in locating disputed boundary lines have been to the end that in so doing the steps of the surveyor who originally projected the lines on the ground may be retraced as nearly as possible.*

If a deed describes the land conveyed by course and monuments and boundary-lines of other tracts, and then declares that the description given is to be according to a survey theretofore made by a person named, such survey is incorporated into the deed and becomes a part of it, and the grantee acquires title only to the land contained within the exterior boundaries of the survey.†

Numerous other cases can be cited in which the principle of acceptance of the original survey is paramount to boundaries, distances, angle, or area. A call for monuments in a metes and bounds description does not necessarily prove that a survey has been made since metes and bounds descriptions that contain calls for monuments can be written without a survey.

Proof of the original survey is usually embodied in the location of the original monuments set to mark the original survey. If, in identifying the lines as run by the original surveyor, there is a discrepancy in course and distance over monuments, the evidence of the actual original location must be beyond doubt. Preliminary lines followed by a different contract are not binding.

Where a surveyor runs lines to meander a body of water or stream, the lines run are not considered lines marked and surveyed; they are lines to aid in the plotting of the monument on paper. The boundary of the monument itself is the true line.

86. Control of Monuments

Principle. *Monuments (natural, artificial, or boundaries) called for in a deed, either directly or by a survey, or by reference to a plat*

* Morris v. Jody, 216 Ky 593.
† Hudson v. Irwin, 50 C 450.

which the parties acted by, are subordinate to senior rights, clearly stated contrary intentions, and original lines marked and surveyed, but are presumed superior to distance, angle, and area.

Biblical importance of monuments was recognized in Deuteronomy by: "Thou shalt not remove thy neighbor's landmark, which they in old times have set" (Deut. 19: 14) and "Cursed be he that removeth his neighbor's landmark" (Deut. 27: 17).

Where parties agree upon definite monuments which fix the boundaries of a parcel of land conveyed by one to the other, such monument should unquestionably control*

Whenever an original survey is made, the surveyor either finds a monument in place or sets a monument. The distance and direction measured between the monuments is dependent upon the skill and accuracy of the surveyors doing the measuring, and, if an error occurs, the error is due to the inability of humans to measure properly. The monuments are fixed in position and, if found undisturbed, are not in error. In deeds written without benefit of survey and including calls for monuments, the presumption is that the parties intended to go to the monuments, otherwise the calls would not have been inserted. Because an original monument is considered as more certain in fixing the location of a line or corner, it is given preference over distance, direction, or area. An uncalled for monument cannot, in most cases, be considered controlling when in conflict with other elements.

Monuments mentioned in a deed, in describing the boundaries of the land granted, control both the courses and distances given in the deed, if there is a conflict, without regard to whether, in fact, the monuments were seen by the parties to the deed or not.†

LIMITATIONS ON THE CONTROL OF MONUMENTS. For a monument to be controlling it must be (1) called for, (2) identifiable, and (3) undisturbed. In written deeds, uncalled-for monuments usually cannot be considered controlling. If it is the intention of the parties to have a monument controlling, it should be so stated in the deed. If a monument has deteriorated beyond recognition, either visual or by witnesses' evidence, the monument is no longer controlling. Once a monument is disturbed, its value as a control

* Norbery v. Todd, 236 NW (Mich) 628.
† Anderson v. Richardson, 92 C 623.

point ceases; but if a monument is merely obliterated and its former position can be identified, the former position will control.

Superiority of monuments over distance, angle, and area is so frequently accepted by the courts in all states that the danger of applying the principle comes from a contrary intent. If numerous other inferior terms in a deed refute the call for a monument, and if the other terms taken together indicate a contrary intent, the reason for the principle is nullified.

Control of Monuments Shown on a Reference Plat. Where a deed refers to a plat and the parties acted with reference to the plat, all the monuments shown on the plat have as much force as if mentioned in the writings itself. If the call for the plat is inconsistent with other parts of the deed, the plat is controlling only where the parties acted with reference to the plat.

Obliterated Monuments. If a monument is merely obliterated, but its former position can be positively identified by the testimony of landowners, competent surveyors, or by other qualified local authorities or witnesses or by acceptable evidence, the position so identified is controlling. Proof sufficient to convince a judge and jury that an obliterated monument has been restored to its original position rests with the surveyor.

87. Control between Conflicting Monuments

Principle. *Where there are conflicts between monuments called for and no senior right is interfered with, the monument most clearly showing the intentions of the parties is controlling. Unless a contrary intent is indicated by the deed wording, the following order of importance is presumed:*

(a) Natural physical monuments control over artificial monuments, record monuments, and meander lines.

(b) Artificial monuments control over record monuments.

(c) Monuments set after the deed was written, and not occupying the spot of an original monument, are not controlling except where the deed calls for a survey to be made.

(d) Where two monuments, otherwise equal, are in conflict, the one in harmony with distance, angle, or area becomes controlling.

(e) Monuments in the form of fences or boundary improvements built soon after the deed was written and in accordance with the original survey will become controlling where several surveyors

would locate the property lines in different places or where the true survey lines are uncertain.

(f) For a monument to be controlling it must be called for or represent a replacement of the original called for; it must be identified, undisturbed, and considered as a part of the deed.

88. Explanation of the Principles. The above order of importance of monuments is subservient to the principle: "the lines as marked and surveyed by the original surveyor are considered most clearly showing the intentions of the parties to a deed." Any monument considered marking the original lines as surveyed may be elevated in importance and outrank an otherwise superior monument. A fence built at the time of the original survey may be a monument marking the lines as originally surveyed, and thus, become controlling over other monuments.

In legal books, record monuments are often classified as natural monuments; hence the statement is sometimes made that artificial monuments may control natural monuments (meaning *record* monuments). To avoid such ambiguity, the word natural *physical* monument was used to clearly indicate that record monuments are excluded from principle *a*.

The above principles have force when monuments are called for. A specified artificial monument in conflict with a natural monument not called for would be construed by the artificial monument unless the intent is clearly indicated by other words. A deed reading "west 200 feet to an iron pin; thence S 1° 02′ W, 200 feet to an iron pin; thence east 200 feet; thence to the point of beginning" would be interpreted by the found iron pins even though the course S 1° 02′ W, 200 feet were found to be adjoining and parallel with an uncalled for river. If the deed had read "west 200 feet to an iron pin marking the Mississippi River, etc.," the deed would be interpreted by the natural monument (river).

Normally deeds are controlled by the monuments called for, but, if other factors show that the call for the monument was inserted in error, and the other factors more clearly show the intent of the parties, the reason for the control of monuments is overcome. Only where monuments most clearly show the intentions, and they usually do, are they controlling. Monuments cannot overcome senior rights. Adverse or title rights may exist along a line of uncalled-for monuments, but this is normally a function of the courts and not the prerogative of the surveyor to decide what these rights are.

The results of the authorities may be stated thus: The lines run and marked on the ground are the true survey, and when they can be found will control the call for a natural or other fixed boundary, and conclusively establish the survey; but when a younger survey calls for an older as an adjoiner, and no lines are found to have been marked for the younger on the side on which the older is called for, the line of the older becomes the division line between the two tracts; or in other words the younger is to be laid so as to adjoin the older. If a line inconsistent with the older survey be actually run and marked for the younger, it must prevail of course if it interferes with no prior right, but if no such inconsistent line be found, the law adopts, for the younger survey, the adjacent lines of the elder.*

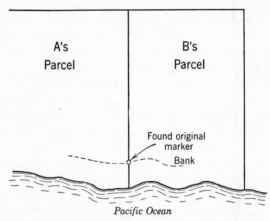

Figure 3-1. Original monuments set upon the shore control the direction of a line but not its terminus

NATURAL PHYSICAL MONUMENTS. A stake placed upon the shore of a lake or upon the bank of a stream is to be used for line (direction) purposes only, whereas the more certain monument, the water, is the determining monument that establishes the termination of the line. Thus, in Fig. 3-1, the original surveyor set a stake upon a bank near the ocean to designate A and B's parcels. Since the water line represents the limit of ownership of the subdivider, and since the surveyor could not conveniently set a stake at a submerged location, it is assumed that the stake set upon the bank was intended only for line and that the water as called for by the plat is the true termination of the line. But if the water were not called for, it is not a consideration of the deed.

* Quin v. Heart, 43 Pa 337.

In a court case* involving the above it was noted,

> Generally, in interpreting boundaries of land, resort must be had first to natural objects or landmarks, next to artificial monuments, then to adjacent boundaries, and thereafter to course and distance, and, whenever a natural object is distinctly *called for* and satisfactorily proved, it becomes a landmark to which preference must be given, because certainty which it affords excludes possibility of mistakes.

ARTIFICIAL MONUMENTS AND RECORD MONUMENTS. Monuments set *prior* to a deed and considered part of the deed are presumed superior to record monuments provided no senior right is

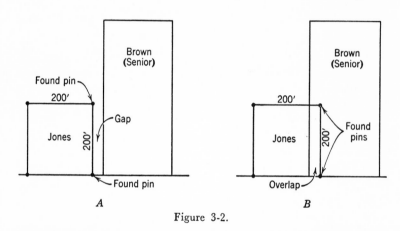

A   B

Figure 3-2.

interfered with. But artificial monuments set *after* the deed is written are presumed subordinate to record monuments. Only those monuments called for or considered a part of the deed are presumed controlling.

Conflicts between adjoiners and artificial monuments may occur as shown in either Fig. 3-2A or 3-2B. Brown's parcel is senior. Jones's property is described as " . . . ; thence, N 89° E, 200.00 feet to an iron pin located in Brown's property line; thence S 1° E, 200.00 feet along Brown's line to an iron pin located in the northerly side of sixth street; thence, etc. . . . ." The gap shown in Fig. 3-2A is vested in neither Jones nor Brown. The intent of the sale was relative to the iron pins as found, not in accordance with the unmarked adjoiner called for. The overlap in Fig. 3-2B belongs to the senior deed (Brown). The only recourse of Jones in Fig. 3-2B

* Earhart v. Rosenwinkel, 25 NE 2nd 268, 108 Ind. App. 281.

is against the seller for misrepresenting the size of the parcel sold. But if the deed were written without the calls for the iron pins, the controlling consideration would be Brown's line regardless of the distance.

MONUMENTS CONTROLLED BY HARMONY. Where two monuments are in conflict, the one in harmony with distance, angle, or surface becomes controlling. If the call is for a creek, the creek nearest to the called-for distance would control (100 CA 629).

UNCALLED-FOR MONUMENTS AND BOUNDARY IMPROVEMENTS. Monuments set after a deed was written are not controlling other than as possible prescriptive points. Monuments in the form of fences or improvements built soon after the deed was written and in accordance with the original survey will become controlling where several surveyors would locate the property lines in different places or where the true survey lines are uncertain. When there is certainty in the location of the boundaries of a parcel of land and when several surveyors would all locate the property in precisely the same place, improvements in the way of buildings, fences, etc., are usually treated as encroachments; but if the survey lines are uncertain from lack of control of known fixed monuments, and several surveyors might place the lines in different places, the fences and improvements are probably better evidence of the original lines of the original parties. The courts accept the most certain evidence to fix the limits of a property. Where the survey lines are uncertain, the courts are loathe to change existing fences as in the following case.*

Where the call of both lots in distance from the line of a street is rendered uncertain by difficulty in ascertaining the true line of the street, some surveyors sustaining plaintiff's line, and others the boundary claimed by the defendant, but there is not uncertainty as to the possession given to plaintiff's grantor by the original owner of both lots, and as to the fence which such grantor was then permitted to erect and maintain, and the subsequent grant by the original owner of the remainder of the land to defendant's grant was bounded by plaintiff's lot, which was then fenced, such boundary must be deemed a monument which will control the call for distance in the description of the defendant's lot.

89. Importance of the Word "to." "To" is a word of exclusion. In a land description "to" flashes a warning to the surveyor, attorney, or title engineer—look for a call that excludes informative

* Powers v. Bank of Oroville, 136 C 486.

calls of distance, angle, or area. "To a stone," "to a stake," "to the corner of Lot 16," "to the point of beginning," are all examples of the usage of the word "to" where the distance, area, or course given yields by presumption to the object or point called for. Surveyors often fail to properly locate points where there is a call for an adjoiner as "S 76° 21' E, 327.21 feet to the southeast corner of that land conveyed to Jones in Book 1276, page 16 of Official Records." This means in effect that Jones's land must be located before the survey can be completed, and that the cost of the survey increases since more than one parcel of ground is to be determined. A perfectly worded deed with exact distances and bearings offers a temptation to heed the distance and bearing and ignore the call for a monument, but such action can only lead to liability.

The exact location of the point that you go to has various meanings under different circumstances. When you go to the ocean you go to the line defined by statute law; if you go to a river, you go to the center or side line of the river, depending upon state laws; if you go to a highway, you go to the center of the highway unless the contrary is stated; if you go to a stake, you go to the center of the stake; if you go to a tree, you go to the center of the tree.

In the absence of any qualifying term, the designation in a conveyance of any particular object or monument as a boundary implies the middle or central point of such boundary.*

90. Control of Distance and Bearings

Principle. *Distance and bearing are presumed superior to surface, and only where distance and bearing more clearly show the intent do they control other elements.*

Distances and bearings quoted are more often informative terms than controlling terms. Dimensions give way to the objects called for; hence, they are frequently more or less in meaning.

Within subdivisions, bearing is considered as inferior and yields to distance. In metes and bounds descriptions where monuments are not called for, *both bearing and distance are essential* for the determination of a line and neither needs to yield to the other. In the case of a call for an adjoiner (record monument), bearing may be held and distance may yield. Thus, "N 10° W a distance of 25 feet to the line of Jones's property" means that you go "N 10°

* Freeman v. Bellegarde, 108 C 179.

W" to the line of Jones's property, and, if the distance is more or less than 25 feet, the distance must yield.

Though courts have agreed that amongst a diversity of calls, preference, everything else being equal, is to be given first to the natural objects called for, next to the artificial objects, and lastly to course and distance indicated, yet, when a discrepancy among the calls is established, and the circumstances in proof show that course and distance are the more certain and reliable evidence of the true locality, then course and distance will prevail.*

Where there are several provisions, i.e., bearing, distance, and a call for a monument, such a construction is to be adopted, if possi-

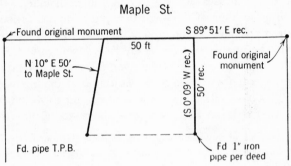

Maple St.

Figure 3-3.

ble, as will give effect to all. Very frequently bearing, distance, and a call for an adjoiner are in conflict, and, where in conflict, neither bearing nor distance is considered superior to the other. The construction is adopted that will give control to the largest number of terms and still recognize the presumed paramount control of a call for an adjoiner. There are three cases, namely: (1) Distance yields, (2) bearing yields, and (3) both distance and bearing yield. A description including all three cases is ". . . thence N 10° E a distance of 50 feet to the southerly line of Maple Street; thence, South 89° 51' E a distance of 50 feet along the southerly line of Maple Street; thence S 00° 09' W a distance of 50 feet to a 1-inch iron pipe; . . ., etc." (see Fig. 3-3). In the first call given, you go N 10° E to the southerly line of Maple Street regardless of whether the distance is 50 feet or not. In the second call, you go 50 feet along Maple Street whether the bearing is S 89°

* Booth v. Upshur, 26 Tex 64.

51′ E or not. In the third call, you go to the 1″ iron pipe whether it is 50 feet or S 00° 09′ W or not. In each case, bearing, distance, or both yielded to the call for a monument, but in each case only that element or elements yielded that was in conflict with the monument.

A consideration of the above discussion and cases leads to the principle:

Principle. *Where bearing or distance or both must yield to a call for a monument or boundary, only the particular element or elements in conflict with the monument yields; neither is presumed as paramount to the other in metes and bounds descriptions.*

The importance of distance measurement depends upon location. In the country where land values are low and distances great, the chances of error are greater and the importance of accurate measurement is less. In a city where land is of high value, distances are short, and accuracy commonly greater owing to more favorable surveying conditions, much more importance is attached to record measurements.

DAMAGES. If a distance call yields to an adjoiner who has senior rights, and if the buyer was misled into believing the distance as given was correct, a damage suit is not precluded. "Thence northerly thirty (30) feet to the right of way of the Southern Railroad"* was cause for recovery of expenses paid by the buyer to purchase several feet of the 30 feet existing within the right of way.

91. Control of Bearing and Distance over Monuments by Harmony

Principle. *Where two monuments are in conflict, and one cannot be distinguished from the other, the one in harmony with distance and angle is controlling.*

Where there is a call for natural objects, and course (bearing) and distance are also given, and where the natural object called for is unique, course and distance are disregarded, but where there are several natural objects equally answering the description, course and distance may be examined to ascertain which is the true object, for in such case they do not control a natural boundary, but only serve to explain a latent ambiguity.†

* Pritchard v. Rebori 135 Tenn 328.

† Yadkin Lumber Co. v. John M. Bernhardt, 162 NC 460. Also see Danziger v. Boyd, 24 NE 482.

92. Coordinates

Principle. *Coordinates, being based upon calculations that are dependent upon bearing and distance, are presumed inferior to monuments, bearing, and distance, but superior to area.*

Coordinates are computed from measurements of distance and angles. In the order of importance of conflicting deed elements, coordinates cannot be presumed to rank higher than the method used to determine them; they are presumed subordinate to monuments. Whether coordinates will outrank other measured distances or angles will depend upon the accuracy of the method used to determine the coordinates. Although coordinates can be established with good precision, not all are. If a monument is found and the coordinates of the monument are precisely determined by an acceptable method, and then the monument is later lost, the coordinates so established will probably form the best available means of re-establishing the former position. Likewise, if, when an original monument is set and the surveyor carefully determines the exact coordinates of the monument, the coordinates, an informational call, will probably be the best means of restoring the corner, if lost; but if the monument is not lost or disturbed, the monument itself is presumed correct irrespective of whether the coordinates were determined correctly or not. Coordinates are an informational aid to assist in replacing a lost monument, not a means to determine where a found undisturbed monument should have been.

93. Area or Surface

Principle for Control. *Excepting where area expressly states the intentions of the parties to a deed, area is presumed as subordinate to other considerations.*

"South 5 acres of lot 13" is a description in which area is the sole factor that establishes the north line of the survey, and in the absence of other calls, area is the controlling element. In a conveyance reading "5 acres no more, nor no less, described as follows," or "exactly five acres," area probably will prevail if an ambiguous description follows. But if the perimeter description is without error, the area becomes more or less. Occasionally area is the deciding factor where alternate lines can be drawn from the written instructions, and area computations fit one of the alternate lines as in the case in which the judge observed,*

Quantity . . . of itself is no description. It does not give boundaries of course (bearing and distance), therefore, metes and bounds will prevail where there is conflict. But when boundaries are doubtful in themselves, quantity often becomes the controlling fact. It often makes the metes and bounds certain. The quantity, taking the eastern ridge as the boundary, approximates the quantity mentioned in the deed, being eleven acres more than the deed calls for. Taking the western ridge for the boundary is added 680 acres, nearly ⅔ as much more, to the deed. Such a discrepancy should not be disregarded in arriving at the proper location of the disputed boundary under the circumstances disclosed in the case.

In the case† where the original surveyor established the first 13 calls in a patent and then, at the instructions of the seller, inserted adjoiner calls for the remainder of the land, the land conveyed follows the lines of the original 13 calls and the adjoiners described even though 600 acres were conveyed instead of 150 as supposed.

94. Point of Beginning. Although every deed must have a point of beginning, it is not to be assumed that the beginning corner is of any more importance than any other corner. A monument called for and found at the second corner often fixes the position of the second corner independently of the first corner. Both corners have equal standing.

95. Construed Most Strongly against Grantor

Principle. *A grant is to be interpreted in favor of the grantee, except that a reservation in any grant, and every grant by a public officer or body, as such, to a private party, is to be interpreted in favor of the grantor.*

Because language used in the instrument was selected by the grantor who is more familiar with the property, the deed should be construed most strongly against the grantor. This rule applies only where two or more meanings are possible, but not where one of the parties misunderstands a clearly expressed written meaning.

The northerly 50 feet of lot 10 as shown in Fig. 3-4 implies that the 50 feet is measured at right angles to the northerly line, thus giving the buyer the maximum possible area. In Fig. 3-5 the

* Winans v. Cheney, 55 C 567.
† Rock Creek Property Co. v. Hill, 162 Ky 324.

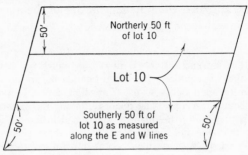

Figure 3-4. The northerly 50 feet of a lot are measured at right angles to the northerly line

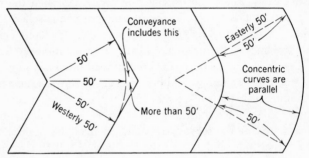

Figure 3-5. At an angle point, the westerly 50' conveys more than 50 feet because of implied parallelism

westerly 50 feet shown actually includes more than 50 feet at the angle point since parallelism is implied by the "westerly 50 feet."

96. Errors and Ambiguous Terms

Principle. *Certain and definite statements will prevail, and erroneous or ambiguous terms may be rejected; but such rejections should be as few as possible.*

Errors in any description may be corrected or rejected if there is sufficient information in the deed to indicate where the errors occur.

A reversal of bearings from N 10° E to N 10° W, as proved by a mathematical closure, may be corrected. A general statement refuted by a particular call may be rejected, but only that part refuted may be rejected.

A call in a survey or deed may be rejected for inconsistency when description enough still remains to ascertain the land with certainty.*

97. Error of Closure and Direction of the Survey

Principle. *In the absence of an analysis showing the location of an error of closure, place the error of closure in the last course which states, "thence to the point of beginning."*

Except where proof indicates otherwise, an error of closure should be placed in the last course. In a series of lots facing a curved street, and described by metes and bounds descriptions none of which would close mathematically, it was shown that, if twice the radius were used, all the lots would close. In cases of this type, the error cannot be placed in the last course, but must be placed where it occurs.

In attempting to trace the description on the ground, the court should follow the footsteps of the surveyor rather than the reverse course.†

If you follow the foosteps of the surveyor, the error of closure would fall in the last course excepting those cases where found monuments or mathematical errors prove otherwise. In the absence of certainty of the point of beginning, and in the presence of certain monuments farther along, the surveys are sometimes backed in, but this procedure is to be avoided except where the intent is clarified. The presumption is that the survey is to be made in the direction of the deed; the contrary must be justified.

If an unsurmountable difficulty is met with in running the lines in one direction, and is entirely obviated by running them in the reverse direction, and all the known calls of the survey are harmonized by the latter course, it is only the dictates of common sense to follow it.‡

98. Direct Line Measurement

Principle. *Unless otherwise stated a distance is measured in a straight line along the shortest measurable distance.*

Ambiguous conditions arising from this rule are shown in Fig. 3-6. Where a distance is intended to be along a line or curve, the

* Vase v. Handy, 2 Me 322.
† Birk v. Hodgkins, 159 C 576.
‡ 137 U.S. 584.

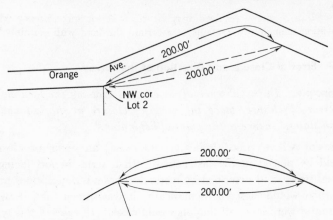

Figure 3-6. Deeds reading "200.00 feet from the northwest corner of Lot 2," may be ambiguous

fact should be so stated. "Beginning at a point in Orange Avenue 200 feet easterly from the NW corner of lot 2" is indefinite, but "beginning at a point in Orange Avenue, 200 feet easterly from the NW corner of lot 2 as measured along the road" is certain.

The law does not declare in favor of a straight line between monuments, where the language employed in the deed shows that a different line was intended. If, in a deed, the boundary line on one side of the land conveyed is described as running from a given monument easterly to a creek parallel with the southerly line of another tract of land, and such line of the other tract of land is not a straight line, but meanders, then the boundary line described in the deed will run parallel with the other line in its meandering, and not straight, and parallel with its general course.*

99. Treatment of Curves

Principles. (1) *Where a curve factor is given as a whole number, the curve factor with the whole number was probably the controlling assumed figure originally and should remain as such.* (2) *Where radius, tangent, and degree of curve are all odd, a prorate adjustment between fixed monuments is indicated.* (3) *Government (city, county, and state) relocated curved street lines are not acceptable for lot location unless based upon original curve stakes.*

* Woodard v. Fratt, 32 Cal 219.

Since curve data are fixed by computation from two known factors, the problem is to fix the most likely control. The usual situation is where the given delta differs from the delta as measured by the resurvey. Almost always the original surveyor assumes one of three factors after the delta has been fixed, i.e.: (1) the radius is assigned a whole number, or (2) the curve is assigned an even degree of curve, or (3) the tangent is assigned a definite amount. Where the radius is an odd number, the chances are that the radius was computed from other data. All even degrees of curvature have odd radius; a check must be made to determine whether the radius was derived from an even degree of curvature (always suspect this where a curve adjoins a former or existing railroad right of way). Where the tangent is an even whole number (center line or side line), the chances are that this was the intended control.

Very frequently in re-running street lines, the highway surveyors locate curves with changed radii or delta or both. Such relocation can be used for defining the recognized street boundaries which may have arisen from prescriptive methods, but cannot be used to locate original lines. It is far safer to relocate lots from known lot corners or block corners and work towards the curve in question.

100. First Stated Conditions

Principle. *Where two factors are in conflict, and nothing else indicates which of the two is correct, the first stated is preferred.*

Although only two elements of a curve are necessary to determine a curve mathematically, three are usually given. If the three, the radius, delta, and tangent are in conflict and all are odd in measurement, the first two stated are preferred. However, if by reasonable analysis one of the three is found to be in error, the one in error should be disregarded. If a correct closure is obtained by using the delta and tangent, the radius given is in error.

101. Written and Character Numbers

Principle. *Where numbers are shown both as figures and spelled out as words, the word will control unless the contrary can be proved.*

The probability of spelling out a word in error is much less than the chance of writing a number erroneously, especially where a decimal point is misplaced.

102. Unit Implied

Principle. *The scale unit of the map is implied to refer to all distances without a character mark on the map.*

The mapping custom of surveyors has been to omit the sign indicating which unit has been employed. Where the scale of the map is given, a comparison between the enumerated distances and the distance scaled will reveal the unit. On a map with a scale 1 inch equals 50 feet, unless the contrary can be shown, it is implied that all numbers unmarked by a unit are in feet.

103. Feet and Inches. Modern surveying practice, except for sectionalized land, calls for measurements to be made in feet and decimal parts of feet. Some of the older survey plats did use inches without stating such fact on the map or placing the customary inch symbol on the inches intended. Only by an examination of the map as a whole, can the intent be determined. The usage of 11, meaning 11 inches, is a clue for proving the intent to be inches; whereas, the usage of numbers above 12, indicating decimal parts of a foot, is a contrary proof.

104. General and Particular Provision

Principle. *A particular intent will by presumption control a general one that is inconsistent with it.*

Most deed descriptions have a general statement to identify the locale or vicinity, and a particular statement which identifies the land from all other parcels in the vicinity. "All that portion of Section 10, Township 15 South, Range 3 East, SBM, more particularly described as follows" is a general description which will be followed by a particular description. If in the particular description the land were clearly described as lying within both sections 10 and 11, the particular facts are controlling and that portion in Section 11, if owned by the grantor, would be conveyed even though not mentioned in the general description. This principle is based upon the fact that a particular thing described in detail is much less apt to be in error than a general statement written without detailed thought.

A deed* reading, "Thirty-one acres in the east side of lot seven in Section fourteen, township seven south, range nine west, together

* Carrere v. Johnson, 149 Miss 105.

with all improvements thereon" and followed by a particular description, "the land hereby conveyed being bounded on the south by the Bay of Biloxi; on the east by the Scale property; on the west by the lands of Martin, and on the north by the north line of lot number seven," is to be construed by the particular description even though only 17.3 acres were conveyed.

But if a contrary intent is shown by the wording, the principle may be overcome. In a will the term "the house and lot known as No. 114 Tenth Street" controlled a particular description which did not include all the land that the house occupied.* The general description showed the intent of the testator, that of willing a house and including all things necessary to enjoy the use of the house. The principle that a general description is not controlling over a specific description applies to cases where the specific description is not ambiguous.†

Particular calls are special locative calls; general calls are descriptive or directory. General calls are merely to direct a person's attention to the vicinity or neighborhood, whereas locative calls are made with care and exactness. General calls cannot be given much credit when in conflict with a particular locative call.‡

Directory calls are those which merely indicate the neighborhood wherein the different calls may be found; whereas *locative calls* are those which serve to fix the boundaries.§

BASIS OF BEARINGS

105. Deflection Method vs. Compass. Direction determinations in early surveys were made employing the compass; later surveys, mostly since 1900, were made using an instrument to measure the angle between lines. The deflection method of determining bearings fundamentally differs from the compass method. To illustrate this difference, an extreme, if not ridiculous, situation, is shown in Fig. 3-7, where a parcel of land (*ABC*) apexing at the north pole is being surveyed. Assuming that points *A, B,* and *C* are fixed in position as shown and that the deflection method is being used, the surveyor would measure the angles at *A, B,* and *C*. At point *B* the

* Gilbert v. McCreary 87 W Va 56.
† Haskell v. Friend, 196 Mass 198.
‡ Stafford v. King, 30 Tex 257.
§ Cates v. Reynolds, 228 SW 695, 143 Tenn 667.

meridian is observed by solar observation. A deed written and based upon the deflection method reads: "Beginning at point B; thence west 500 feet; thence N 27° E to the north pole; thence due south to the point of beginning." Obviously, from the drawing, it is impossible for the course N 27° E to be a true bearing. But by the deflection method all bearings are computed relative to one line AB. Contrasting this with the compass method of determining bearings, the surveyor would set up at B, take a reading on C, correct for magnetic declination, and record the true bearing. Likewise at C he would make an observation on A to determine the true bearing, and at A he would take a reading on B. The resultant description from such a survey would be "beginning at point B; thence west 500 feet; thence north to the north pole; thence south to the point of beginning." A line that is true west at every point is a curved line, BD. An argument might ensue as to the meaning of the first call "west 500 feet." Is it line BC or curve BD? An observation taken at C and in the direction of B would reveal that the bearing of line CB is N 63° E and not west as observed at B. The bearing of the line BC actually changes at every point as you travel from B to C.

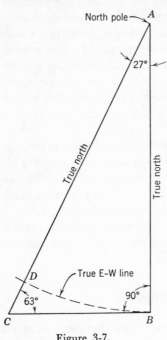

Figure 3-7.

The differences arising from land being located by the deflection method and by the compass method decrease as land is situated nearer to the equator and as land decreases in size. Within a local area, on continental United States, the differences are negligible.

In modern descriptions the following presumption exists:

Unless the contrary is stated, it is presumed that every bearing given in a present-day metes and bounds description refers to the same basis at the same point, and that the bearing of every line is constant throughout its length.

This presumption is exactly right if the original surveyor or deed author used the deflection method to compose his description. The presumption is equally valid for descriptions written from data obtained from a compass survey, provided the area of the survey is small and not near the north or south pole.

Very seldom in modern surveys does a surveyor find it necessary to make astronomical observations. Where a new parcel is carved from an older subdivision, the bearings as given on the older map are assumed to be correct; new lines are deflected from the older lines, and bearings are computed. If a deed calls for a line and defines that line as having a definite bearing, succeeding lines are surveyed relative to the line called for.

In the east, especially in the original colonies, the usage of the compass was prevalent before the development of the deflection method. Many early deeds failed to state whether their basis of bearing was magnetic or true. In some states the presumption is that magnetic was used in older deeds; in others true north is the presumption. Often, where there is a marked difference between magnetic north and true north, the facts as observed on the ground will disclose which is correct. If the original surveyor used the deflection method, succeeding surveyors, in order to follow the footsteps of the original surveyor, must use the deflection method to re-establish deed lines.

Three conditions arising in descriptions lead to the following principles for the determination of the basis of *deflected* bearings:

Principle 1. *Where the bearing of a known line is given in a metes and bounds description, the bearing as given is assumed to be correct; successive courses are surveyed relative to the given bearing whether the given bearing is astronomically correct or not.*

Principle 2. *Where a land description refers to a map and no basis of bearing is stated, it is implied that the map bearings are to be used, and all bearings in the description are referred to the same basis.*

Principle 3. *Where no basis of bearing is given or implied by a call for a map, true or magnetic bearings are to be used, depending upon the presumption in the particular state.*

Referring to Fig. 3-8, a description reading "Beginning at the NW corner of Pueblo Lot 1204, from which the northeast corner bears N 89° 50′ E; thence S 40° E, 850 feet to the true point of beginning; thence, etc." implies that the angle to be turned from the north line of Pueblo lot 1204 is 50° 10′ and not 50° 40′ as figured from the true astronomical bearings. Should the deed read "Beginning at the northwest corner of Pueblo lot 1204 as shown on the map of View Crest; thence S 40° E, 850 feet to the true point of beginning; thence, etc.," principle 2 applies. Where the View Crest map shows the bearing of the north line of Pueblo lot 1204 to be N 89° 50′ E, an angle of 50° 10′ would be turned from said line. "Beginning at the northwest corner of Pueblo lot

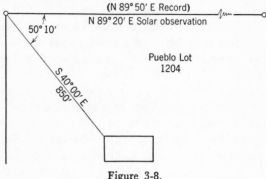

Figure 3-8.

1204; thence S 40° E, 850 feet to the true point of beginning; thence, etc." makes it necessary to use astronomical or magnetic bearings where no bearings are given on the map of the Pueblo lands. In this last case (principle 3) the turned angle is 50° 40′ where the presumption is that true astronomical bearings were used.

COMPASS BEARINGS. As previously noted, the magnetic bearing of a line is subject to daily variations, annual variations, and magnetic storm variations. Where an old description has magnetic bearings based upon a compass survey, the problem today is to determine the difference between magnetic north as it existed at the date of the original deed and as it exists today. It is well known that two compasses may give substantially different bearings for the same line at the same time. Considering this, the surest way to determine the difference between magnetic north as it existed at the time of the survey and as it exists today is according to the following principle:

Principle. *If an original line of a deed can be identified, and if it were originally described by a measured magnetic bearing, the difference between the original record bearing and the present measured magnetic bearing is the correction to apply to other record bearings of the same deed.*

But the original lines are not always identifiable. Lacking an original line to determine the difference between the present and the former declination, the next best procedure is:

Principle. *If a line can be found in the vicinity whose magnetic bearing was reliably determined at the time of the deed, determine on that line the change in magnetic bearing from the date of the deed to the present time. Next, correct the bearings of the lines being surveyed by the amount of correction noted.*

In the absence of direct methods of determining declination variations with time, tables published by the government (Magnetic Declinations in the United States in 1945, Samuel A. Deel, *U. S. Government Publication* 664, Coast and Geodetic Survey) should be consulted. The annual change of declination may be small, but over a period of time it becomes significant. The change may accumulate for many years in one direction and then change to the opposite direction. Because of the many uncertainties in applying theoretical corrections, the following should be considered as a principle of last resort.

Principle. *In the absence of a direct method of determining declination changes between given dates, and in the absence of reliable local data relative to declination changes from a given date, apply the magnetic declination corrections as given in the Coast and Geodetic Survey tables.*

"OF" DESCRIPTIONS

106. "Of" Descriptions within Subdivisions and Adjoining Streets. Land conveyed by an "of" description, such as the "easterly 50 feet of lot 2" as shown in Fig. 3-9, presents an ambiguity. Ownership of a lot within a subdivision extends to the center line of the street; hence, the easterly 50 feet of lot 2 could be measured from the center line of the street. But, in the minds of the public, the side line of the street and not the center line is the limits of private ownership, thus causing the 50 feet to be measured from the

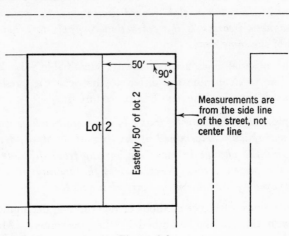

Figure 3-9.

side line. In keeping with the principle "where two meanings can be construed from a written instrument, the meaning giving the greater advantage to the grantee shall be used," and in keeping with the intent of the sale as understood by most people, the measurements are made from the side line of the lot in accordance with the principle:

Principle. *Where an owner conveys a portion of a lot of a subdivision by an "of" description, the owner conveys that portion of the lot called for by measuring from the side line of the street. Vacations or openings of streets do not alter original lot lines.*

However clear it may appear that the owner of a lot holds title to the center of the adjoining street, subject to the public easement, and that the boundary of the lot is technically, therefore, the center of the street, in view of the fact that the owner of such lot or land has no right to the possession or occupancy of any portion of such street, the word "lot" as generally and customarily used does not include that portion of the street. In the absence of any circumstances indicating that a more unusual and technical meaning of the word "lot" was contemplated and intended by the grantor, it will be presumed that the grant of a fractional part or of a given number of feet of a certain lot or parcel of land conveys the given fractional part or number of feet of that portion of the lot or parcel of land which is set apart for private use and occupancy.*

* Earl v. Dutour, 181 C 58.

In Fig. 3-10 a condition is shown where care must be used in conveying the east or west 25 feet of the ownership shown. Lot lines never change due to a street opening or closing. Because of the vacation of the street, the east 25 feet of the ownership is properly described as the westerly one-half of the street now vacated and not the easterly 25 feet of lot *B*. The west 25 feet of lot *B*

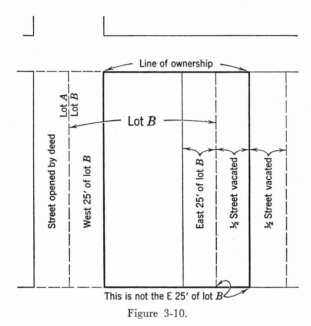

Figure 3-10.

describes a portion of a street opened, whereas the east 25 feet of the west 50 feet properly describes the 25 feet immediately adjoining the west side of the ownership.

107. "OF" Descriptions within Metes and Bounds Descriptions and Adjoining Streets

Principle. *Where an owner conveys a portion of a metes and bounds survey by an "of" description, the owner conveys from his boundary line or causes the measurements to be made from his boundary line, even though the boundary line is in a street.*

In metes and bounds descriptions, the reverse principle to that given for subdivisions usually is implied. Where the "easterly 50 feet of the following described property" is conveyed as in Fig. 3-11, the property conveyed is the easterly 50 feet of that part described even though part of the land described lies within a public street.

108. Direction of Measurement

Principle. *Where an owner conveys an "of" description by lineal measurements, it is presumed that the measurement is at right angles to the boundary line from which the measurement is made, unless otherwise specified.*

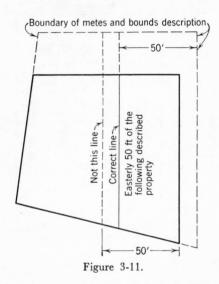

Figure 3-11.

Figure 3-4 shows a typical case where the "northerly 50 feet" of a lot, and where the "southerly 50 feet as measured along the easterly and westerly lines" of a lot give different areas. As in all measurements of this type, the greatest advantage is given to the buyer where alternate meanings can be interpreted. However, where the method of measurement is specified as in the "southerly 50 feet" of Fig. 3-4, the method as specified should be used since alternate meanings do not exist. In Fig. 3-5 are shown the correct property lines for curves and angle points in lines where lineal measurement "of" descriptions are used. It is interesting to note that where an angle point exists as shown in Fig. 3-5, there is more than the called-for distance conveyed at the angle point.

109. Proportional "Of" Conveyance

Principle. *Where a fraction of the whole is conveyed, as the west one-half, it is presumed that the conveyance is based upon area measurement unless otherwise stated.* (*See Fig. 3-12.*)

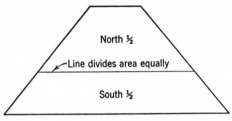

North ½
← Line divides area equally
South ½

Figure 3-12.

This principle is not in harmony with the Federal statutes which specify the method to be used for sectionalized land. Thus, the north one-half of the northwest one-quarter of section six might be considerably less in area (especially in a closing section on a correction line) than the south one-half of the northwest one-quarter. In general, proportionate conveyances under state laws are based upon acreage; under Federal laws for sectionalized land, acreage is not considered.

Occasionally, in sectionalized land where there is an odd-shaped lot bordering on a lake or land-grant line and the land is divided *after it has passed under state jurisdiction,* the question arises as to the intent of the sale where half is sold. The south one-half of lot 4 as shown in Fig. 3-13 would be divided, according to state laws, into two parts of equal area. But by the Federal prin-

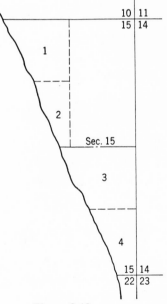

Figure 3-13.

ciple the south half would be determined by a line extending west from the mid-point of the easterly line of lot 4. Any reference to "according to Federal government survey methods" implies that the lot would be divided by linear measurements. A few of the states have adopted statute laws similar to Federal laws, and thus it becomes mandatory that the Federal rules be applied. Where division by acreage is intended, it is advisable to state "one-half the acreage of lot 4."

A deed calling for the north one half of a lot facing on the Au Gress River and not indicating a division line, is to be divided so as to make the parcels equal in area; a division such as to give each one half of the river front, is erroneous.*

Strictly speaking, any line can divide a lot into two halves, especially where the deeds state the northerly one-half and the southerly one-half. In a written description of a proportional or fractional conveyance the direc-

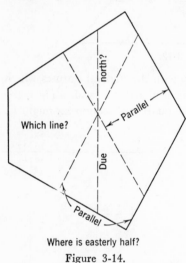

Where is easterly half?
Figure 3-14.

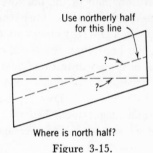

Where is north half?
Figure 3-15.

tion of the dividing line should always be given.

Proportional conveyances, where the method of locating the dividing line is specified as "the south one-half as measured along the easterly line," are divided in accordance with the method specified. "Along a line" cannot be an area measurement nor does it imply equal areas; the line would be divided in half.

110.   Indeterminate Proportional Conveyances. Indeterminate proportional conveyances are those in which the direction of the dividing line is not given or implied. Any area may be divided into half by a multitude of lines, and, where the direction of the dividing line is not given, the conveyance may be indeterminate, as shown in Figs. 3-14 and 3-15. A scrivener who fails to define the

* The Au Gress Boom Company v. Whitney, 26 Mich 42.

direction of the dividing line when writing a proportional conveyance is dedicating to the future a headache for the parties on either side of the dividing line and an unsolvable problem to surveyors. Such descriptions should and could be avoided by a few carefully inserted words in a document so that a clear and concise intent is conveyed rather than a dual meaning left to the fighting instincts of future owners. Under certain conditions the direction of the dividing line is revealed by the geometric shape of the whole parcel or by the wording of the deed.

111.   Angular Direction of the Dividing Line in "Of" Descriptions

Principle. *Where the easterly and westerly lines of a lot are shown as parallel on the original map, and in fact are nearly parallel, and where the easterly one-half and westerly one-half are conveyed, the dividing line between the easterly and westerly half is made on the mean bearing of the two lines.*

Figure 3-16 illustrates this principle as applied to two conditions. Lot A was originally shown as having due north lot lines that

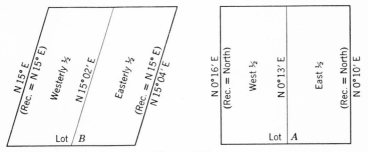

Figure 3-16.

proved to be North 0° 10' 00" East and North 0° 16' 00" East when actually surveyed. Since two parcels were sold, the east one-half and the west one-half, the problem of the surveyor is to divide the area into two equal areas and use a line equitable to both parties. Because the original lot lines were shown as parallel, the dividing line should be as nearly parallel to the sides of the lot as possible or, in other words, on the average bearing of the two sides. This principle can be overcome by other factors more clearly showing the intent, such as stakes set at the time of the division and being parallel with either the west or east line. This principle cannot be applied where the deeds read "the east one-half" and "all except the east one-half" since it is then inferred that the east one-half is intended to be a parallelogram and the west one-half is what is left. The usage of the east one-half, west one-half, north one-half, or south one-half should be avoided unless the original lot lines were due east, west, north, or south. Easterly, etc., are the proper terms, which do not imply that the dividing line must be astronomic north or west. In the case of lot *B*, Fig. 3-16, where the original lot lines were shown as parallel and where the easterly and westerly halves were conveyed, there is the implication that the dividing line should

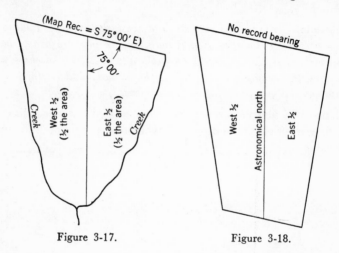

Figure 3-17.   Figure 3-18.

be as nearly parallel with the easterly and westerly lines as possible or on the average bearing of the lines.

But this principle is of little value where the supposedly parallel lines are in fact considerably out of parallelism. In one such case the court ruled that after the grantor had sold the easterly one-half he could sell only his remainder. The easterly half was laid off by parallel lines, and the westerly half received the remainder.

Nonparallel Lines

Principle. *Where the easterly and westerly lines of a lot are not parallel or north and the lot is divided into the east half and west half, make the dividing line run north and south.*

A deed reading "the east one-half" of the land shown in Fig. 3-17 would be staked by turning 75° from the northerly property line at a point that will divide the lot into two equal areas. The record map bearing, S 75° 00′ 00″ E, determines the basis of bearings (where a deed calls for a map, the data shown on the map become a portion of the written description), and, since the line is to be north, the angle of 75° properly defines north according to the map referred to. Where no record bearing exists on the called-for map as in Fig. 3-18, only an astronomical observation can properly divide the lot into the east one-half and west one-half. In neither figure is there an implication that the dividing line is to be parallel with a particular line.

East Half of Lot and the Lot Except the East Half

Principle. *When a deed reads "East one-half of lot 1" and the second deed reads "lot 1, except the east one-half," it is commonly assumed that the west line of the east one-half is parallel with the east line of the lot, provided the east line of the lot is nearly in a cardinal direction.*

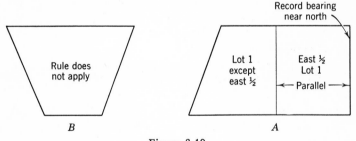

Figure 3-19.

In Fig. 3-19 is shown the application of this rule and also a case where it does not apply. In Fig. 3-19B, if the deeds were written the easterly one-half and all except the easterly one-half, the common practice would be to make the dividing line parallel with the easterly line.

The southeast one-half as shown in Fig. 3-20 was ruled to be a line parallel with the N 63° E line and not on the diagonal line as shown.*

* Pruett v. Robinson, 192 SW 537, 108 Texas 283.

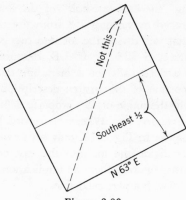

Figure 3-20.

112. Acreage "Of" Descriptions. The same general rules of Section 109 that apply to proportional descriptions (the north one-half of lot 1, etc.) apply to acreage conveyances. The direction of the dividing line, as in proportional descriptions, should always be stated when a new deed is written.

A description reading "the north 10 acres" of the land shown in Fig. 3-15 allows two interpretations, each equally valid. Similarly the "easterly 10 acres" of the land shown in Fig. 3-14 is an indeterminate area. But there are certain general principles for acreage descriptions that can be stated.

Principles. *In the absence of other qualifying terms, a given area of land on the side of a tract will include such quantity in the form of a parallelogram.*

If a given area of land is to be laid off on a given line, the shape is presumed to be a square.

If a given area of land is to be laid off in the corner of a given parcel of land, the shape is presumed to be as nearly a paralellogram with equal sides as the circumstance permits.

Chief Justice McClendon in a Texas case* stated,

Where land is described generally by acreage out of the corner or off a side of a larger tract, the courts will construct a survey of the designated acreage, by lines drawn parallel with the designated line or lines of the larger tract; not, however, because the parties have so stated in

* Woods v. Selby Oil & Gas Co. 2 SW 2nd 895, 12 SW 2nd 994.

their writings, but because the writing is silent on the subject, and the presumption that they so intended is deduced from what men ordinarily do under like circumstances.

The conditions were as shown in Fig. 3-21. The south 75 acres and the north 80 acres of a 155-acre parcel were leased within two days of each other. Area *A*, containing an oil well, was claimed by the lessee of the 75-acre parcel on the grounds that the lessor stated that his intentions were to lease the north 80 acres and then lease the remainder. But the court ruled that the south 75 acres

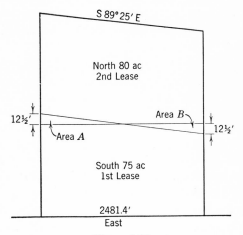

Figure 3-21.

must be laid between parallel lines, and hence the lessee of the south 75 acres had no interest in the area *A*.

A description of "nine acres in the southwest corner of the SE¼ of the SW¼ of section 1, T8N, R4W" was construed in accordance with

A conveyance of a definite quantity of land in or off of a specified corner of a designated tract is, under a well-settled rule of construction, the grant of a corner quadrangle, of equal sides, extending to the corner.*

Also a description reading, "15 acres more or less off the southwest corner of the NE¼," was construed to mean "exactly 15 acres to be taken in a square body located in the southwest corner of the land."†

* Daniel v. Williams, 58 S 419, 177 Ala 140.

† Early v. Long, 42 S 348, 89 Miss 285.

113. Ambiguity. All too often ambiguous statements or phrases in deeds are difficult to interpret and require field information. In Fig. 3-22, the "east 50 feet" is indeterminate where a curve return cuts off the corner. Better practice is to write the "east 50 feet as determined by a line parallel to the most easterly

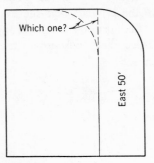

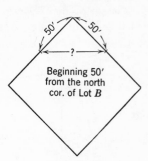

Figure 3-22. Avoid "east 50 feet" where there is a corner cut off on radius return

Figure 3-23.

line of the lot and its northerly extension." "Beginning at a point 50 feet from the most northerly corner of lot *B*" as shown in Fig. 3-23 indicates two possible points. In Fig. 3-24, the southwest one-quarter can be interpreted in two ways. The rear 15 feet and the west 50 feet in Figs. 3-25 and 3-26 can be solved only by physical

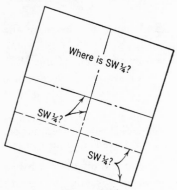

Figure 3-24.

evidence on the ground or parole evidence of witnesses. Figure 3-27, the case of the double exception, can and should be avoided by the deed author, who should never use double exceptions without checking for dual meanings. "Lot *B*, except the north 50 feet, except the west 75 feet," is clear until the second exception is made. What does the "except the west 75 feet" refer to, the north 50 feet or lot *B?*

Deeds being interpreted most strongly against the seller sets up a condition in which a double exception may cause the seller to part with more land than he intended to.

In Fig. 3-28, ambiguity is obtained where a deed reads the "east 20 feet of lots 9 and 10," owing to the dual meaning of (1) "lot 10 and the east 20 feet of lot 9," or (2) the "east 20 feet of lot 9 and the east 20 feet of lot 10." In a deed it is better to state the whole lot or lots first, and then follow with the part lots. In

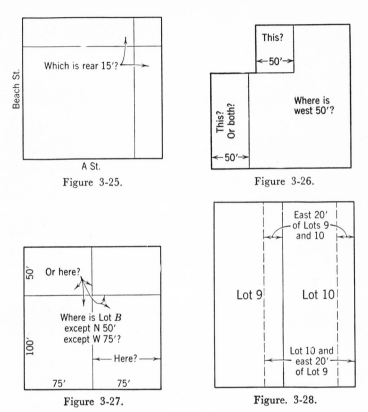

Figure 3-25.

Figure 3-26.

Figure 3-27.

Figure. 3-28.

Fig. 3-28, the sale would be construed most strongly against the seller unless the contrary could be proved.

The land conveyed to a person and the land described to a person can be entirely different points as shown in Fig. 3-29. Where land abuts a road in a subdivision, by common law and statutes, title to the road vests in the owner of the abutting land. The land described in this instance would be lot 27 excluding the road, whereas the land conveyed would include lot 27 and the road up to the center line.

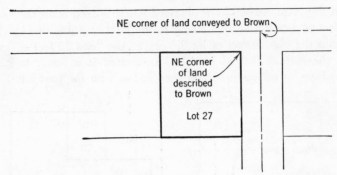

Figure 3-29.

"Thence along the west line of lot D to the mean high tide line; thence 150 feet along the mean high tide line; thence . . . " is ambiguous as shown in Fig. 3-30 because the mean high tide line changes with erosion of the shore line. The point of beginning of the next course could change with every storm.

Interpretation of intent is difficult in deeds containing double calls of the form: "thence N 10° E a distance of 200 feet to a point

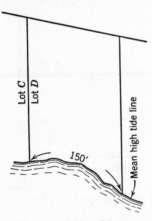

Figure 3-30. Distances along a body of water may change with erosion

in the north line of lot 13, said point being 120 westerly from the north-easterly corner of said lot and also being 110 feet easterly from the north-westerly corner of said lot." If there is surplus or deficiency, both being clauses cannot be right. If the N 10° E, 200 feet is in agreement with one of the two distances, then that one would be controlling. But if the N 10° E, 200 feet is not in agreement with either tie to the lot corners, then a prorate is indicated, provided no senior right is interfered with.

Deeds of the form "thence N 10° E a distance of 200 feet to a point in the northerly line of lot 13, said point being S 89° W, 120 feet from the northeasterly corner of said lot; thence N 89° E, 120 feet to the northeasterly corner of said lot; thence, etc.," would be construed by the tie distance. The N 10° E, 200 feet becomes more or less in character because of the extra emphasis placed upon the N 89° E, 120 feet.

OVERLAPS AND GAPS

114. Calls from Two Directions

Principle. *When writing a legal description, avoid deed calls from two directions.*

This condition arises where portions of lots are sold from two directions as the east 50 feet and the west 50 feet of a 100-foot lot. Frequently a surplus or deficiency exists within a lot, and where the above form is used there is usually an overlap or gap. The proper way to describe the parcels is "the easterly 50 feet of lot 1" and "lot 1 except the easterly 50 feet."

When an overlap exists between two parcels, the senior or first owner receives what is coming to him and the junior owner has the remainder. Where there is a gap, and the two parcels do not meet, neither has title to the surplus since the original grantor did not sell it. Thus an owner sold the west 12 acres and the east 8 acres of a parcel reported to be 20 acres by original government measure. An accurate survey revealed that instead of there being 20 acres as supposed, the said 20 acres was found to be 22½ acres owing to surplus in the section. Since the original owner had not sold the 2½ acres, title was vested in him.

ROADS AS BOUNDARIES AND ROAD DESCRIPTIONS

115. Conveyances to Center Line of Public Roads Presumed

Principle. *A metes and bounds description along a road must be written to definitely exclude the road, otherwise in those cases where the grantor owns the bed of the road it will be presumed that the conveyance intended to pass title to the center line of the road, subject to public easements.*

An owner of land bounded by a road or street is presumed to own to the center of the way; but the contrary may be shown. Such terms as "along said road" do not exclude the road. "Along the east side of said road,"* "the side line of said road," "excepting the road," and "excluding the road" are definite statements showing clear intent to exclude the road. Unless the deed clearly states that the road is excluded, or clearly indicates so by its language, the

* Severy v. C.P.R.R. Co., 51 Cal. 194.

conveyance is to the center line of the road provided the grantor owns the bed of the road. Reference to a stake in the side line of a road, along with a distance that extends only to the side line of the road, does not exclude conveyance to the center line because stakes are normally set on the side line whether the conveyance is to the center line or not. For the grant to extend to the center line, the grantor must have title that extends to the center line.

The above principle is just and based upon necessity. A person who has sold all his land adjoining a road is not interested in the maintenance or improvement of the road and should not have title interest in the road. Where improvements are made on a road and assessments are made, normally the costs are paid by the adjoining owners; however, if title to the road is vested in a third person, questions of the legality of the assessments arise. To circumvent these troubles, most states have statutes in accordance with the above principle.

116. Conveyances along Private Ways

In the construction of deeds, where lands are bounded on or by a way, either public or private, the law presumes it to be the intention of the grantor to convey the fee title of the land to the center of the way, if the title extends so far. This presumption is of course controlled, whenever there are words used in the description showing a different intention.*

But in Maine† the reverse was held; i.e., where land is bounded by a private way in Maine, the fee is limited to the side line (*see American Jurisprudence,* Vol. 8, page 781).

117. Road Descriptions. *Strip Conveyances.* Roads are frequently described as a strip, i.e., "a strip of land 60 feet in width, lying 30 feet on each side (not either side) of the following described line." Where the road ends or begins on a diagonal line, the side lines must be extended or shortened to terminate on the diagonal line.

In Fig. 3-31, danger areas, which are not usually covered by strip descriptions, are shown. Where the road is a straight line a recital stating, "extending and shortening the side line so as to terminate at the property line" is usually sufficient to cover area *A* shown.

---

* MacCorkle v. City of Charleston, 105 W Va 395, 142 SE 841. See also 187 Ky 453, 90 Ky 426, 106 Md 644, 184 Mass 452, 128 NY 253, 224 Pa 554.

† Bangor House Proprietary v. Brown, 33 Me 309.

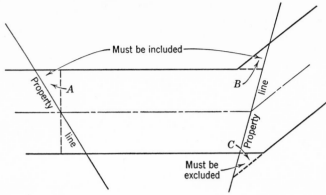

Figure 3-31. Strip conveyances should be written to include or exclude areas *A, B,* and *C*

Where a curve is involved, *continuing* instead of extending is preferable. Parcel *C* is best described as a separate exception.

118. Easements.   Definitions.   An easement is a right of use which one person or several may have in the land of another.   The easement may be *encumbering,* i.e., be within the fee title, or it may be *augmenting* (lying outside the fee title).   An *appurtenant* easement—one essential to the land such as a street—passes automatically with the fee title, whether recited or not.

Principle. *A fee simple title is presumed to be intended by a grant of real property, unless it appears from the grant that a lesser estate was intended.*

Where the word easement is omitted from a description that was intended to be an easement, fee title may pass. A title reading "30-foot strip of land for road purposes" passes fee title subject to a road easement.   "Reserving the west 25 feet for road purposes" may not create an easement, but may reserve the 25 feet in fee title subject to an easement for road purposes.

USAGE OF EASEMENTS.   The use intended for an easement should be specifically stated.   Several easements may be granted to the same strip of ground, but the right of the senior easement cannot be interfered with.   Where the width of the easement is not stated it is assumed that it is intended to be wide enough for the holder of the easement to enjoy his privilege.

WHAT EASEMENTS PASS WITH PROPERTY.   A transfer of real property passes all easements attached thereto, and creates in favor thereof an easement to use other real property of the person whose estate is transferred in the same manner and to the same extent as such property was obviously and permanently used by the person whose estate is transferred.

119. Summary and Interpretation of the Principles. In court cases certain things are presumed to be true until the contrary is proved; thus, if a letter is duly written, sealed, addressed, stamped, and placed in a mail box, it is presumed to be delivered unless the contrary can be proved. Each of the above principles can be considered in the same light; they are presumed to be correct until a contrary intent can be proved.

When interpreting conflicting terms within a deed courts apply the rule or rules of construction that most clearly show the intent of the original parties to the deed. To state definitely that one construction always controls another is to err. The foregoing principles aid in interpreting what the courts declared to be the normal manner in which intent is expressed. To determine the intent of each term of a deed without considering each term in the light of all other terms, is to err; the intent is to be gathered from all the terms of the deed, and the circumstance under which the deed was written and the facts on the ground. Many of the principles given above have force where only one other term is in conflict. Thus a call for a monument is normally given precedence over calls for distance, angle, and area; but where several other terms in the deed contradict the call for the monument, and where the acceptance of the monument voids all other considerations in the deed, the principle that monuments control is overcome by a contrary intent.

In Fig. 3-32 are shown the facts found on the ground for a deed reading, " . . . to a 1-inch iron pipe being the true point of beginning; thence, N 1° 10′ E, 200 feet to a stone mound; thence, N 89° 50′ E, 200 feet to a 1-inch iron pipe; thence, S 10° 10′ W, 200 feet to a 1-inch iron pipe; thence, S 89° 50′ W, 200 feet to the point of beginning." Considering the first call alone "N 1° 10′ E, 200 feet to a stone mound," the stone mound found at that point would be considered as correct whereas the stone mound found at N 10° 10′ E would be rejected in accordance with the rule stated in paragraph 86. However, the remainder of the deed shows a contrary intent. A mathematical closure and the finding of three other monuments in agreement with one another all indicate that

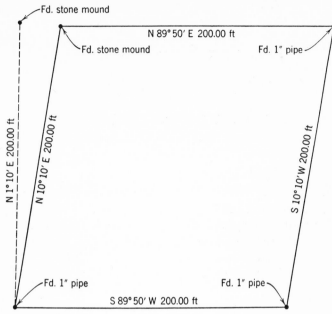

Figure 3-32.

a typographical error caused the N 10° 10′ E to become N 1° 10′ E. Only by considering all the terms of the deed can a proper intent be arrived at.

The theory of majority probability (advanced by Mr. William C. Wattles in his book *Land Survey Descriptions*) whereby all factors are balanced, giving each its proper weighted value, forms a logical approach to a complex deed problem.   Mathematical correctness, location of monuments, location and age of lines of possession, superiority of one call over another, previous survey records, the seniority of adjoiner deeds, common customs of other surveyors, and all other factors must all be examined, weighed, and balanced to arrive at a proper location.

Locating Subdivisions
and Conveyances
Lacking Senior Rights

120. Contents. Unless the contrary is stated, parcels of land created at the same time, by the same person, and by the same instrument, all have equal rights, and none can be said to have prior rights or seniority over the other. Subdivisions, proceedings in partition, wills, and simultaneous partitioning of property fall within this classification. By far the greater amount of discussion in this chapter will be centered around the location of streets, blocks, and lots within subdivisions existing within jurisdiction of state laws. Sectionalized land location, regulated by Federal laws, will be presented in Chapter 5.

121. Subdivisions. A subdivision is a division of land into parcels with the following conditions fulfilled: (1) a map or plat is made showing all the divisions of land; (2) the map or plat is filed with or by the governing agency in compliance with its subdivision laws.

If lots are sold in accordance with a plan or map, and no other consideration exists other than the map, no one lot can be said to be senior to any other lot. All lots being created at the same moment of time, i.e., at the moment of filing the map, are of equal standing. A deficiency in a block found to exist within a platted subdivision must be divided among the several lots in proportion to frontages as indicated on the plat, without regard to the sequence of their sale by the proprietor.*

But if lots are sold in sequence and the lots are added on the map after they are sold, senior rights may exist.

The positioning of subdivision lots on the ground presents essen-

* O'Brien v. McGrane, 27 Wis 446.

tially the same legal elements as those presented for metes and bounds description except that certain modifications are caused by the absence of the title holders' senior rights. In a metes and bounds description the owner of the senior title receives all that is coming to him and the junior title holder has the remainder. Within a subdivision, any excess or deficiency is divided among several lots.

Excepting Federal subdivisions, lands subdivided within a state are governed by the state laws, and relocation of boundaries must be done in accordance with the rules of the state.

Lot and block conveyances, according to a plan, offer the minimum of written language on the face of the deed; however, this does not necessarily mean that a lot and block description is the simplest conveyance to establish on the ground. Many older subdivisions and some poorly surveyed modern subdivisions present difficult conditions to the person attempting to re-establish the true deed lines. Litigation arising from ambiguous lines and figures on maps has produced numerous common laws.

The exterior boundaries of a subdivision may or may not have senior conveyance considerations, depending upon the original deed of the subdivider. If the deed defining the boundary of the subdivision is junior to the adjoiner, then all lots adjoining the senior deed are junior in character to the adjoiner. Lots within a subdivision may be junior to an adjoiner of the subdivision, but never to another lot within the same subdivision. Because the boundaries of a subdivision may be defined by a metes and bounds description or may be defined by a lot and block description or may be a free line, the principles given in the following pages for the establishment of subdivision boundaries and corners are applied.

ESTABLISHMENT OF SUBDIVISION BOUNDARIES AND CORNERS

122. Principle. *The boundaries and corners of a subdivision are determined by the lot lines of an older subdivision or by the boundary lines of a metes and bounds description. Rules applicable to the establishment of lots or metes and bounds descriptions are applied to the boundary lines as explained in the following or foregoing pages.*

Frequently it is necessary to re-establish subdivision boundaries from the stakes set within the subdivision. Conditions arise where the boundary of an old subdivision, erroneously monumented at the time the subdivision was made, must be established without reference to any of the stakes set within the subdivision. Two sets of subdivision boundaries then exist: the true boundary lines and the

True ¹⁄₁₆ corner
N 70° 50′ W 101.23 ft

Sec. 3

Center section

Fd. orig.
subdivision
corner

Hillside Acres
Map 1992
W ½ SW ¼ Sec. 3

Subdivided
without title

Figure 4-1.

boundary lines assumed to be true at the time of the subdivision. When Map 1992, Hillside Acres, was recorded the northwest corner was noted as "set 2-inch iron pipe at fence corner post in boundary of long standing." Upon properly surveying the west half of the southwest one-quarter of Sec. 3, T 13 S, R 4 W, SBM, the conditions were as shown in Fig. 4-1. On the east side of the subdivision, more than 100 feet of land was subdivided which did not belong to the subdivider, and on the north side part of the subdivider's land was not included within the subdivision. This leads to the principle:

123. Subdivision Boundaries Wrongly Monumented

Principle. *A subdivider who subdivides another's land cannot convey title to the land improperly monumented. However, after a period of time, a person may acquire title to an improperly monumented strip of land by prescriptive methods.*

LIMITATIONS ON THE PRINCIPLE.   A subdivider who subdivides another's land may later purchase the adjoining land, and, by after rights, automatically clear the title to the land subdivided.

In the case of Hillside Acres (see Fig. 4-1), title to the triangular strip of land on the east side could not pass since the subdivider did not have title to the land.   Under certain circumstances where a person occupies land with color of title, pays taxes on the land, etc., he may acquire a fee title by adverse rights (see Section 63).   If you, as a surveyor, are hired to survey the east half of the southwest quarter of Sec. 3, and you find the encroachment of Hillside Acres on the east half as above, you would note the encroachment on your map whether you considered the land lost by adverse rights or not.   The surveyor should point out to the client what rights the adjoiner has to encroachments of long standing and also advise the client to see his attorney.   Along land-grant lines, especially where the grants are several miles long, subdivisions are frequently found to overlap or not touch the true grant lines.   Where the cost of running out the true line is excessive, surveyors often fail to establish the line properly.   For further discussion of subdivision boundaries improperly monumented see Establishment of Lots, Sections 146 to 155.

124. Subdivision Boundaries Incorrectly Described

Principle. *A subdivider who incorrectly describes the boundaries of a subdivision but owns all the lands monumented conveys title to the land improperly described.*

An owner petitioned the county court to lay off a town on the north 40 acres of his holdings, but the town was actually laid off, under his direction, extending into his south 40.*   Though the plat was filed showing the town to be wholly within the north 40, all sales of the land by lots and blocks conveyed the land as monumented.

* 158 Ark 321.

CONTROL OF CONFLICTING ELEMENTS
WITHIN A SUBDIVISION

125. General. The control afforded conflicting elements *within* a subdivision, but not necessarily the boundaries of a subdivision, are expressed in the following rules. The boundaries of a subdivision, as described in the map title or the subdivider's title are controlled either by the rules for metes and bounds surveys or by the rules of construction for a larger subdivision from which the new one was carved. The rules as presented in the following pages are to be interpreted as applying to lots within a subdivision or to a portion of the lots within a subdivision, but not to the boundary lines of a lot abutting on a subdivision, unless specifically included.

126. Intentions of the Parties. *The intentions of the parties to a subdivision are paramount to all other considerations.*

By most state laws, the subdivider must subdivide and survey his land before offering any one lot for sale. The intent of size and shape of all lots is thus determined and caused to be surveyed by the subdivider. The monuments as set by the original surveyor, within a subdivision, to show the lines as marked and surveyed, express the intent of the subdivider, and, where the monuments, so set, most clearly express the intent of the subdivider, they become the paramount control for resurvey within a record subdivision. This is not true for the boundary lines of a subdivision, where prior conditions, prior surveys, or prior deeds may dictate otherwise.

127. Permanence of Lines

Principle. *Once a lot, street, or block line within a subdivision is established by the original surveyor and the land is sold in accordance with the original plat, the lines originally marked and surveyed are unalterable except by resubdivision. Subdivision boundary lines may be an exception.*

If land is to remain fixed in position and not altered by every resurvey, the principle must stand. It would indeed be folly to alter the lines of a survey and the location of the improvements thereon, just because the original surveyor failed to set his monuments in the measured position called for. The entire foundation for the stability of the land depends upon the above rule.

All of the rules of law that have been adopted for guidance in locating disputed boundary lines have been to the end that in so doing the steps of the surveyor who originally projected the lines on the ground may be retraced as nearly as possible. No rule that has been adopted to accomplish that end is more firmly established than that courses and distances are controlled by marked and fixed monuments.*

LIMITATIONS ON THE PRINCIPLE. This principle does not apply to the lines of later surveyors or to subdivision boundary lines other than free lines. If a later surveyor establishes lines and purports them to be the original lines of the original surveyor, they can be accepted only if they are in fact the original lines. Later surveyors are not empowered to place the lines in any other position than those established by the original surveyor, and, if the later surveyors establish the lines erroneously, the lines must be re-established in their original position. Where the original surveyor of a new subdivision establishes the boundary lines of the new subdivision erroneously, and the subdivider did not own the adjoining land nor has he acquired title to it since the new subdivision was filed, the boundary lines erroneously established cannot be considered unalterable unless title by after rights, prescription, agreement, estoppel, or other unwritten means has set in. The boundaries of the newer subdivision when not in agreement with the original subdivision determining the boundaries may be altered because of the permanence of the lines of the older subdivision.

The boundary lines of older subdivisions, established in error, often become the true boundary lines by prescriptive title. If the boundaries of a subdivision have been in error and improvements have been maintained along the erroneous lines for the statutory limit, it is safe to assume that the adjoiner would be barred from asserting his rights to the true line.

128. Control of Original Monuments within a Subdivision

Principle. *In a lot and block description, subdivision monuments called for on the plat, or monuments set by others to perpetuate the position of the original monuments called for, if properly identified and undisturbed, control the position of the original lot lines.*

In descriptions of the type, lot 2, block 3, map 2701, nothing other than data given on the map are called for by the writings.

* Morris v. Jody, 216 Ky 593.

Where the map is the sole written consideration, original monuments are paramount.

Monuments, as placed by the original surveyor of a subdivision, represent the true location of the lines as run by the original surveyor, and as such have prior rights over any informative call for angles, distance, or surface. Errors in the measurements of distance, angles, or surface occur, but the location of original monuments, if undisturbed, is certain and conclusive as to the original location of the lines run by the original surveyor. Calls on plats for distance, angles, or surface are informative terms to aid in the location of monuments; the monuments mark the lines as run.

A plat is a subdivision of land into lots, streets and alleys, marked upon the earth and represented on paper.*

The monuments or marks placed upon the ground by the surveyor in making a survey, constitute the survey, and the courses and distances are only evidence of the survey. Although evidence based on courses and distances from other known points is admissible as evidence to fix a corner, where no corner is found, it is not admissible to change the location of an original corner of the survey when found.†

And numerous other court cases can be cited that recognize the control of the original monuments.

In Iowa‡ the surveyor set original monuments and a few years later set other monuments in the correct position as indicated by his field notes. An original monumenting error caused a loss of about 4 feet in Cottage Grove Ave., a gain of 4 feet in University Ave., and a shifting of all lots by about 4 feet. Since the earliest purchasers had found the original stakes and relied upon them and constructed improvements in accordance with them, the court ruled that the original stakes must control. The original surveyor had no right to alter the position of the lots after the new owners had acted with respect to the stakes set even though they were not in accordance with his plat and field notes.

Where a monument is found, but not identified as an original monument set by the original surveyor or as a replacement of an original monument, the control given the monument is often subordinate to distance and angles given on the original map. An uncalled-for monument, with exceptions as noted in Section 134,

* McDaniels v. Mance, 47 Iowa 504.
† Gordon v. Booker, 97 Cal 586.
‡ Tomlinson v. Golden, 157 Iowa 237.

cannot be considered an original monument and cannot be given priority over distance or angle as given on the original map. In older subdivisions where all the original stakes are gone as well as the records of any replacement of original stakes, the burden of proving that existing city engineers' monuments or tie points are replacements of original stakes is impossible. If the tie points are in agreement with street and building improvements, and the improvements represent monuments built upon the original lines, the tie points can be accepted. Further discussion is presented under Uncalled-for Monuments (Section 134).

129. Title Monuments

Principle. *Monuments other than the original monuments or replacements of the original monuments may become title monuments by prescriptive, agreement, estoppel, or other means; however these monuments cannot be used to determine original lines of the subdivision.*

A monument found but not located in accordance with the written deed or map may be a correct title monument, yet it may not be an indicator of the original lines of a subdivision. Where a monument within a subdivision becomes a title monument by agreement, estoppel, adverse rights, judicial proceedings or any other means and where the monument is not an original, the monument, although binding on the adjoiners of that particular line, has no effect on the location of the original lot lines of the original surveyor; i.e., it is local in character.

130. Control of Monuments Over Plats. *Original monuments set upon the ground, except where the intent is clearly otherwise, control facts given upon a plat.*

The lines marked upon the earth represent the true full-scale map of the subdivision; the lines as marked upon paper are a short-hand representation of what the surveyor purported to do. Where there is an inconsistency between the map and the facts on the ground, the map must yield to the facts on the ground.* When facts cannot be established on the ground, i.e., the lines were never run on the ground, or are completely lost, the data on the map are the best available evidence.

* O'Farrel v. Harney, 51 C 125.

According to most state laws, where land is described by lot and block numbers and several parcels are simultaneously created by the filing of a map, the land must be surveyed before the sale of any one lot. In such cases the lines as marked by the original surveyor represent the intentions of the subdivider and control resurveys.

131. Identification of Monuments

Principle. *After due allowance has been made for weathering, deterioration, and other disruptive forces, the monument and its markings should be substantially the same as the record describing the monument. In the absence of visual evidence of a monument, location of a former monument can be determined by competent witnesses who saw the monument and remembered its location.*

Time takes its toll of all monuments; some faster than others. From the standpoint of permanence, stability, visibility, and certainty of identification, concrete monuments rank high, iron stakes intermediate, and wood stakes low. Pine stakes rot and disappear after a short span of life; in locations of a moist type, 5 years is the most that can be expected. Redwood is well known for its resistance to decay and termites. In the Eureka Lemon Tract many of the original 2-inch × 2-inch redwood lot corner stakes were found after a 60-year existence, and, from the excellent state of preservation, another 60 years could be expected. In the National Ranch 3-inch × 3-inch × 4 foot scribed redwood posts, set for corner locations, were found well preserved after 82 years.

Iron stakes in some locations are not nearly as permanent as is generally supposed. At one location a ¾-inch iron pipe (ungalvanized) was almost completely rusted away at the end of 4 years, whereas at another location little rusting took place in the same length of time. At the end of 25 years 2-inch pipes (ungalvanized) set at Sunset Cliffs were completely rusted, whereas the redwood cores, driven in the pipes, were in good condition.

Of all the devices invented by man, the bulldozer disrupts more stakes than any other. Monuments yield to the power of the dirt-happy dozer operator, pushing the earth around at will. In one subdivision after all improvements were in, not a single lot stake or boundary stake was left—construction work destroyed them all.

132. Record Descriptions of Monuments. Surveyors in describing monuments are often careless, the usage of pipe sizes being an example.   Common sizes of pipes do not measure the same as the stock designation.   A 1½-inch pipe measures 2 inches outside diameter.   In reporting the size of a set pipe, many take the actual outside measurement, but others give the stock designation.   If the outside diameter of a 1½-inch pipe is measured, it should be noted as 2 inches O.D. and not as a 2-inch pipe.   Early survey records were notoriously poor in monument descriptions; usually none was given.   Most modern laws have rectified this by requiring descriptions of all monuments set.

133. Principles for the Presumed Control between Conflicting Monuments within Subdivisions.   *Two or more monuments in conflict with one another are given control in the following order of presumed importance:*

(*a*) *Original natural physical monuments called for control over artificial monuments, record monuments, and meander lines.*

(*b*) *Original artificial monuments control over record monuments.*

(*c*) *Original monuments set to mark the boundary lines of the subdivision or original monuments set along the boundary line may yield to senior rights.*

(*d*) *Uncalled for monuments may become controlling by common report.*

(*e*) *A series of boundary improvements built soon after the original stakes were set, in agreement with one another and long acquiesced to by adjoining owners, are sometimes better evidence of original survey lines than are measurements of angles and distances.*

(*f*) *Where two monuments, otherwise equal, are in conflict, the one in harmony with distance, angle, or area becomes controlling.*

A major portion of the surveyor's work when he is surveying a lot within a subdivision is the relocation of monuments set by the original surveyor or the relocation of points set to perpetuate original monument locations.   Land surveyors might be considered detectives who have specialized in the art of finding and relocating monuments and lines run by the original surveyors.   In the absence of found monuments, other factors, such as distances given on a plat, become controlling and will be discussed under the establishment of streets and lots.

134. Explanation of the Principles.   The above principles are similar in meaning to those given in Section 87.   Except along the boundary lines of subdivisions, senior rights do not exist, thus accounting for the greater importance of monuments within subdivisions.

Any principle given to determine the control between different types of monuments is merely a rule of construction to put in force the intentions of the parties, and any rule of construction is rebuttable and may be overcome by contrary evidence.   In conveyances, natural physical monuments in the form of lakes, rivers, and the like are given preference because of the certainty of their identification. Artificial monuments representing the lines as originally marked and surveyed are given preference over record monuments such as the line of the adjoiner, because of the greater certainty of location. But along subdivision boundaries artificial monuments cannot overcome senior rights, unless prescriptive rights have ripened into a fee.

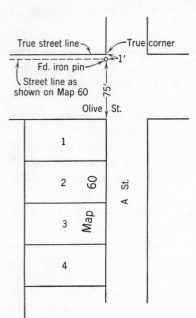

Figure 4-2.

CONTROL OF ARTIFICIAL MONUMENTS. If artificial monuments set or used by the original surveyor represent the lines as actually run by the original surveyor, the artificial mounments are presumed superior to record monuments. Thus, in Fig. 4-2, the original surveyor assumed in error that the iron pin found at the northwest corner of Olive and A streets was the true corner and started a subdivision from the erroneous point. To relocate a lot within this subdivision the surveyor should use the pin as his starting point and overlook the indicated call for the record monuments (street line). The street as originally staked is 76 feet wide, and is unalterable except by conveyancing. In a New Jersey case, very similar in nature, the opposite was held. The court reasoned that the unmarked street was a natural monument (?) that should control the artificial monument.

MEANDER LINES. Artificial monuments set by a surveyor to meander a natural monument, such as a lake, river, or ocean, must yield to the more certain monument, i.e., the water line. Meander lines are run for the purpose of plotting the natural monument being meandered and should not be considered as marking the boundaries or limits of the natural monument.

Where a meander line of land included in a patent is run to approximately locate a shore line and to afford the means for calculating the area of the land granted, the shore line constitutes the real boundary.*

UNCALLED-FOR MONUMENTS. Monuments that are not called for are uncertain; to be controlling they must be proved. If they are found in the proper position for angle and distance, they automatically become the correct corner marker. If they are not in the measured position, they cannot be accepted without substantial evidence showing that they are in the position of the original stakes or that they have been accepted by common report.

Unfortunately in many older subdivision surveys a statement explaining what monuments were set was not required by law; yet we know that the lands were surveyed and points were set. A statement on a map "Surveyed by Wheeler in 1880" is conclusive proof that the land was surveyed, and it must be presumed that monuments were set (115 C 481). Notes taken at the time of early surveys amounted to private property, and as such have been lost as the years advanced. In some instances a thorough resurvey reveals consistent types of corner material set by the original surveyor. In Rancho Mission, 4 inch × 4 inch redwood posts about 3½ feet long, set 1 foot in the earth and stenciled with black paint indicating the corner numbers shown on the original map, were found as corner monuments. In a superior court case involving lot line location in Wadsworth's Olive Grove, 2½ inch × 2½ inch × 18 inches redwood stakes were accepted as the original stakes even though not mentioned on the original map. In each of the above, the principle that a monument should be called for before it is controlling is defeated because of the preponderance of evidence proving what was actually set, even though not described on the maps.

This principle is sustained by the court in their findings.†

In an action to quiet title involving a disputed boundary between lots, referring to a map uncertainly locating the line, and no field-notes of the survey for the map are indicated, it is proper for the court to receive the

* Curtis v. Upton, 175 Cal 322; and Watson v. San Pedro, 169 C 520.
† Andrews v. Wheeler, 10 CA 614.

best evidence obtainable to determine the location as a matter of fact, and in so doing so, was important to inquire as to the location of such stakes and monuments as were commonly recognized, accepted and used in lieu of lost or destroyed original monuments, and in the absence of more certain evidence, these stakes and monuments would be sufficient to support a finding as to the location of the boundary.

In this case the court accepted parole descriptions of the old monument found but not described on the original map. One surveyor testified, "In making surveys here in the city (Los Angeles) the last 13 years I have had occasion to retrace a great many of those Hancock corners. There were a few of them left and that was one of the last to go."

COMMON REPORT. By reputation certain markers are commonly accepted by surveyors and others as being correct, even though they cannot positively be proved to be correct. As time progresses and the records of replacement of original property monuments are lost, surveyors become more and more dependent upon the acceptance of monuments whose history is lost in antiquity. If people accept a monument, and especially if numerous surveyors accept a monument, the monument is said to be the true marker by *common report*. Monuments that can neither be proved to be correct nor incorrect and are commonly accepted as being correct may be accepted by common report, but a monument that can positively be proved to be incorrect, though accepted by many as being correct, cannot be accepted by common report. Mere measurements from distant objects does not disprove a monument. But finding an original monument not in agreement with a ½-inch pin accepted by common report certainly casts doubt upon the pin. For a monument to be accepted by common report the following factors need to be present: (1) the monument is commonly accepted by people as being correct; (2) the monument is in a position that represents a spot marked by an original surveyor or a spot that could have been marked by an original surveyor; (3) the monument cannot be disproved.

IMPROVEMENTS AS MONUMENTS. A resurvey, made after the monuments of the original survey have disappeared, is for the purpose of determining where they were, and not where they ought to be.* If the original monuments of an original survey are lost and a series of old fences, old buildings, or other aged boundary indica-

* Diehl v. Zanger, 39 Mich 601.

tors are in agreement with one another, it is usually presumed that the improvements were built upon the original lines of the original surveyor and stand as monuments representing the original lines. This has more force where it can be shown that the improvements were made soon after the original stakes were set.   Many tie points are set in accordance with this principle.   Where there is uncertainty as to the city tie points representing the position of the original monuments, and where several surveyors are uncertain as to the true location of the original monuments, the courts will frequently settle upon a fence of long standing as being the better evidence of a boundary line.   Acceptance of improvements is a principle that should not be applied if there is better evidence of the original positions of the monuments.

Associate Justice Cooley in 1878* stated in his opinions:

This litigation grows out of a new survey recently made by the City Engineer.   According to this survey the practical location of the whole plat is wrong, and all the lines should be moved four or five feet east . . . . When an officer proposes thus dogmatically to unsettle the landmarks of the whole community, it becomes of highest importance to know what was the basis of his opinion.   The records in this case fail to give an explanation.

Nothing is better understood than that few of our early plats will stand the test of a careful and accurate survey without disclosing errors.   This is true of the government surveys as of any others, and if all the lines were now subject to correction on new surveys, the confusion of lines and titles that would follow would cause consternation in many communities. Indeed the mischiefs that must follow would be incalculable, and the visitation of the surveyor might well be set down as a great public calamity.

But no law can sanction this course.   The surveyor has mistaken entirely the point to which his attention should have been directed.   The question is not how an entirely accurate survey would locate these lots, but how the original stakes located them.   No rule in real estate law is more inflexible than that monuments control course and distance . . . the city surveyor should therefore, have directed his attention to the ascertainment of the actual location of the original landmarks, and if those were discovered they must govern.   If they are no longer discoverable, the question is where they were located; and upon that question the best possible evidence is usually to be found in the practical location of the lines, made at the time when the original monuments were presumably in existence and probably well known.   As between old boundary fences, and any survey made after the monuments have disappeared, the fences are by far the better evidence of what the lines of a lot actually are.

* Diehl v. Zanger, 39 Mich 601.

Also Justice Hand* noted:

In case of a disputed boundary line in a town, city or village, where the monuments from which the town, city or village was platted are lost or destroyed, the courts ought not to disturb boundary lines between lot owners which have been acquiesced in for years and upon which the lot owners have erected improvements.

135. Distance, Direction, and Area

Principle. *Within a subdivision distance, direction, and area are presumed subordinate to the intent of the subdivider, the lines as marked and surveyed, and original monuments. Distance is presumed superior to direction and area, and direction is presumed superior to area.*

Because of the inherent errors of the compass, which was used in early surveys, distance was always considered more certain than direction and more nearly expressive of the intentions of the subdivider. With present-day surveying methods, direction can be measured with as much certainty or even greater certainty than distance. This is especially true where accurate triangulation methods were used in the original location of property lines and calculation was depended upon for distance. As yet the courts have not recognized this fact, and the rule that distance in subdivisions is superior to direction, even in modern surveys, is still followed.

Area, being a computation dependent upon both bearing and distance, must be considered subordinate to the means from which it was determined.

136. Apportionment Principle. *In the absence of senior rights, excess and deficiency found to exist between original monuments are distributed among the lots in proportion to the original record measurement of the lots.† This is a principle of last resort.*

The original recorded distance between two monuments as noted by the original surveyor is the original record distance. Later surveys may show record measurements to be in error. The difference between the two measurements is the excess or deficiency. Where excess or deficiency occurs and where several parcels of land have

* Westgate v. Ohlmaher, 251 Ill 538.

† Coppin v. Manson, 144 Ky 634; Blaze v. Pyles, 350 Ill 344; Nilson v. Kann, 314 Ill 275; Anderson v. Wirth, 131 Mich 183.

a right to the surplusage or shortage, it is distributed among all the parcels in proportion to the original record linear measurement or, as commonly known, by proportionate measurement. Proration of surplus or deficiency is to be regarded as the last resort, and can only be applied after all hopes of locating the position of original monuments or original lines are exhausted.

Subdivision maps and proceedings in partition are unlike metes and bounds descriptions where a deed for a certain portion of land is made to one person, designating specific boundaries of the land conveyed, and afterward a deed is made to still another person for another portion of the land, designating other specific boundaries. The grantor, in the case of metes and bounds descriptions, would have no power to again convey any part of the property that he had previously conveyed to the first grantee. But those claiming under the same subdivision map, the same proceedings in partition, the same decree, or the same will, all have equal rights to their full quota of land.

When a city lot is subdivided, and a plat of the subdivision recorded, and the actual aggregate frontage is less than is called for by the plat, the deficiency must be divided between the sub-lots in proportion to their several frontages as indicated by the plat, without regard to the order of their alienation by the proprietor.*

Where several tracts are surveyed in one block, but the lines of division are not run between them and subsequently the block is found to contain more land than the aggregate amount called for by the survey of the tracts within it, the proper course is to divide the surplus proportionally among the several tracts.†

When ruling was made on a case involving excess acreage and involving part of the "Gore" in Burnham, Maine, according to the plan by Charles Hayden, it was stated:

It must be presumed, in the absence of circumstances showing the contrary, that variance arose from an imperfect measurement of the whole piece of land. Grantees of lots laid off on a particular plot hold in proportion to their respective conveyance.‡

In any conveyance where senior and junior rights exist, the junior deed has title to the remainder; thus excess and deficiency do not exist and proration cannot apply.

* O'Brien v. McGrave, 27 Wis 446, in 1872.
† Parks v. Baynton, 98 Pa 370.
‡ Susi v. Davis, 133 Me 354.

137. Proportionate Measure.* Proportionate measure is used to relocate a lost point in the exact proportion as the original measurements. Proportionate measure is based upon distance. In the absence of record linear measurements and the presence of area measurements, area may be used.

SINGLE PROPORTIONATE MEASURE. Single proportionate measure is used on a single straight line between original points; the distance between all points originally reported on the said straight line must have the same proportion between the original record distance and the present distance. An example of this would be in a rectangular block of six lots, 50 feet each, where the present measurement is 300.6 feet. By proportionate measure and in the absence of found original lot corners, the 0.6 foot would be distributed among the lots in equal amounts; or, since all the lots are the same size, each lot would now measure 50.10 feet in width.

DOUBLE PROPORTIONATE MEASURE. Re-establishing a lost point by measuring from four known points is called double proportionate measure. This is applicable where land is subdivided into a checkerboard pattern, as for example, sections of land. See Section 175.

ACREAGE PROPORTIONING. In a few of the early subdivisions, acreage only was shown. In such case, proportionate amounts of acreage are the only means of establishing lost boundaries. All other methods should be exhausted before acreage is resorted to.

ESTABLISHMENT OF STREETS OR BLOCK CORNERS

138. Establishment of Streets. Streets are established by the following methods listed in their usual order of importance: (1) by natural monuments, (2) by artificial monuments and lines actually run at the time of making the plat, (3) by improvements, (4) by the line of nearby streets where called for, (5) by the data given on the plat, and (6) as a last resort, by proportional measure. Since the lines of streets and blocks are usually one and the same thing, the establishment of street lines normally establishes block corners.

139. Establishment of Streets by Natural Monuments

Principle. *Natural physical monuments where called for are presumed to control street lines.*

* Annotations A.L.R. 97-1227.

Figure 4-3 shows a portion of Bird Rock subdivision with Ocean Boulevard existing between blocks 20, 21, and the ocean.   This defines the boundary of Ocean Boulevard as being riparian and extending to the ocean regardless of the distance given or scaled on the original map.   To do otherwise in this case would defeat the intentions of the subdivider, who has shown clearly by his plat that he intended the street to extend all the way to the ocean.

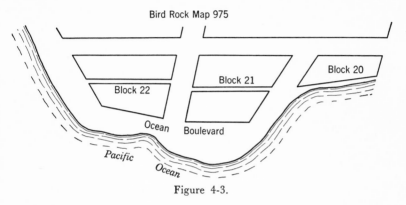

Figure 4-3.

140. Establishment of Streets by Artificial Monuments and Lines Actually Run at the Time of Making the Plat

Principle.   *After natural physical monuments, artificial monuments that represent the actual lines run by the original surveyor at the time of making the plat are presumed to control street lines irrespective of whether the courses, distances, and street improvement agree with the plat or not.*

Identified original monuments set by the original surveyor and found undisturbed will control the street line as shown in Fig. 4-4. Street A was found to measure 50 feet between monuments instead of 40 feet as indicated on the original map.   The adjoining lots cannot each receive 5 feet extra by narrowing the street; the artificial monuments found definitely establish the street line.   Similarly, if the record measurement is greater than the actual width indicated by monuments, the street cannot be widened at the expense of the adjoining lots.   In the above the subdivider's intentions are clearly shown by the markers set at the time of the subdivision.   The fact that the map maker erroneously noted 40 feet instead of 50 feet does not alter the facts on the ground.

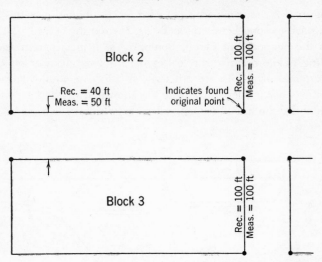

Figure 4-4.   Streets are not record width where original monuments indicate otherwise

Owners of land south of Cheltenham Ave. in St. Louis* could not claim 20 feet of the surplus in the subdivision merely because they were entitled to a pro-rata share of the entire subdivision. Stones placed in Cheltenham Ave. by the original surveyor fixed the position of the street; all surplus belonged to the land north of the street.

An artificial monument representing the lines as marked and surveyed by the original surveyor becomes controlling over record monuments (boundaries), as in Fig. 4-2, where the survey started from an erroneous iron pin. The record monument (north line of Olive St.) even though called for on the map must give way to the iron pin which represents the lines as marked and surveyed. Olive Street is then 76 feet wide instead of 75 as indicated on Map 60.

Street improvements not built in accordance with the original stakes set by the original surveyor cannot change the street alignment; the original control is conclusive and cannot be altered. This does not preclude a city or other governing agency from claiming the streets by prescription; it merely means that a street claimed by prescription, if properly described by written title, must be described in accordance with the original lines as marked and surveyed by the original surveyor if such lines can be proved.

* Williams v. City of St. Louis, 120 Mo 403.

141. Establishment of Streets by Improvements

Principle. *In the absence of natural monuments or evidence of lines actually run by the original surveyor, improvements, such as curbs and paving, which were installed in accordance with the original survey monuments, are presumed controlling.*

The duty of the surveyor is to relocate lines as they were originally run by the first surveyor; curbs located properly when the original stakes were available are the best evidence as to where the original lines were run, and as such are controlling. The court* observed:

> In determining the line of a street, measurements upon such street are of more value than measurements taken elsewhere; and if they or the places where they were cannot be located, the boundaries of the street as actually opened and used should be ascertained; and if such location has been generally acquiesced in by the public, by lot owners and by the municipality, in the *absence of more certain evidence,* it will be conclusive.

When the reason for the principle ceases, i.e., the improvements were not built in accordance with the original stakes, so does the principle. Because the engineer failed to place his construction stakes in accordance with the original stakes, does not allow the street to be moved in position to cover a construction blunder. Where a street is long used by the public, and the location of the improvements are not in accordance with the original monuments, the public may acquire a right, by prescription, to that portion improved. This *does not* alter the original street lines; they are unchangeable. Where by reasonable analysis it can be shown that the original street lines and the present improvements are not in agreement, the original block corners may not be in the side lines of the streets as obtained by prescription.

Home Ave. was constructed and staked by locating the street from Swan's Addition, which was a resubdivision of a portion of Wadsworth's Olive Grove. When attempting to locate Home Ave. as shown on Wadsworth's Olive Grove, the surveyor measured the record distance as shown on said map and set the side line markers for Swan's Addition. He failed to note that the measurements extended to the center line of the street and thus located the street

* Orena v. City of Santa Barbara, 91 Cal 621.

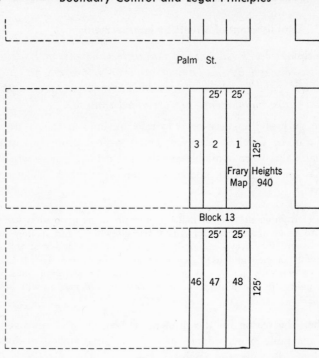

Figure 4-5.

incorrectly by one-half its width.   In Superior Court it was ruled that the starting of a survey from the side line of Home Ave. as established by Swan's map was improper for the establishment of a lot in Wadsworth's Olive Grove.   Home Ave. had been built and improved for more than 20 years in its incorrect position; yet the improvements alone, unless built in accordance with the original stakes, are insufficient to control original lines.   If there had been a lack of evidence to show where Home Ave. should have been with respect to Wadsworth's Olive Grove, the court might have ruled differently.

142. Establishment of Streets by the Line of a Nearby Street

Principle.   *In the absence of artificial monuments and evidence of the lines as marked and surveyed, where a street is plotted as being the continuation of a nearby street or commencing at a nearby street, the line of the nearby street is presumed to control.*

The call for the line of a street is a call for a record monument, and as such is presumed to control over distance and angle. Figure 4-5 shows part of Frary Heights subdivision where Palm Street is shown as a continuation of the street of the adjoining subdivision. In the absence of finding original monuments within the subdivision of Frary Heights, the continuation of the line of Palm Street as found in the adjoining subdivision is proper. This principle is defeated where found original monuments indicate the street line is not a continuation of the adjoining street.

143. Establishment of Streets by Plat

Principle. *In the absence of evidence covered by the foregoing principles, the exact width of the street as given on the plat and the distances and angles are presumed to govern street location. Occasionally a measurement index is applied.*

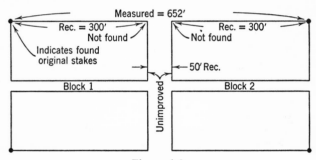

Figure 4-6.

In the absence of monuments, streets are given the width called for on the plat, regardless of excess or deficiency that may exist within a subdivision. In Fig. 4-6, two original 2-inch × 2-inch hubs found two blocks apart measured 2 ft in excess of the record distance. The proper procedure is to give blocks 1 and 2 exactly half of the surplus (1 foot each) and give the street exactly 50 feet as called for by the map. The rights of the public to a street are thus protected by the courts so that deficiency or excess cannot exist within a street except where the original monuments set by the original surveyor indicate otherwise. In a few jurisdiction a measurement index is applied.

MEASUREMENT INDEX. Not all surveyors are in agreement with

the theory that excess or deficiency is not to be prorated in the width of the street. If the original surveyor, establishing monuments within a subdivision, used a long or short tape, the streets as well as the blocks would be equally long or short. The uniform excess or deficiency is referred to as the measurement index. In Long Island City, Queens, N. Y., the chain used to tie point was 100.08 feet instead of 100.00; the custom is to prorate 0.04 foot in a 50-foot street. In San Diego, California, Horton's Subdivision has a fairly uniform surplus of ½ foot to a 300-foot block, yet streets are always staked at exactly 80.00-foot width and all surplus given to the blocks.

A measurement index can be applied where there is a uniform overage or shortage in many blocks within the same subdivision, but cannot be applied where there are erratic measurements that do not indicate a uniform error. In a subdivision where the blocks are supposed to be 300 feet each and the actual measurements indicate 300.25, 300.35, and 300.30 feet, it might be assumed that the original tape was in error. But if the measurements were 299.75, 300.25, and 300.00 feet, no measurement index exists.

Only one court case* was found in which excess and deficiency was distributed within a public way, wherein 43.8 feet shortage was divided between two lots and an alley. The weight of reason is against such a procedure. Before the establishment of any subdivision, street widths that are acceptable to the public are determined by the governing agency and the subdivision is accepted by the public agency upon the condition that the streets are of a certain definite width. The size of lots are determined by the whims of the subdivider, the desires of the purchasers, and the minimum area requirements of the planning agency. The tendency of all subdividers is to make the streets of minimum width so as to have a maximum amount of land for lots. The streets are definite and fixed whereas the lots are variable.

144. Establishment of Streets Where Width Is Not Given

Principle. *If the street width is not given on the plat, the width as scaled on the map will govern as the last resort.*

The complete absence of any other acceptable evidence on the ground makes it necessary to use scaling as the only means avail-

* Coop v. Lowe Co., 263 Pac 485—Utah.

able to determine street width.   Scaling should be considered as the last resort.

145. Establishment of Streets by City Engineers' Monuments

Principle. *Offset monuments set by the city engineer to perpetuate the position of the original monuments of the original surveyor, control street lines.   Offset monuments not based upon adjacent original monuments, are afforded control only in proportion to the accuracy with which they were set in accordance with the foregoing rules.   City engineers' monuments long acquiesced to are presumed to be correct; the contrary must be proved.*

Just because a city engineer or his assistants set a monument does not prove the monument to be correct.   Where a monument is set by measurements of angle and distance from other known original monuments, the monument so set cannot be considered as controlling except where it is in agreement with the data given on the map.   This is well illustrated in the case* where the original town of Sacramento was surveyed by Sutter in 1848 or 1849.   The city engineer in 1878 established the street lines by starting at points many blocks apart and prorating in the intervening streets.   Evidence showed that the Sutter survey and the stones set in the 1878 city survey were not in agreement.   A surveyor in 1911 established a lot with respect to the 1878 stones and overlapped a fence.   The court observed:

> In this action in ejectment and for damages for the unlawful detention of land, which involved the location of the boundary line between two lots in a city of Sacramento, upon the dividing line of which a fence has existed for probably 40 years, or more, it is held that in view of the meager character of the evidence of the real boundary line as fixed by the original survey of the city (Sutter survey) and in accordance with which the deeds of the parties were made, and of the disputed strip in the enclosure of the defendant, the court was justified in finding that the plaintiffs had failed to establish any title to the property in controversy.

Here the court accepted a fence as better evidence than uncertain monuments.   It is to be noted that, although the stones set in the later survey were not acceptable for the location of lot lines within a block of the subdivision, they might be acceptable for the deter-

* Perich v. Maurer, 29 CA 293.

mination of the street lines. Streets can be acquired by usage of the public even though not based upon an original survey.

In the case* where the city had passed an ordinance making all surveys not conforming to the new points established by the city engineer as nul and void, the court observed:

An ordinance of a city providing that a certain monument shall from that date of the ordinance be the initial point of the town survey and of all locations of lots and streets, and that all surveys made thereafter, that shall deviate from such initial point shall be null and void, is void, and not admissible in evidence to show enlarged rights against the city. The city council cannot change the location of streets by such a resolution, or affect the rights of land owners under grants previously made, nor can it lay down rules of evidence by which the courts are to determine the location of the points or lines of the survey.

In this case a landowner was attempting to move his fence some 16 feet to include a portion of the street that was long recognized by improvements. The shift in the lot position was brought about by using the point of beginning as mentioned above.

Where a deed from a city bounded the land granted by a street which had been previously located and surveyed by a city surveyor, and the grantee had for many years held possession of and fenced the lot nearly according to such location and survey, and the street was in use by the public accordingly, the fact that a new survey of the street is afterwards made, changing its line so as to exclude therefrom a strip of land adjoining the lot granted, cannot entitle the grantee to remove his fence to the line of the street as fixed by the new survey, so as to include such strip in his lot, but he is restricted to the lot as bounded by the line of the street as *originally* surveyed.

In determining the boundaries of city lots the line as originally located on the surface must govern; and a line shown by monuments as platted by the city authorities and acquiesced in for many years must control course and distance, and cannot be overturned by measurements alone.†

Summarizing the three court cases above, it can be said that city engineers' monuments are not controlling where they were not correctly set with reference to the original stakes. However, where city engineers' monuments have long been acquiesced in and used by surveyors and the public, they will be *presumed to be correct* except where the contrary can be shown.

* Orena v. City of Santa Barbara, 91 Cal 621.
† Dasier v. Dalto, 140 C 167.

ESTABLISHMENT OF LOTS WITHIN SUBDIVISIONS

146. Effect of Mathematical Error

Principle. *Excess or deficiency within a block, caused by a mathematical error in a lot, is given to the lot in which the error occurs.*

In block 9 of Mission Beach (Fig. 4-7), the length of the north line of lot *D* is indicated as being 66.58 feet; yet the scaled distance is 96 feet more or less. Mathematically the lot will not close by

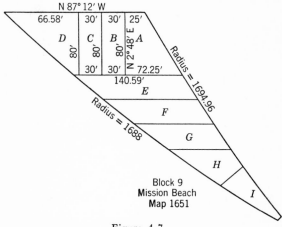

Figure 4-7.

30 feet more or less. If each lot were to receive a portion of the surplus, the lot corner common to *D* and *C* would shift some 24 feet west of that pictured and the intent that lot lines are about 90° to the north line and parallel with each other is defeated. The proper method is to give lots *A, B,* and *C* their record distance, which will automatically correct the mathematical error of lot *D* by establishing the length of the north line of lot *D* at about 96 feet.

147. Excess or Deficiency Confined to a Block

Principle. *Excess or deficiency occurring within a block should not be prorated among other blocks.*

Excess or deficiency in the land platted into lots, blocks, and streets along with an absence of original markers does not always indicate that intervening streets should be located by proration. If possible, each block should be treated as distinct* and the shortage or surplusage therein apportioned among the lot owners. Proration is a principle of last resort, and once a street is established by one of the means previously discussed, the street lines are unchangeable. Just because block 1 in Fig. 4-8 is 1 foot short and block 2 is 1 foot long does not mean that the location of B Street can be moved 1 foot east in order to give blocks 1 and 2 each

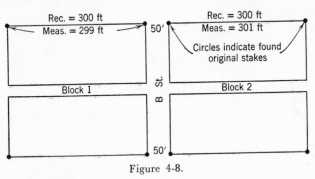

Figure 4-8.

exactly the record measure. All the shortage existing in block 1 is prorated among the lots of block 1, irrespective of the surplus in an adjoining block. Only if B Street were not established by improvements, possession, or found points, could blocks 1 and 2 each receive an equal frontage between streets.

148. Excess or Deficiency Distribution within Blocks. When measuring a line and excess or deficiency is found, it cannot be assumed that the error of measurement occurred in any one part of the line, but in all of the line. The original surveyor probably had a chain that was either too long or too short, and the error would occur in all parts of the line. Where a subdivision shows ten lots of equal frontage, it is logical to assume that any small excess or deficiency should be distributed among all lots equally and not given to the end lot.

Excess or deficiency distribution is applicable where several parcels were created simultaneously by proceedings in partition or by subdivision. Proration of surplusage and shortage cannot apply

* Anderson v. Wirth, 131 Mich 183.

to metes and bounds descriptions where a senior grant exists, to blocks with undimensioned end lots, to errors the location of which can be established, to lines where monuments fix the location of the error, or to lines where points are fixed by improvements made in accordance with the original stakes.

Where land is plotted into lots, blocks and streets, and surplus exists, the surplus is to be divided among the lots.*

Where in platting a village it turns out that by mistake the blocks are not so long as the plat represents, the deficiency must be apportioned between the lots of the block according to their apparent size as shown by the map.†

And many more.

149. Single Proportionate Measure

Principle.   *Excess or deficiency existing in a straight line between fixed monuments within a subdivision is distributed among all the lots along the line in proportion to their record measurements.*

In the absence of any agreement or question of title by adverse possession, where a block has been platted into lots and the lots sold, a shortage in the block will be prorated among the several lots.   Complainant, therefore, when it received its deed, the property being described as the north half of lot 5 and the south half of lot 6, and not by metes and bounds, did not get paper title to 50′ frontage, but only received paper title to the north half of lot 5 and the south half of lot 6 after the same had been prorated by reason of the deficiency.‡

This principle is intended to apply to the distribution of small errors and small differences between present measurement and original measurements.   Where gross errors occur, a different rule often, but not always, applies.   Where the block is abutting upon a subdivision line, extreme caution should be exercised in locating lots by proration since the principle frequently does not apply.

Figure 4-9 shows the application of proration to a block where the block corners are fixed by monuments.   Angles at the block corners must be measured to show the angles for any one lot, but the angles have no influence on distribution of excess or deficiency for it is based entirely upon linear measurements.

* Coppin v. Manson, 144 Ky 634.
† Qunnin v. Reimers, 46 Mich 605.
‡ Nilson v. Kahn, 314 Ill 275.

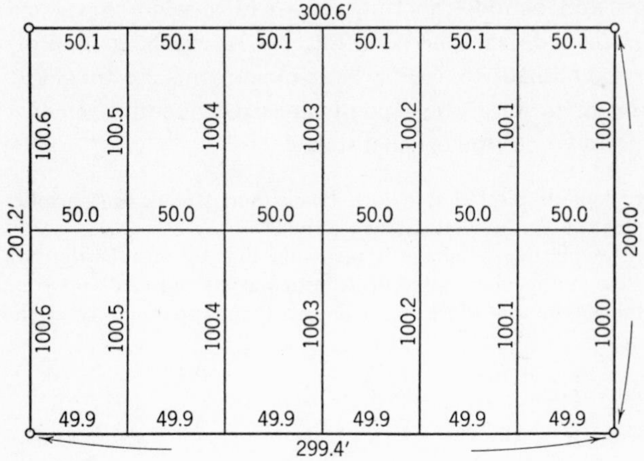

Original lot size 50 × 100 ft

Figure 4-9. Errors of measurement are divided proportionately between the lots

150. Single Proportionate Measure on Curves

Principle. *Excess or deficiency existing between fixed monuments on a curve is distributed among the lots along the curve in proportion to their record linear measure.*

In Fig. 4-10, the length of the curve along Le Roy Street was found by actual measurement to be 8.40 feet short of the original measurements. The beginning and end of the curve was fixed by street improvements and by monuments set by the city engineer; no trace of the original markers could be found. Since the beginning and end of the curve was fixed by presumption and could not be altered, lots 4, 5, and 6 must take all the deficiency. The fixed monuments preclude lot 7 from being short in measurement.

Proration along a curve is controlled by the same rule that governs single proportionate measure; i.e., each segment of the curve has the same proportionate length of the total curve as is shown on the original map. The new length of lot 6 is calculated as follows:

$$127.09 \times 44.62 \div 135.49 = 41.85 \text{ feet}$$

The lot frontage then becomes 2.77 feet short of the record measurement.

Frequently the city engineer establishes a curve that is not based upon the original curve points, because the curve data given on the

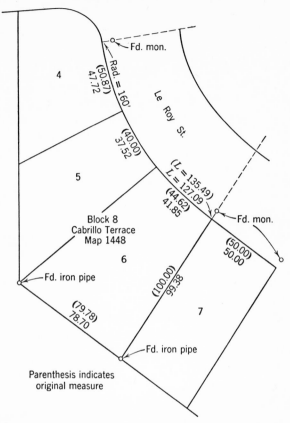

Figure 4-10.   Proportionate distribution of errors along a curve

map are out of agreement with the stakes set on the ground or because the stakes as set are not a true curve.   Any survey locating lots from a curve alignment not in agreement with the original stakes is done so with poor foundation for the survey.

151. Distribution of Excess and Deficiency beyond a Monument

Principle.   *Excess or deficiency cannot be distributed beyond any undisturbed original monument.*

Undisturbed original monuments are fixed in position and cannot be overridden by proration even when the monuments are found in the middle of the block.   Using the same block as shown in Fig. 4-9, the distribution of excess and deficiency is modified by the found monuments as shown in Fig. 4-11.

Judge Marshall in 1897* when commenting on the establishment of lot corners from known corners found within a block as compared to remote block corners, observed:

The unvarying rule to be following in such case is to start at the nearest known point on one side of the lost corner, on the line on which it was originally established; to then measure to the nearest known corner on the other side of the same line; then if the length of the line is in excess of that called for by the original survey, to divide it between the tracts connecting such two known points, in proportion to the lengths of

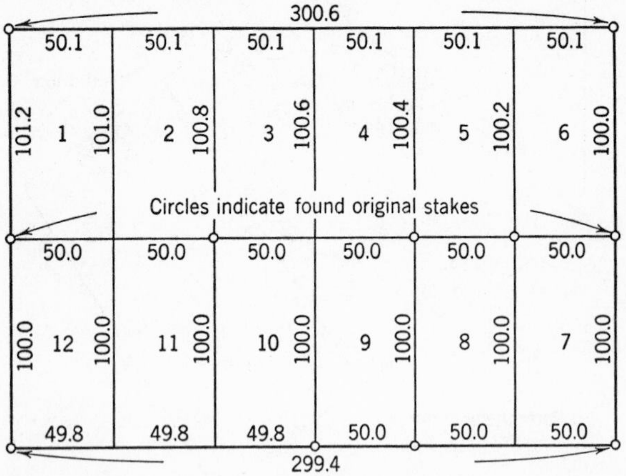

Figure 4-11. Errors of measurement are distributed proportionately between found original monuments

the boundaries of such tracts on such line, as given in the survey . . . . The method always followed in re-establishing corners is to measure the line connecting the nearest known corners, on the same line, on either side of the lost corner, and then divide the excess, if any be found, as before stated.

152. Establishment of Lots Where the End Lot Measurement Is Not Given

Principle. *Where the end lot measurement is not given, all the excess or deficiency is presumed to be given to the end lot.*

Where the original subdivider failed to give a dimension to the last lot in the block, it can be assumed that the subdivider intended

* Lewis v. Prien, 98 Wis 87.

to place all the excess or deficiency in the last lot. The fact that the last lot scales differently from the amount of land on the ground does not alter the principle. This situation frequently occurs along the boundary of a subdivision where the subdivider was uncertain as to his true boundary line. In Fig. 4-12 is shown the condition in block 13 with the general note that all regular lots are 100 × 100 feet. Since lots 3 and 4 are true remnants of lots, all excess or deficiency is given to lots 3 and 4 regardless of the scaled distance. Lot 3, which scales 100 feet, will receive 150 feet.

In New Jersey* a map showed 50 lots, 48 of which were regular with a width of 25 feet each, two were irregular and undimen-

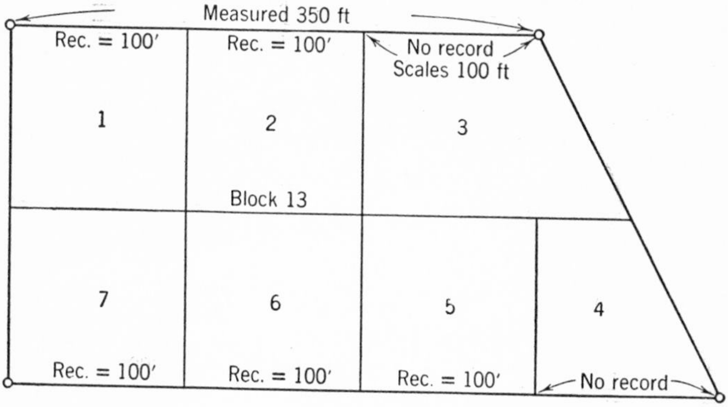

Figure 4-12.

sioned; the court ruled that the regular lots would receive 25 feet each and the undimensioned lots would receive what was left over even though they did not get the amount of land that the map appeared to give them.

153. Remnant Principle. *Where excess or deficiency is given to an irregular-shaped lot at the end of a block, the method is called the remnant rule. Few jurisdictions accept it.*

An end lot designated as 75.38 feet† was given a block deficiency of 21.6 feet on the theory that, if the subdivider had known that the deficiency existed, he would have made the last irregular lot smaller in size and would have maintained all other regular lots at 25 feet. Blocks along a subdivision boundary often utilize this rule

* Baldwin v. Shannon, 43 NJL 596.
† Barrett v. Perkins, 113 Minn. 480.

but for a different reason (see Section 159). No other case was found supporting the remnant rule.

In Michigan* the rule of apportionment of deficiency between lots of a block must stand irrespective of the end lot being fractional except where the contrary is proved.

The majority opinion on the remnant rule is well expressed by Judge Cassoday.†

Had the plat given the specific dimensions of each lot of the several lots fronting on Jefferson Street except lot 1, and given no dimensions of that, then such absence of the dimensions of that lot would have evinced an intention that it should include whatever should be left after setting off the several lots of which the specific dimensions had thus been given, whether the same should be more or less, but where, as here, the specific dimensions of each and all of the several lots fronting on Jefferson Street are given upon the plat, and there is no lot in the block of which the specific dimensions are not thus given, there seems to be no substantial reason why such excess should be given wholly to one lot merely because its dimensions, as given upon the plat, differ from those of other lots.

154. Establishing of Lots Where No Lot Measurement Is Given

Principle. *In the absence of physical evidence on the ground and in the absence of measurements given on the plat, scaling of the plat must be resorted to.*

Some early subdivisions failed to mention how big the subdivided lots were. On one map where ten lots, each scaling 50 feet, were shown, only 450 feet were found to exist on the ground. Since several houses were built by measuring 50 feet from each end of the block, a tangled legal snarl ensued. One of the unoccupied lots was finally purchased, and the block was resubdivided to adjust the houses within the land occupied. Scaling in this case indicated that there were ten lots of equal size about 50 feet each. Facts on the ground showed the existence of only 450 feet or 45 feet per lot. Scaling could not be relied upon to establish any fact other than that the lots were of equal size; the physical evidence on the ground was better evidence of the intent of the lot sizes.

Paper shrinks or expands with changing moisture conditions. A map reproduced by the dry process or the wet process will give a resulting print different in scale from the original. A map drawn

* Quinnin v. Reimers, 46 Mich 605.
† Pereless v. Magoon, 78 Wis 27.

on a scale of 1 inch equals 100 feet cannot be scaled sufficiently accurate to determine whether a distance intended to be 50 feet is either 48 or 52 feet. Because of these facts, scaling must be considered poor evidence to be relied upon only as the last resort.

155. Lots with Area Only Given. Where a subdivision shows area only, the proration of any excess or deficiency presents almost insurmountable difficulties. Area is a computation depending upon two linear measurements and directions, any of which can be altered. Sometimes area errors can be localized by the existing streets or lines of possession. Location of property lines from area data is considered a last resort to be applied after all other means have failed.

Where in an instrument of conveyance of real property the quantity of land to be conveyed is stated, the statement is not to be viewed as a factor in establishing boundaries unless the more particular description given is indefinite and uncertain.*

ESTABLISHING LOTS ADJOINING SUBDIVISION BOUNDARIES

The foregoing discussion has been confined to lots within a subdivision but not adjoining the boundary of a subdivision. Lots abutting a subdivision boundary frequently require special attention where there was an error in the establishment of the original boundary line and at a later date the true boundary was recognized. The question of adverse rights often enters into these cases.

156. Establishing Lots Adjoining Subdivision Boundaries Correctly Established

Principle. *Where the boundaries of a subdivision were correctly staked originally, the foregoing principles for the establishment of lots are applied.*

157. Establishing Lots Overlapping the True Subdivision Boundaries

Principle. *Lots abutting on a subdivision boundary line cannot extend beyond the title interest of the original subdivider except as noted in chapter 2.*

* 169 Cal 505.

This principle is best explained by the following illustrations. The map of Middletown Addition filed in 1871 shows a picture plan and a general note giving the street widths, block sizes, and lot sizes. On the original map, the boundary line of the subdivision was shown as in Fig. 4-13. When the boundary was run out from known existing monuments on the ground, about 12 feet of the subdivision was not in existence. Lots 8, 9, 17, and 18 cannot

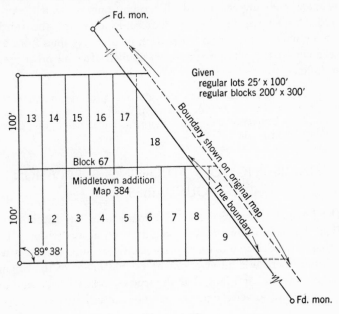

Figure 4-13.

extend beyond the true boundary because the subdivider did not own the land and could not extend beyond his ownership, nor can the deficiency be distributed among all the lots in the block, since the original lot lines are unchangeable. The proper procedure in this block is to give each lot in the block 25 feet and place all the excess or deficiency in the lots adjoining the subdivision boundary.

Figure 4-14 shows block 21 of New San Diego, Map 456, where the subdivider subdivided part of the bay of San Diego in error. Since title to the tidelands could not be conveyed, all of lots D, E, F, G, and H and parts of I, J, and C do not exist on the ground. Complete blocks are shown in this subdivision, which are wholly below the mean high-tide line, the limit of private ownership in

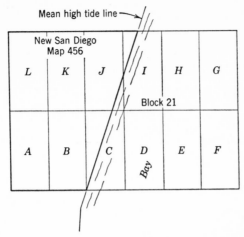

Figure 4-14.

California. Adverse occupation of government land cannot ripen into a fee title; so, regardless of line of occupation, land below the mean high-tide line cannot be privately owned.

LIMITATIONS ON THE PRINCIPLE. As previously noted, title to land can be transferred by estoppel, adverse rights, agreement, and other unwritten means.

158. Lots Not Touching the True Boundary of the Subdivision

Principle. *Where the original subdivider failed to subdivide all his land as shown by found original monuments, do not extend the lot lines beyond the limits of the original monuments. Title to the unsubdivided land remains in the original subdivider.*

When surveying College Park Unit 2, Map 2218, the surveyor failed to subdivide all the land owned by the subdivider by the amount shown in Fig. 4-15. The original stakes for lot 6 were found, and no doubt existed as to the original location of lot 6. The fact that there was a strip of land varying in width from 10.6 to 12.94 feet, not subdivided by the subdivider, does not give lot 6 a title interest to the strip.

LIMITATIONS ON PRINCIPLE. This rule cannot apply to small insignificant errors, nor to cases where the original subdivider's monuments cannot be found. Where a subdivider indicates by his title that he subdivided all his land, and no monuments on the ground

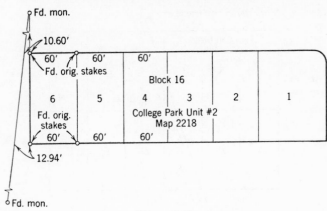

Figure 4-15.

indicate otherwise, it must be presumed that all his land was intended to be subdivided.

In Washington* 4½ feet surplus was found to exist between the street and the subdividers true boundary line. The court ruled that, where the lots as marked on the plat occupy the entire space between the north and south boundaries of the tract, the excess must be apportioned among the lots.

159. Proration of Excess and Deficiency in Blocks Closing on Subdivision Boundaries

Principle. *A considerable excess or deficiency existing in blocks adjoining a subdivision boundary is prorated only as a last resort.*

Considerable error in the closing block of a subdivision may indicate an error in the original location of the subdivision boundary. If an error existed in the original boundary location of the subdivision, and if at a later date the boundary were moved to fit the true deed location of the subdivision, it is not advisable to move the lots by proration to fit the new boundary. Lots once established are unalterable.

There must be reasonable proof showing that an error probably existed in the original subdivision boundary location. If there are ten blocks in a subdivision, nine of which measure very close to the original record and the tenth, existing next to the subdivision bound-

* Booth v. Clark, 59 Wash 229.

ary, is found 30 feet short, the inference is that the original boundary line was erroneously established and later moved to the true location. However, if the subdivision consists of only one block and the block is found 30 feet in error, proof is lacking to show on which end of the block the error might have occurred, and in such a case the only equitable solution is to prorate the error.

Blocks abutting upon subdivision boundaries cause no end of grief to surveyors and landowners. Although a lot within a block that adjoins a subdivision boundary may be insured by a title company without fear of liability provided it is described by lot number instead of size, the location and size of such a lot on the ground may be in serious doubt. Two possible solutions exist: (1) prorate the error; and (2) give the error to the end lot. If the error were brought about by a relocation of an incorrect original boundary line, the error would be applied where it occurred, i.e., next to the boundary line. But if the error were not due to the boundary line being moved from its original location and no evidence exists to localize the error in one lot, the error would be prorated. This is a question of proof, the burden of which is placed upon the surveyor.

160. Locating Lots from Boundary Lines

Principle. *It is safer to locate lots from the interior of a subdivision rather than from the boundary line of a subdivision.*

Proved interior lots and street locations within a subdivision are a safer starting line for staking the lots within a subdivision. The frequency of error in locating boundaries is far more common and is dangerous to use. Any lot or street within a subdivision should be located from the data on the map itself and not from a relocated boundary line of an adjoining subdivision.

LIMITATIONS ON PRINCIPLE. Rarely the original lot lines of some of the early subdivisions were never staked on the ground, and in such cases the lots can only be relocated from the boundaries of the subdivision.

PROCEEDINGS IN PARTITION

161. General. A court decree resulting from proceedings in partition vests title in the various parties at the same time and by the same decree; none can be said to be senior to the other. Unless there is a definite statement limiting a party to a definite quantity of land, all are presumed to have a proportionate share of surplusage or shortage.

162. Establishing Lines Determined by Proceedings in Partition. In many proceedings in partition a map or plan is made showing the division between the various allotments, and, where the allotments are described by the map, the division lines between the various parcels are determined by the same principles as given previously for subdivisions. The map is treated like any other filed or recorded subdivision map. If the allotments are described by written language and there exists a gap or overlap between the allotments, the gap or overlap is prorated among the allotments.

The procedure for determining property lines resulting from proceedings in partition is clearly stated: *

First: If the monuments or marks on the bounds for the corners of the several allotments can be found, such marks or monuments must govern, and distance and bearing must be disregarded.

Second: If the monuments or marks on the ground are lost or obliterated, parole evidence may be introduced in connection with the record to show their location.

Third: If no monuments were set, except theoretically on paper, the proper location of these monuments will be determined by prorating the distances as given in the records, according to the length of the frontage of the several allotments.

Fourth: If the actual computed sum of the lengths of the several allotments as given exceeds the length of the tract partitioned, it will be construed that the decree means that, upon the hypothesis that the entire length of the whole tract is as stated, then the length of each assignment shall be (proportionately larger than) as given; but if it be less, the assignments of allotments must lose in like proportion.

WILLS

163. Establishing Boundaries of Allotees of Wills. All heirs receiving land under a will have equal standing, and unless there are contrary words, each is to share in any surplusage or shortage. Where by the terms of a will the testator intended to give all his land to his heirs, and the tract is found to contain excess as shown by the sum of the acres given to the different heirs, the surplus will be prorated among the said heirs proportionate to the named acreage of each.†

* McAlpine v. Reicheneker, 27 Kan 257.
† Bennett v. Simon, 152 Ind 490.

SIMULTANEOUS DESCRIPTIONS

164. Definition. Simultaneous descriptions are those that divide a larger parcel into parts by instruments executed at the same time. The deeds may be written similarly to metes and bounds descriptions, but, since they are simultaneously written and created at the same time, no one is senior to another.

165. Proration. Two deeds executed at the same time by the same seller, and each calling for the line of the other as a division line, will be construed to convey the entire tract and any excess or deficiency will be divided between the two in proportion to the quantity owned by each.*

ESTABLISHING PROPERTY DESCRIBED BY BOTH METES AND BOUNDS AND SUBDIVISION DESCRIPTIONS

166. Ambiguity resulting from double descriptions of the same parcel of land can and should be avoided by deed authors. "Lot 4, block 2, according to map 1240 being also the following described land; beginning at the southeast corner of block 2; thence west 150 feet to the true point of beginning; thence, north 100 feet; thence west 50 feet; thence, south 100 feet; thence, east 50 feet to the true point of beginning" is a description that invites troubles. The block shown in Fig. 4-16, being long in all directions, causes the two described parcels to be in different locations. If the seller owned all of block 2 at the time of the sale, certainty of location would be impossible.

In Louisiana a square described as #2670 on a map and also described as bounded by Paris Ave., Hamburg, Manuel, and Fowy Streets was controlled by the monuments called for and the possession of the owner rather than the erroneous square number.†

In some areas of the United States, particularly the older regions, double descriptions are more prevalent. Occasionally three or four rewrites of the same land create numerous ambiguities. If it can be shown that the new description was intended by the scrivener to be the same as the old description, the new description should be interpreted in that light. If this cannot be shown, the grantor then

---

* Sellers v. Reed, 46 Tex 377.
† Lassus v. Gourgott, 169 La 577.

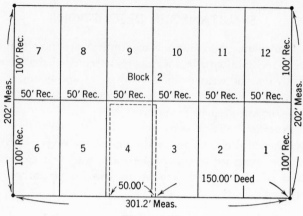

Figure 4-16.

remains as the owner of any unconveyed land. But the grantor cannot convey that which he does not own; hence any land included that did not belong to the grantor is not conveyed.

167. Summary. The principles of law that determine a particular property location are simple; the applications of the principles are difficult. Principles for locating land can be stated, but, if they are incorrectly applied, they are of little value. The fundamental principle, "The intentions of the parties to a deed as expressed by the writings are the paramount considerations when determining the order of importance of conflicting elements," may be a simple statement, but its application is complex. In the chapter on metes and bounds surveys and in this chapter, the application of this principle and other principles was expanded by reviewing the thoughts of the courts as expressed by numerous court decisions.

Basically the principles that apply to the relocation of metes and bounds descriptions and subdivision descriptions are the same, but they are modified by differences in senior rights and statute laws. The method to be used in subdividing land is regulated by law; hence the intent of the subdivider is often determined by the procedure prescribed by law. In this chapter the means of surveying and relocating former subdivided lands within states was discussed. But these principles cannot be applied 100% to land subdivided by the Federal Government. Federal statutes determining the procedure for laying out subdivisions differ from state statutes, and the application of legal principles must be modified by the statute laws.

In the following chapter is given the procedure for locating land originally surveyed under Federal Government jurisdiction.

The major difference between the location procedure for a subdivision description and that for a metes and bounds description is senior rights.   Because of senior rights in metes and bounds descriptions, a discussion or an application of the subject of proportionate measurement was precluded.   In this chapter and the following chapter the application of double and single proportion is discussed.

CHAPTER 5

Sectionalized
Land System

---

168. Within the continental United States almost all the public domain has been surveyed by the sectionalizing system. Retracement of the original lines as originally surveyed by the government surveyors and the division of sections into smaller parcels are problems confronting landowners. This chapter is devoted to the proper procedure for retracement surveys and the proper legal methods of subdividing sections of land.

LEGAL PRINCIPLES OF RETRACEMENTS

169. General. The intentions of the parties to a deed are paramount to all other considerations. Government subdivisions were done in accordance with statutory law, and any intent on the government's part must be interpreted from the statutes and the rules and regulations delegated to the Superintendent of Surveys or Surveyor General. In accordance with the statute, "The boundary lines, actually run and marked in the surveys returned by the surveyor-general, shall be established as the proper boundary lines of the sections or subdivisions for which they were intended," original lines surveyed by the original government surveyors are the best evidence of the intent of the government; the monuments and lines as surveyed become the control for relocation of sections of land. It is axiomatic that, before any retracement can be initiated in the field, a copy of the original field notes must be obtained along with any other records that show the findings of others in the particular area.

158

170. Conflict between Federal and State Laws

Principle. *All state laws that are in conflict with the Federal statutes and land department principles have been declared void in so far as the boundaries of any former patented parcel of public lands is concerned.*

This principle applies to the original patentee's boundaries and to land divisions made prior to a territory becoming a state. After land passes under state jurisdiction, further divisions into smaller parcels are regulated by state laws. A proportionate conveyance by state law conveys a fractional part of the acreage of a parcel whereas, by Federal law, area is not considered. If a person within a Federal territory patents the southwest quarter, his land boundaries are determined by the Federal laws. But if at a later date, after the territory was admitted as a state, the land is divided by selling the north half of the southwest quarter and the south half of the southwest quarter, the division is within the jurisdiction of the state laws. It is only by custom and court interpretation that Federal principles are followed. It is a matter of intent. If the words "according to government survey" are used, the general interpretation is that the Federal principles are called for. In a few court cases one-half of a parcel has been interpreted to mean one-half of the area of the parcel. If the proportionate conveyance applies to a parcel made irregular by a body of water, the courts are more prone to inquire whether the intent was acreage or not.

171. Lines As Marked and Surveyed

Principle. *"The boundaries of the public lands, when approved and accepted are unchangeable, except by resubdivision."**

The strength of the above principle comes from the statutes of the United States and the interpretations that the courts have placed on the statutes. "The boundary lines, actually run and marked in the surveys returned by the surveyor-general, shall be established as the proper boundary lines of the sections or subdivisions for which they were intended."†

The basic principle for all surveyors is contained in the above principle; the footsteps of the original surveyor are to be followed;

* "Restoration of Lost Corners," page 6.
† U.S.C., title 43, sec. 752.

the boundaries originally surveyed cannot be changed.   The duty
of the surveyor is to locate the lines exactly as run by the original
surveyor, and to gather sufficient evidence so that a judge and jury
can be convinced that the re-established line is the original line run
by the original surveyor.   What constitutes proof that the original
survey is followed is contained in the following pages.

The government may subdivide its land, and then, at a later date,
it may decide to resubdivide the same land.   The second subdivision then supersedes the first subdivision, but the second subdivision
cannot overcome the bona fide rights of a patentee who acquired
title under the first subdivision.

172. Monuments

Principle.   *"The original township, section, and quarter-section
corners must stand as the true corners which they were intended to
represent, whether in the place shown by the field notes or not."**

This is a logical sequence of the principle: "The boundaries of
the public lands, when approved and accepted, are unchangeable."
The monuments set at the time of the original survey are the best
evidence as to where the original boundaries were established; as
such the monuments must remain unchangeable.   *United States
Code,* Title 43, section 752, states in part: "All the corners marked
in the surveys returned by the surveyor-general shall be established
as the proper corners of sections, or subdivisions of sections, which
they were intended to designate."

173. Proportionate Measure or Proration

Principle.   *Lost corners are to be relocated by proportionate
measure, i.e., "the new values given to the several parts, as determined by the re-measurement, shall bear the same relation to the
record lengths as the new measurement of the whole line bears to
that record."*†

Existing original corners cannot be disturbed; consequently discrepancies between the new and those of the record measurements will not in
any manner affect the measurements beyond the identified corners, but
the difference will be distributed proportionately within the several intervals along the lines between the corners.‡

* *Ibid.,* page 6.
† *Ibid.,* page 12.
‡ *Ibid.,* page 10.

In a subdivision where there is a difference in measurement between the original surveyor and the recent surveyor, it must be concluded that the difference occurred in all parts of the line unless the
contrary can be proved beyond any reasonable doubt.   In government surveys many corners were set on a single line, whereas others
were set checkerboard fashion with cross ties.   Single proportionate
measure is applied to measurements along a single line, whereas
double proportionate measure is applied to checkerboard type surveys.

174. Single Proportionate Measurement

*Definition: "The term, single proportionate measurement, is ap-
plied to a new measurement made on a line to determine one or
more positions on that line."**

The classic example of single proportionate measure is the restoration of a lost quarter-section corner as shown in Fig. 5-1.   Section

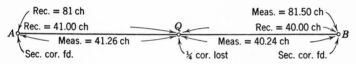

Figure 5-1.   Single proportionate measure

corners *A* and *B* are known; the record distance from *A* to the lost
quarter corner *Q* was 41 chains; the record distance from *Q* to *B*
was 40 chains; the present measure from *A* to *B* is 81.50 chains.
Quarter corner *Q* is restored in the exact proportion of the original
record, i.e., (41 ÷ 81) × 81.50 or 41.26 chains is the distance from
A to *Q* and (40 ÷ 81) × 81.50 or 40.24 chains is the distance from
Q to *B*.

United States Code, title 43, section 752 states in part: " . . .
and the length of such lines (section lines) as returned shall be held
and considered as the true length thereof."   The original reported
length is presumed to be the correct length, and any discrepancy in
measurement that exists is presumed due to the recent surveyor.   In
resurvey it is rarely found that the new measurement agrees with
the old; hence, the new survey must be adjusted so that it will be in
proportionate agreement with the old survey.   Or, in other words,

* *Ibid.*, page 12.

the new chain must be adjusted in length so that it agrees with the original measure. Actually this is done by mathematics as illustrated in the above example.

By law and by court ruling, original monuments are fixed in position and cannot be moved. Proportionate measure cannot extend beyond any fixed point or fixed monument and is applicable only to lost points between original monuments.

Not all lines surveyed were straight lines as in the above illustration. Corners on a standard parallel or east-west township lines were originally set on a curved line, and any restored corner that is located in the footsteps of the original surveyor must be on the same curved line.

175. Double Proportionate Measurement

Definition: "The term, double proportionate measurement is applied to a new measurement made between four known corners, two each on intersecting meridional and latitudinal lines, for the purpose of relating the intersection of both."*

In order to restore a lost corner of four townships by double proportionate measurement, a retracement will first be made between the nearest known corners on the meridional line, north and south of the missing corner, and upon that line a temporary stake will be placed at the proper proportionate distance; this will determine the latitude of the lost corner. Next, the nearest corners on the latitudinal line will be connected, and a second point will be marked for the proportionate measurement east and west; this point will determine the position of the lost corner in departure (or longitude). Then through the first temporary stake run a line east or west, and through the second temporary stake a line north or south, as relative situations may determine; the intersection of these two lines will fix the position for the restored corner.†

It is to be noted that original reported bearings play no part in the restoration of a corner by double proportionate measurement; distance in a subdivision is superior to angle.

Double proportionate measurement is illustrated by Fig. 5-2, which shows the conditions in a hypothetical problem. To restore the lost section corner common to sections 25, 26, 35, and 36 as shown in Fig. 5-2, the surveyor located the southeast (marked *A*)

* *Ibid.*, page 13.
† *Ibid.*, page 13.

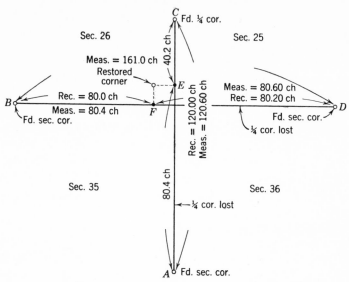

Figure 5-2. Double proportionate measure

and northwest corner (B) of section 35, and the west quarter corner (C) and southeast section corner (D) of section 25. A straight line from A to C is run and found to measure 120.60 chains, whereas the original recorded government measure was 40 chains for each half mile or a total of 120.00 chains. The surplus of 0.60 chain is divided into three equal parts of 0.20 chain each. A temporary point is established at E exactly one-third of the way between C and A or 40.20 chains south of C on the line AC. On the east and west straight line between B and D, is established a temporary point at F, the position of which is computed as follows:

$$\text{Distance } BF = \frac{161 \times 80}{80 + 80.2} = 80.40 \text{ chains}$$

$$\text{Distance } FD = 161.00 \times \frac{80.20}{80 + 80.2} = 80.60 \text{ chains}$$

From the proportionate point F a line is run due north (astronomical) and from the point E a line is run due west; and their point of intersection determines the restored position for the lost section corner.

176. Importance of One Line over Another

Principle. *"The principle of the precedence of one line over another of less original importance, relative to single or double proportionate measurements, in order to harmonize the restorative process with the method followed in the original survey, thus limiting the control, is recognized."*

When the public lands were originally surveyed, certain lines were established without reference to other lines. If the footsteps of the original surveyor are to be followed, restoration work should be pursued in the same manner as that used by the original surveyor; thus, lost corners on a base line should be relocated without reference either to later set closing corners or to later set quarter corners located a half mile to the north. Exterior township lines were surveyed before the subdivision of townships into sections; lost corners on township lines are restored by proportionate means, utilizing only the corners along the township lines. Closing corners must be moved up to the line closed upon. Lost quarter corners can be located only after the section corners are located or restored.

177. Original Field Notes

Principle. *The plat and all the original field notes become a part of the grant. Errors on a plat are subordinated to the field notes.*

In a Supreme Court case† it is stated,

It is a well settled principle that when lands are granted according to an official plat of the survey of such lands, the plat, itself, with all its notes, lines, descriptions and landmarks, becomes as much a part of the grant or deed by which they were conveyed, and controls so far as limits are concerned, as if such descriptive features were written out upon the face of the deed or the grant itself.

Government field notes are the only source from which descriptive information, describing the type of corners used and the type of objects found on lines, can be obtained. Witness trees and bearing objects commonly noted in the field books are seldom described in the legal description conveying title to property. The best evidence of where and how the original lines were run is contained in the field notes.

* *Ibid.,* page 13.
† Cragin v. Powell, 128 US 691, 696.

In case of discrepancy between the field notes and the plat, the plat must give way to the field notes; and the land department may properly correct the plat so as to conform to the field notes.*

178. Closing Corners

Principle. *A closing corner not actually located on the line that was closed upon will determine the direction of the closing line, but not its legal terminus; the correct position is at the true point of intersection of the two lines.*

Once a line is run and established, it cannot be altered at a later date. If the surveyor failed to place the closing corner upon the true line closed upon, the original line cannot be changed to fit the new corner; the closing corner must be moved to the line closed upon. This rule applies to closing corners on standard parallels, correction lines, land-grant lines, or the last-set double corner. Where a new township is being surveyed or an old one being re-surveyed and double corners are set along the township lines, the second corner set must be considered a closing corner.

Where large land grants were given by the Mexican Government, the closing corners set along the grant lines by the original surveyors were frequently grossly in error, one-quarter of a mile being not uncommon.

IDENTIFICATION OF CORNERS AND LINES

179. Definitions:

An *existent corner* is one whose position can be identified by verifying the evidence of the monument, or its accessories, by reference to the description that is contained in the field notes, or where the point can be located by an acceptable supplemental survey record, some physical evidence or testimony.†

An *obliterated corner* is one at whose point there are no remaining traces of the monuments, or its accessories, but whose location has been perpetuated, or the point for which may be recovered beyond reasonable doubt, by the acts and testimony of the interested landowners, competent surveyors, or other qualified local authorities, or witnesses, or by some acceptable record evidence.‡

A *lost corner* is a point of a survey whose position cannot be determined, beyond reasonable doubt, either from traces of the original marks

---

* Harrington v. Boehmer, 134 Cal 196.

† *Ibid.,* page 9.

‡ *Ibid.,* page 9.

or from acceptable evidence or testimony that bears upon the original position, and whose location can be restored only by reference to one or more inter-dependent corners.*

An *accessory to a corner monument* is any bearing object, bearing tree, pit, or thing, given in the original field notes as having a definite relationship in bearing and distance to the corner.

A *memorial* is any durable article deposited along side the monument which will serve to identify the corner location in case the monument is destroyed. Metal, a quart of charcoal, glass, stoneware, and marked stones are common memorials.

180. Monuments, Identification

Principle. *After making due allowances for natural changes, a monument to be identifiable should not differ greatly from the following:*

"(1) The character and dimensions of the monument in evidence should not be widely different from the record; (2) the markings in evidence should not be inconsistent with the record; and (3) the nature of the accessories in evidence, including size, position, and markings, should not be greatly at variance with the record."†

Accessories are considered part of the monument; their identification, without finding the monument, fixes the position of the monument and restores obliterated corners to their original location.

Prior to any attempt to resurvey a section of land, the original government field notes must be examined for a description of the topography, monuments, bearing objects, witnesses, and line markers. In some states, where all original surveys have been completed, the original notes have been turned over to the states; in others, the original notes are in the Government Land Office.

Accessories to monuments, such as bearing trees or bearing objects, are considered part of the monument itself, and often afford the only means of identifying corners. It is axiomatic that a search for a monument includes a search for all accessories.

Material used for early monuments varied; stones, stone mounds, and wooden posts were common. Where undisturbed by humans, stone mounds are frequently found in excellent condition after 75 years. Unfortunately most of the corner stones have been de-

* *Ibid.,* page 10.
† *Manual,* paragraph 354.

stroyed where cultivation or construction work has been in progress. Although stone mounds may be visible, most people have little or no respect for them; the relative ease with which they can be moved has caused considerable trouble. When surveying in the back country a surveyor often finds recently built stone mounds that mark a spot that a local resident wishes to keep in mind, sometimes the spot is supposed to represent the corner being searched for. By reading the signs of age, the difference between new and old mounds of stones can be detected and fraudulent corners can be rejected. When a stone mound is found, it is wise to lift and examine each stone carefully. Bottom stones should leave an imprint of their shape in the ground. During a period of years, dirt falling or being washed into a stone mound will cause the lower stones to be imbedded in the dirt. Leaves undecayed under the stones afford an excellent means of detecting recently built mounds. Stones freshly picked up from the ground have a weathered side on top and a lighter color underneath. Seeds falling in the shade between the rocks present favorable germination conditions which often cause bushes and shrubs to grow out of the mounds.

Posts or wooden stakes originally set as corner material are seldom found in later years. Hardwoods and available woods for early markers rotted readily and lasted but a few years. Some woods, such as redwood and cedar, last longer than present-day iron stakes. In the early government surveys redwood was not generally available; woods used were found locally and had poor time-enduring qualities. Wooden fence posts of hardwoods or pines seldom last more than a few years (2 to 5 years); to expect a hardwood post set for a corner to last 70 years is unreasonable. Occasionally well-defined pits and an earth mound set as accessories to a post are found. Usually the pits are filled from years of rains, and the mound is washed down until hardly recognizable.

Often the best evidence of a corner location is found in bearing objects or trees. Identified blazed witness trees are far better evidence as to where a corner was set than is an easily movable rock mound, out of conformity with the bearing trees. A call for a rock mound 3 feet south of a 6-foot high boulder presents a case where the only 6-foot boulder in the vicinity was better evidence of the original location than was a rock mound 70 feet away at a fence intersection of doubtful origin. The mound could be moved, but the boulder could not.

Blazed bearing trees can be positively identified by the growth rate of the tree. After a period of time, a blaze becomes obliterated and only a scar will be visible. By carefully removing the regrowth on the tree, the original scribing can be read. The date of the original blaze can be determined by counting the ring growth of the tree. In searching for bearing trees it must be borne in mind that the trees in question would be larger in diameter than the original recorded size.

The prime object of all surveys is to relocate the original lines of the original survey exactly as they were run by the original surveyor. The evidence of the original survey is usually embodied in the monuments set on the original survey; consequently the most important duty of a surveyor is ferreting out the evidence of former survey lines as shown by monuments.

181. Map or Plat Reference by Others

Principle. *Where an acceptable map or plat shows the found location of the original corner, the corner, if obliterated, should be relocated by said map or plat.*

Before a corner can be considered lost, a thorough and complete search must be made of all available records that might shed light on the corner location. Subdivision maps, record of surveys, state, county, and city road surveys, power and water companies' right of way maps, and government topographic maps in the vicinity should all be inspected. Title companies often have unrecorded maps available. Private survey records are a good source of information.

182. Testimony of Old Residents

Principle. *The original location of a corner may be restored at a spot pointed out by an old resident, who saw the original corner and knows where its former location was. The witness evidence testified to has no more weight than would be given in court; i.e., it should not be hearsay, etc.*

The fact that a surveyor may take oaths for the establishment of facts relating to old survey corners and lines is well recognized. In California the state law provides:

Every licensed land surveyor or registered civil engineer may administer and certify oaths: (*a*) When it becomes necessary to take testimony for the identification or establishment of old, lost or obliterated corners. (*b*) When a corner or monument is found in a perishable condition and it appears desirable that evidence concerning it be perpetuated. (*c*) When the importance of the survey makes it desirable to administer an oath to his assistants for the faithful performance of their duty. A record of oaths shall be preserved as part of the field notes of the survey and a memorandum of them shall be made on the record of survey filed under this article.

It must be ever remembered by the surveyor that the oath must consist of facts within the perception of the witness. To testify as to what his neighbor observed is not permitted; it is hearsay. To testify that a stone existed in the present road before the construction of the now existent road and that the stone existed on the prolongation of the present fence is proper testimony and should not be disregarded by the surveyor.

A corner will not be considered as lost if its position can be recovered satisfactorily by means of the testimony and acts of witnesses having positive knowledge of the precise location of the original monument. The expert testimony of surveyors who may have identified the original monument prior to its destruction and thereupon recorded new accessories or connections, etc., is by far the most reliable, though land owners are often able to furnish valuable testimony. The greatest care is necessary in order to establish the bona fide character of the record intervening after the destruction of an original monument. Full inquiry may often serve to bring to light various records relating to the original corners, and memoranda of private markings, etc., and the engineer should make use of all such sources of information. The matter of boundary disputes should be carefully looked into insofar as adverse claimants may base their contentions upon evidence of the original survey, and if such disputes have resulted in a boundary suit, the record testimony and the court's decision should be carefully examined relative to any information which may shed light upon the position of an original monument. The testimony of individuals may relate to knowledge of the original monument or the accessories, prior to their destruction, or to any other marks fixing the focus of the original survey, and the value of such testimony may be weighted in proportion to its completeness and agreement with the calls of the field notes of the original survey, also upon the steps taken to preserve the location of the original marks. All such evidence should be put to the severest possible tests by confirmation relating to known original corners and other calls of the original field notes, particularly on line trees, blazed lines and items of topography.*

* *Manual*, paragraph 355.

Testimonial evidence given by a person involved in a dispute should be regarded with suspicion, since it might be made to better his position. Better evidence comes from disinterested parties.

183. Common Usage

Principle. *Under special conditions a corner location can be accepted by common usage of a point.*

Frequently highways are located along section lines. Where a road has been commonly accepted as the section line and there is no evidence to the contrary, the road is the section line by *common report.* In the absence of other means, the location of an obliterated section corner can be relocated at the center-line intersection of two such roads which are commonly reported as being the section lines in question.

184. Identification of Lines Run

Principle. *Where the direction of a line can be determined from the mean position of line trees or blaze markers, the direction so established will be controlling where the corner monument is lost. Sometimes a stream or canyon crossing becomes controlling, especially where the crossing is close to a corner.*

In the original notes many features of topography were described so that it is sometimes possible to locate a line by trees or natural objects called for. In older surveys very little evidence of the original lines are left; only by careful, diligent search in the immediate vicinity can traces be found. Due weight must be given to line trees, crossings, and other topographic features in proportion to its certainty of location.

The boundary lines, actually run and marked in the surveys returned by the surveyor-general, shall be established as the proper boundary lines of the sections or subdivisions for which they were intended.*

RESTORATION OF LOST CORNERS

185. Principle. *All lost corners are to be relocated by proportionate measure with due regard to the principle of the precedence*

* U.S.C., title 43, sec. 752.

of one line over another of less original importance. Lost land-grant corners are to be restored in accordance with the rules for metes and bounds surveys.

All lost corners must be restored by proportionate measure so that all interested parties receive an equitable share of existing excess or deficiency. Restoring a corner by proportionate methods should be regarded as the last resort; all other evidence that might reveal the original location must be exhausted. It is far better to accept a long-standing fence corner commonly accepted as the section corner than to try to establish a new corner by proportionate measure.

When it becomes necessary to restore a lost corner, the procedure used varies somewhat, depending upon the original importance of the line on which the corner was located. The rules for restoration of lost corners as set out in the *Manual of Surveying Instructions* have been developed with a view to giving proper recognition to the various factors incident to the establishment of an original corner, the object being the restoration of the lost corner as nearly as possible to its true original position. Thus, on a standard parallel which was originally projected as a line independent of other surveys, the lost corners are properly re-established by single protraction.

186. Restoration of Lost Standard Corners on Standard Parallels, Correction Lines, and Base Lines

Principle. *Lost standard corners will be restored to their original position on a base line, standard parallel, or correction line, by single proportionate measurement on the true line connecting the nearest identified standard corners on opposite sides of the missing corner or corners, as the case may be. Proper adjustment should be made to secure the correct latitudinal curve. Closing corners are not to be used for either direction or measurement.*

The term "standard corners," as used above, will be understood to mean all corners which were established on the standard parallel during the original survey of that line, including but not limited to, standard township, section, quarter-section and meander corners. Closing corners or other corners purported to be established on a standard parallel after the original survey of that line, will not control the initial restoration of lost standard corners.*

* "Restoration of Lost Corners," page 17.

In rare cases wnere a closing corner was set on the standard parallel at the calculated position of the closing corner and at the time of the survey of the standard parallel, such a corner controls the direction of the standard parallel.

Since corners originally set on standard parallels were set on a curved line, the lost corners must be restored on the original curved line connecting the nearest identified standard corner on each side. Lost corners on curved lines are restored by single proportionate measure on the curved line by first setting a temporary proportional corner on a straight line, then measuring over the proper correction for the earth's curvature.

187. Restoration of Lost Township Corners on Principal Meridians and Guide Meridians

Principle. *Where the principal meridian or guide meridian was established by alignment in one direction only, lost township corners on such lines shall be restored by single proportionate measurement. Where guide meridians were established as part of the scheme of township boundaries, all surveyed in the same system under a single contract, the township corners located thereon should be relocated by double proportionate measurements.*

Where guide meridians were run as independent lines before the subdivision of township lines, cross ties did not exist and restoration work should proceed on the basis of single proportionate means. However, under most contracts, guide meridians were established as part of the general scheme for the township boundaries with cross ties to other township lines. Where this occurred, double proportion should be used to restore lost township corners.

188. Restoration of Lost Township and Section Corners Originally Established with Cross Ties in Four Directions

Principle. *Where lost regular township corners common to four sections and lost regular section corners between township lines were originally established with ties from four directions, the lost corners will be re-established by double proportionate measurements.*

This rule is applicable to township corners not set on a base line, principal meridian, and occasionally guide meridians. Most guide meridians were originally established as an integral part of the establishment of the township lines with cross ties in four directions; hence, lost township corners on guide meridians are usually restored by double proportionate means. The rule is also applicable to most lost section corners common to four sections and located between township lines. Where lost section corners between township lines were established by alignment in one direction only, such as corners along a sectional correction line or sectional guide meridian, single proportionate measure will be used.

Although the original east-west township lines were run on a curve, it is not necessary to re-run the lines on a curve where double proportion is used since the final result will be identical whether curved or straight lines are employed. Proportionate methods cannot extend beyond an identified original corner regardless of whether it is a quarter corner, section corner, meander corner, or a rarely set sixteenth corner. Once a corner is found undisturbed, its position is fixed and cannot be altered by proportionate means.

189. Restoration of Lost Corners along Township Lines

Principle. *All lost section and quarter-section corners on the township boundary lines will be restored by single proportionate measurement between the nearest identified corners on opposite sides of the missing corner, north and south on a meridional line, or east and west on a latitudinal line, after the township corners have been identified or relocated. An exception to this principle will be noted in the case of any exterior the record of which shows deflections in alignment between the township corners.**

The strength of this principle lies in the fact that township lines were established before the subdivision of sections within a township. The corners being originally set on a line without cross ties should be re-established on the same line without cross ties. The east-west township lines were curved lines and the relocated lost corners must also be placed on a curved parallel of latitude. Single proportion cannot extend beyond a township corner that must be re-established by double proportionate means.

190. Restoration of Lost Township and Section Corners Where the Line Was Not Established in One Direction

Principle. *Where the line has not been established in one direction from the missing township corner, the record distance*

* *Ibid.*, page 17.

will be used to the nearest identified corner in the opposite direction.*

This principle is applicable where double proportion would be normally used, but cannot be applied because a line was not established in one direction. In Fig. 5-3, the northwest section corner, the north quarter corner, the southeast section corner of section 1,

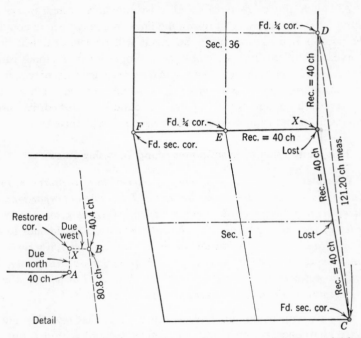

Figure 5-3. Restoration of a lost township corner originally established in three directions

and the east quarter corner of section 36 are all known. The townships to the east were not surveyed. Corner X, the lost township corner, is to be relocated. Run a line exactly 40 chains, the record distance, due east from point E and set a temporary point at A. Since due east means due east in the direction called due east by the original surveyor, the prolongation of line F–E would be considered as due east. Next set a point proportionate measure at B on a straight line from D to C, or 80.80 chains from C proportionate

* *Ibid.,* page 14.

measure. Run a line from *B* due west and run a line from *A* due north. Their point of intersection at *X* is the lost corner.

191. Restoration of Lost Corners Where the Intersecting Lines Have Been Established in Only Two Directions

Principle. *Where the intersecting lines have been established in only two of the directions, the record distances to the nearest identified corners on those two lines will control the position of the temporary points; then from the latter the cardinal offsets will be made to fix the desired point of intersection.**

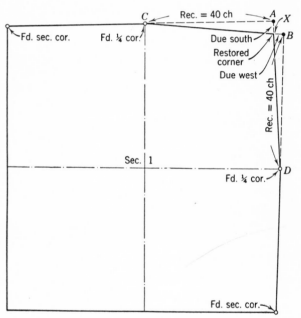

Figure 5-4. Restoration of a township corner originally established in two directions

This principle is applicable in Fig. 5-4, where the north and east quarter corners are known and the northeast section corner (also township corner) is to be set. The other townships were never surveyed. Run a line 40 chains due east from *C*, and set a temporary point *A*. Run a line 40.0 chains (record distance) due north from *D*, and set a temporary point at *B*. Run a line due west from

* *Ibid.*, page 16.

B and a line due south from *A*. The point of intersection *X* is the lost corner.

192. Quarter-Section Corners in Regular Sections

Principle. *"All lost quarter-section corners on the section bounda-ries within the township will be restored by single proportional measurement between the adjoining section corners, after the sec-tion corners have been identified or relocated."** An exception oc-curs where the original lines had angular deflection.

The importance of one line over another is recognized by this rule, in that section corners must be relocated before the restoration of a lost quarter-corner. Lost regular quarter corners, whether located on standard parallels, sectional correction lines, or any other line, are restored by single proportionate measure between the sec-tion corners located on each side of the missing quarter corner. Where the original line run was a curved parallel of latitude, the relocated quarter corner must also be placed on the original curved line. If the quarter corner was originally placed upon a line that showed angular deflections, the restored corner must be relocated with the angular deflection.

193. Quarter-Section Corners Where Only Part of a Section Was Surveyed Originally

Principle. *"Where a line has been terminated with measurement in one direction only, a lost corner will be restored by record bearing and distance, counting from the nearest regular corner, the latter having been duly identified or restored."†*

194. Closing Section Corner on a Standard Parallel

Principle. *"A lost closing corner on a standard parallel will be re-established on the true line that was closed upon, and at the proper proportional interval between the nearest regular corners to the right and left."‡ The only corners that will control the direc-tion of the line being closed upon are (1) standard township, stand-ard section and standard quarter corners, (2) meander corners ter-*

* *Ibid.*, page 19.
† *Ibid.*, page 20.
‡ *Ibid.*, page 19.

minating the survey of the standard parallel, and (3) closing corners in those cases where they were originally established by measurement along the standard line as points from which to start a survey.

Figure 5-5 shows a standard parallel and sections 2 and 3 whose lines closed upon the parallel when surveyed from the south towards the north. The corner common to sections 2 and 3 is to be restored by proportionate means. Since the lost corner was originally set

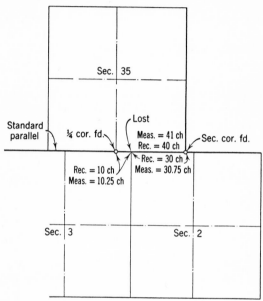

Figure 5-5. Restoration of a lost section corner on a correction line

upon the standard parallel, it must be reset upon the line at a proportionate distance from the next regular corner to the right and left. Closing corners were not set at the time at which the standard parallels were run and cannot be considered as determining the direction of the parallel; only those set as part of the standard parallel when it was originally run may be used. In the above example, the record distance from the closing corner to the nearest regular corner to the east was 30 chains and was 10 chains to the quarter corner to the west. Recent measure revealed 1 chain surplus between the found regular corners, which is divided into 0.75 chains and 0.25 chains by proportion so that the new distance to the regular section corner to the east becomes 30.75 chains.

195. Lost North Quarter Corner in a Closing Section

Principle. *Where the north quarter corner on a closing section was originally set and lost, the lost corner will be re-established on the closing line at a point at the proper proportionate interval between the nearest found or relocated corners to the right and left.*

The north quarter corner of a closing section on a standard parallel was not normally set. For the establishment of this corner, see the discussion under subdivision of sections (Article 202).

196. Lost Meander Corners, Nonriparian

Principle. *"Lost meander corners, originally established on a line projected across the meanderable body of water and marked upon both sides will be relocated by single proportionate measurement, after the section or quarter-section corners upon the opposite sides of the missing meander corner have been duly identified or relocated. Where a line has been terminated with measurement in one direction only, a lost corner will be restored by record bearing and distance, counting from the nearest regular corner, the latter having been duly identified or restored."*

The actual shore line of a body of water is considered the correct terminus of a line; the meander corner controls the direction of the line. The restoration of a lost meander corner would be required infrequently.

197. Meander Lines, Riparian

Principle. *A meander line platted as the boundary of a riparian owner is not the true boundary; the bank of the body of water represents the true boundary.*

The purpose of meandering any body of water is to obtain information that will aid the plotting of the body of water on maps. The shore line itself is the best evidence of the true location and will govern.

Where a survey was fraudulent or grossly inaccurate in that it purported to bound tracts of public lands upon a body of water, when in fact no such body of water existed at or near the meander line, the false meander line and not an imaginary line to fill out the

* *Ibid.,* pages 19 and 20.

fraction of the normal subdivision marks the limits of the grant of a lot abutting thereon, and, upon discovery of the mistake, the Government may survey and dispose of the omitted area as a part of the public domain.*

198. Meander Lines, Nonriparian

Principle. *After locating the positions of the meander corners on the section lines, the record meander courses and distances are run, setting temporary angle points; the closing error from the last*

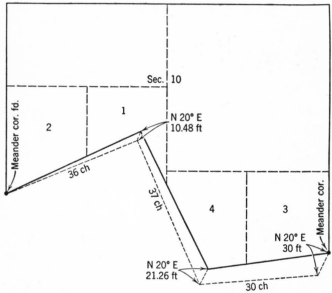

Figure 5-6.   Restoration of a lost nonriparian meander line

meander course to the section line meander corner is noted. The error of closure is balanced out by the compass rule. This is attained in the field by moving each temporary angle stake on the bearing of the closing error a distance that is in proportion to the length of the closing error as the sum of the courses to the angle point is to the sum of all the courses.

The method used is illustrated in Fig. 5-6. The resurvey, beginning on the west side of the section at the found or re-established

* *Manual,* page 366.

meander corner, is run eastward on the bearing and distances of the original notes. After setting temporary stakes at each angle point, the closing bearing and distance from the last temporary stake to the true meander corner is noted, or, as illustrated, N 20° E, a distance of 30 feet. From each temporary stake the true corner is set on the bearing of the closing line a proportionate distance. The first temporary point would be moved 30 times $^{36}/_{103}$ or 10.48 feet, as illustrated.

As previously pointed out, meander lines seldom represent true property lines and the necessity for using the above principle is rare.

199. Irregular Exteriors

Principle. *Where boundaries that would normally be straight lines were originally established in an irregular manner, the resurvey will follow the irregular procedure.*

Where a township line was partially surveyed and later completed by surveying from another direction, an angle point at the junction of the two lines would be perpetuated in resurvey methods. Recent retracements of township lines for the purpose of resurveying a township frequently uncovers deflections in alignment along the township lines. New corners set upon such lines have an original-record angular alignment and must be resurveyed taking the angular deflections into account.

200. Summary. A summary of the usual means by which a lost corner within a township is restored is shown in Fig. 5-7. The letter S indicates that the corner, if lost, is to be relocated by single proportionate measure on a straight line. The letter S' indicates single proportionate measure on a curved parallel is to be used. The letter D signifies that double proportion is used. C indicates a closing corner that is re-established on the line closed upon. Any irregular procedure as indicated by the original field notes might alter the restoration methods. A sectional correction line acquires the stature of a township line, and all corners on the correction line, when lost, are restored by single proportionate measure.

SUBDIVISION OF SECTIONS

201. Subdivision by Protraction. Sections of land, being the minimum area normally surveyed, are too big to completely serve

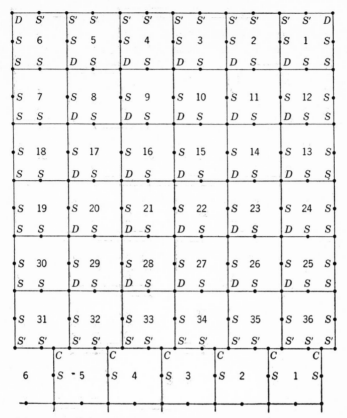

D	S'		S'	S'		S'	S'		S'	S'		S'	S'		S'	S'	D

Figure 5-7. Chart showing the normal methods of restoring lost corners.
S = single proportion. S' = single proportion on a curved parallel.
D = double proportion. C = closing corner

the purpose of disposal of the public land. Where an entryman may patent a quarter of a quarter of a section, the section must be subdivided further to allow proper delineation of the land boundaries; the process is known as subdivision by protraction. Upon the original township plats are shown dotted lines which indicate the intent of the government in disposing of parcels less than a section in size. Together with the Federal land statutes and land plats subdivided by protraction, the surveyor can determine the proper procedure for the survey of portions of sections.

Regular sections of land as shown on the official plats have straight dotted lines concerning opposite quarter corners to indicate that quarter sections are to be subdivided by running lines connecting opposite quarter corners. Further dotted lines to indicate smaller divisions of land are omitted except where irregular conditions exist, such as shown in Fig. 5-8. All quarter-quarter section lines not shown on the plat, Fig. 5-8, are assumed to be of regular size as required by statutes. Irregular-sized parcels and quarter-

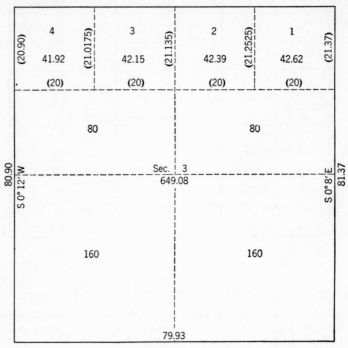

Figure 5-8.

quarter parcels containing irregular measurements are given lot numbers on the plat to distinguish them from regular parcels.

202. Establishing the North Quarter Corner of Closing Sections on a Standard Parallel and Other Quarter Corners Not Originally Set

Principle. *Where an original quarter corner was not originally set, as in the case of sections closing on a correction line or sections closing on a range line with double corners, place the missing corner on the correction line at a point between the found or relocated*

*closing section corners a distance that is proportional to the meas-
urements used for the acreage calculations on the original plat.
The missing corner is usually set midway between closing section
corners except in section six where it is usually 40 chains proportional measure from the northeast or southwest closing section corners.*

By an older principle, when a township was being subdivided, the
last section lines, run west to intersect the west line of the township,
did not have to meet the township line at the same point as the
formerly set section corner. Double corners existed: the original
section corner for the sections west of the township line and the
newly set closing section corner for the sections east of the township
line. By such a rule, the quarter corners for the sections east of the
township line, namely, 6, 7, 18, 19, 30, and 31, were never set. The
quarter-section corner found is applicable only to the sections west
of the township line.

The north quarter corner of sections 1 to 6, inclusive, was seldom
set where the north line of the township was a correction line.

Prior to the establishment of the missing quarter corner, the
found closing section corners must be tested for alignment. If
found off the line closed upon, they must be moved up to the line
closed upon. From the acreage figures on the original plat, the
distances used for computing the original acreage can be recon-
structed. For the purpose of illustration, section 3 shown in Fig.
5-8 gives the original measurements of a section whose north
quarter corner was never set. Figures in parenthesis are those computed by the rules of protraction. Since 1 acre is 10 square chains,
the acreage of lot 1 is $20 \times (21.37 + 21.2525) \div 2 \times \frac{1}{10}$ or 42.62
acres. Where the original width of lot 1 was 20 chains, the acreage
was determined by the sum of the lengths of the east and west lines.
Conversely, where the sum of the east and west sides equals the
acreage, 20 chains was the assumed original width. Since each of
the lots in Fig. 5-8 can be proved to be 20 chains wide by computation, the missing quarter corner would be set midway between the
found or relocated closing section corners to the east and west.

203. Establishment of Center Lines and Center Quarter Corners

Principle. *The method to be followed in the subdivision of a section into quarter sections is to run straight lines from the established
quarter-section corners to the opposite quarter-section corners; the*

*point of intersection of the lines thus run will be the corner common
to the several quarter sections, or the legal center of the section.**

And the boundary lines which have not been actually run and marked
shall be ascertained by running straight lines from the established corners
to the opposite corresponding corners.†

In sectionalized land when conveyances are made of a portion of
a section, such as the west half, the conveyance is not based
on acreage, but upon using the rule as given above.   This is mark-
edly different from conveyance under state laws where the west half
of a lot in a subdivision conveys exactly one-half the area of the lot.
The west one-half of a section is seldom if ever exactly one-half of
the total area of the section.   The rule for dividing a portion of a
conveyance by acreage is based upon common law; whereas the rule
for subdividing a portion of a section is based upon statutes of the
Federal Government.

The establishment of the center quarter corner is provided for
by law and should be followed in every case where a complete section was originally established.   Where part of a section was established on an early survey and the remainder on a later survey, conditions might arise whereby an angle point exists at the center of a
section.   Also in rare cases where the original surveyor established
the true center of a section at the time of the original survey, the
monument so set would be controlling even though set improperly
by error on the part of the original surveyor.

204. Establishment of Quarter-Quarter Section Lines and Corners

Principle. *Preliminary to the subdivision of quarter sections, the
quarter-quarter or sixteenth-section corners will be established at
points midway between the section and quarter-section corners, and
between the quarter-section corners and the center of the section,
except on the last half mile of the lines closing on township boundaries, where they should be placed at 20 chains, proportionate measurement, counting from the regular quarter-section corner.   The
quarter-quarter or sixteenth-section corners having been established
as directed above, the center lines of the quarter section will be run
straight between opposite corresponding quarter-quarter or sixteenth-section corners on the quarter-section boundaries.   The in-*

* "Restoration of Lost Corners," page 25.
† U.S.C. Title 43, Sec. 752.

tersection of the lines thus run will determine the legal center of a quarter section.*

In every case of the division of a quarter section the line for the division thereof shall run north and south . . . on the principles directed and prescribed by the section preceding.†

The section preceding states,

And the boundary lines which have not been actually run and marked shall be ascertained by running straight lines from the established corners to the opposite corresponding corners.

205. Fractional Sections Center Line

Principle. *"The law provides that where opposite corresponding quarter-section corners have not been or cannot be fixed, the subdivision-of-section lines shall be ascertained by running lines from the established corners north, south, east, or west, as the case may be, to the water course, reservation line, or other boundary of such fractional section, as represented upon the official plat. In this the law presumes that the section lines are due north and south, or east and west lines, but this is not usually the case. Hence, in order to carry out the spirit of the law, it will be necessary in running the center lines through fractional sections to adopt mean courses, where the section lines are not due cardinals or to run parallel to the east, south, west, or north boundary of the section, as conditions may require, where there is no opposite section line."‡*

But in those portions of the fractional townships where no such opposite corresponding corners have been or can be fixed, the boundary lines shall be ascertained by running from the established corners due north and south or east and west lines, as the case may be, to the water-course, Indian boundary line, or other external boundary of such fractional township.§

This statute is interpreted by the courts as noted above.

206. Procedure for Retracement Surveys. From the discussion and principles presented it is obvious that most of the following steps are necessary when a retracement survey of sectionalized public lands is being made:

* "Restoration of Lost Corners," page 27.
† U.S.C. Title 43, Sec. 752.
‡ "Restoration of Lost Corners," page 27.
§ U.S.C. Title 43, Sec. 752.

1. Obtain photostats or copies of the original field notes and original plat or plats.

2. Search the records for subsequent surveys (road surveys, record of surveys, etc.) and previous court findings.

3. Contact old residents and adjacent landowners involved in the retracement (mainly for testimony purposes).

4. Obtain copies of the deeds or patents of parties adjoining the lines being run.

5. Locate the corners that are needed. If the corner is existent, physical evidence of the corner will be found. If the corner is obliterated, supplementary records or testimony will be used. If the corner is lost, the application of the rules of proportionate measure will be made.

6. Set replacement monuments or new monuments where necessary.

7. Subdivide the section in accordance with the foregoing rules.

8. File a record of the survey showing all points found, the methods used, and a description of all monuments set.

The primary purpose of a resurvey is to follow exactly in the footsteps of the original surveyor. Monuments as set by the original surveyor afford the principal means of locating the original lines as run; hence courts will give major consideration to the evidence of corner monument location.

207. Interpretations of Description.   When legal description of portions of a section are being written, certain pitfalls should be avoided. When conveying a portion of a section, avoid using acreage except as a secondary call; thus the east 80 acres of the NE quarter is not the same as the east one-half of the NE one-quarter even though the government plat shows the E one-half of the NE one-quarter as being 80 acres. The east 80 acres is 80 acres no more and no less. "The east one-half of the NE one-quarter, being 80 acres" is the E one-half of the NE one-quarter and the "being 80 acres" is a secondary call of lesser importance. Distance calls such as the east 20 chains of the NE one-quarter should not be used when the E one-half of the NE one-quarter is intended. Here again, the east 20 chains is not the east one-half nor is it the east 80 acres.

"Beginning at the southeast corner of section 2, thence west 20 chains, thence north 20 chains, thence east 20 chains, thence south

20 chains" does not describe the SE one-quarter of the SE one-quarter as intended. If the term "according to Government measure" or "as shown on the Government plat" is included, the SE one-quarter of the SE one-quarter is conveyed.

208. Summary. The object of all retracement surveys is to follow the footsteps of the original surveyor and relocate the lines as originally run. The purpose is not to determine by measurement where the lines ought to have been established, but to determine where they were in fact originally established. The first consideration when a section of land is being resurveyed is to determine what the original surveyor purported to do by reading his original notes. The next step is to identify the original lines as set by the original surveyor. If the lines are lost, they are to be re-established as nearly as may be in accordance with the original notes. Once a line is established by survey and deeds are made in accordance with the survey, the lines are to be considered unalterable except by resubdivision. Irregularities incorporated in the original survey are to be incorporated into the resurveys.

The principles given in the preceding two chapters were formulated as common law by the courts to put in force the principle, "The boundaries of land once subdivided and accepted are unalterable except by resubdivision."

CHAPTER 6

Locating Reversion Rights

209. Reversionary Rights. Unless there is a clear contrary intent in a conveyance to a public body, it is presumed that dedicated roads create only an easement for the public whereas the title to the road remains in the grantor of the easement.* Extinguishing an easement by proper agencies causes the full rights to the land to revert to its former owner, disencumbered of the public use. Reversion is not àn altogether accurate term since the land does not revert owing to a lack of alienation in the first place. Upon discharging the public burden, private rights revive.

210. Revival of Public Easements. Once a public easement on land has been extinguished, it can be revived only by a new dedication or condemnation.

211. Private Rights in Easements. Removal of a public easement extinguishes public but not private rights. Easements granted by the owner of the bed of the street, or by the owner prior to the dedication of the street, either by voluntary or prescriptive means, remain in force.

212. Ownership of the Bed of Streets

General Principle. *"Unless there is a contrary statement in the conveyance or there is a statute nullifying the rule, the public acquires only an easement in highways."*†

Legislatures may provide for the taking of a fee to the land appropriated for street purposes, but any intention to take all proprietary interests must be plainly declared by the statute. Thus, in Iowa a statute providing that an acknowledged and recorded

* 144 Ky 634.
† American Law Review 2-25, 18-1018, and 11-551.

plat of a subdivision dedicates all accepted streets in fee simple
retains fee title in the public body after the streets are vacated.*
In the absence of proof to the contrary, ownership is presumed to
lie in the abutting owner.

By the *Dutch law* the ownership of the bed of streets during
the Dutch occupancy of New York was vested in the state. Upon
accession of the British into power the rule no longer applied, but
streets dedicated before the adoption of the British common law
belong to the state in fee.†

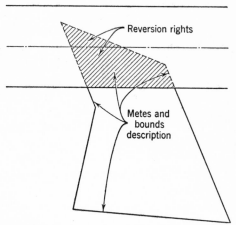

Figure 6-1. Reversion rights are determined by property lines that existed
prior to dedicating the street

213. Division of Private Ownership in Streets

Principle. *The ownership lines in the street are determined by
the ownership lines as they existed before the dedication of the
road easement. A private conveyance of land abutting on a road,
the fee to which belongs to the adjoining proprietors, is interpreted,
if possible, to pass fee to the center line thereof; the contrary must
be stated.*

Metes and bounds descriptions often delineate the limits of private ownership in a street as shown in Fig. 6-1. Where the bounds
within a street are given, the necessity for assuming the center of

* Lake City v. Fulkerson, 122 Iowa 569, 98 NW 376.
† Appleton v. City of New York, 114 NE 73, 219 NY 150.

the street as the boundary does not exist.   Deeds may expressly exclude the street, but, unless they do, the inference is that the street is included.   The assumption that the grantee takes title to the center of the street is based upon the idea that the owners on each side contributed their land in equal amounts.   When such is not the fact, the assumption does not arise.

Subdivision maps filed in most states do not show the limits of private ownership within the streets, yet the streets are mere easements.   When a lot within a subdivision is sold, the subdivider normally (but not always) conveys legal title of the lot without mention of the street, but, according to common law, title to the center of the street is also included.   This is just.   After all the lots within a subdivision are sold, the subdivider has no further interest in the road nor would he want any part of the improvements, taxes, or maintenance assessed against the land in the street.

The only noted exception to the above was in Maine* wherein, when the subdivision plat failed to show lines extending beyond the side lines of the street, the court ruled that the limits of ownership was the side line of the street.

The assumption that ownership extends to the center line of the street is not rebutted by the fact that the dimensions as stated carry the land only to the side line of the street, or by the fact that property markers are in the side line of the street.   Deeds do not ordinarily describe property beyond the limits where the grantor has exclusive rights.   Surveyors frequently set stakes in the side line of roads even when knowing that the true property line is the center of the road.

In Texas† refusal to pay street assessments on the grounds that their metes and bounds description went along the street but did not include the street led to the court finding that deeds to a city lot, fronting or abutting on a street, by metes and bounds, carries fee to the center of the street, unless it contains clauses expressly declaring a contrary intention.

214. Words Excluding and Including Conveyance to Center Line of Street.   The assumption that an owner owns to the center line of a street can be overcome by definitive statements to the contrary.   Such words as "along the side line of the street," "exclusive of the street," "excepting the street" will prevent title in the

* Sutherland v. Jackson, 32 Me 80.

† Texas Betulithic Co. v. Warweck, 293 SW 160.

bed of a street from passing. Such words as "bounded by the highway," "fronting on the highway," "to and along the highway," "with and by the highway," and "in line of highway" can be construed to mean "along the center line of the highway" and are usually taken in that light in the absence of other words of exclusion.

Descriptions of property on a highway and without words expressly including the highway, but with words granting an easement in the highway, are construed to indicate an intent not to convey the bed of the street. The fact that it was necessary to convey an easement indicates that the fee to the bed did not pass.

APPORTIONMENT OF REVERSION RIGHTS

215. The problem of apportioning the limits of ownership arising from the presumption that fee up to the center line of the street is conveyed is sparsely found in the court records. Within subdivisions, where the limits of private ownership are seldom defined, the problem becomes complex on curved and irregular streets. The following rules, partially based upon the customs of surveyors and a few court cases, represent the accepted practice.

216. General Principle. *Unless a deed or map indicates otherwise, reversion rights extend from the street termini of the property lines to the center line or thread of the street in a direction that is at right angles to the center line of the street.*

Prolongation of the lot line to the center line of the street is not recognized as a means of determining the rights in the bed of a street. Dotted lines opposite lot 1 in Fig. 6-2 illustrate the difficulties that result from an attempt to prolong lot lines. Who would own area *C*?

In making street assessments for paving a street, the adjoining property owner must pay for the paving in front of his property in accordance with the above principle. If assessments are paid on that basis, reversion rights should follow the same lines.

217. Reversion Rights of a Lot on a Curved Street

Principle. *The reversion rights of a lot in the middle of a block extends radially to the center line of the street.* (See Fig. 6-3.)

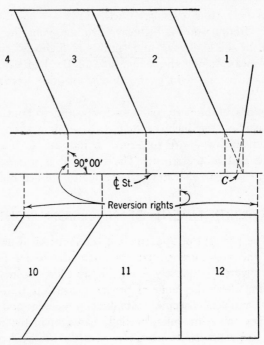

Figure 6-2. Reversion rights, unless otherwise indicated, are at right angle to the center-line of the street

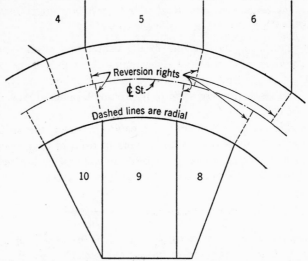

Figure 6-3. Reversion rights, unless otherwise indicated are on radial lines

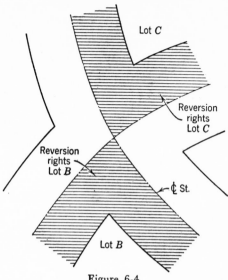

Figure 6-4.

Radial lines are at right angles to a tangent of a curve. If the previous principle is interpreted in a broad manner, this principle can be considered a special application of the former principle. Figure 6-3 illustrates the more common applications of the principle.

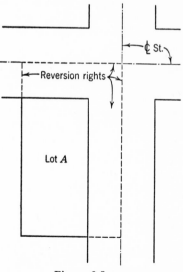

Figure 6-5.

218. Lots at an Intersection

Principle. *Lots adjoining an intersection have reversion rights up to the center line of the intersection of the streets.* (See Figs. 6-4 and 6-5.)

Lots adjoining a street intersection receive the lion's share of the land vacated with just cause. Where a street is paved next to a corner as in Fig. 6-5, the corner lot must pay for the assessment of the intersection and is entitled to all the land that it pays assessments on. Where an intersection is curved as shown in Fig. 6-4, the revision rights also extend to the center line as determined by a curved line.

219. Lots Adjoining a Subdivision Boundary

Principle. *Reversion rights of a lot adjoining a subdivision boundary extend along the boundary line of the subdivision and cannot extend beyond the boundary line.*

In Fig. 6-6, lot 1 of Map 70 and lot *A* of a different subdivision, along with the reversion rights of each lot, are shown. The previous principle that reversion rights of a lot within a subdivision

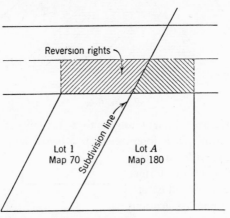

Figure 6-6.

are at right angles to the center line of the street cannot apply in this example owing to the lack of title interest of lot *A* in Map 70. Under certain circumstances lots adjoining a subdivision may have reversion rights beyond the center line of the street as shown in Fig 6-7 where all of the street reverts back to lot 7.* The subdivision on the north side of the street certainly has no title interest in the street adjacent to lot 7. Where the public easement is vacated, the land must revert to the former owner, or in this case to the lots south of the street.

220. Lots at an Angle Point in a Road

Principle. *Reversion rights at an angle point in a road extend on the bisection of the angle.*

* See also Oberhelman v. Allen, 7.0. App. (Ohio) 251.

Reversion rights are indicated by the bisecting line in Fig. 6-8, where there is an angle point. Lot 4 will receive a greater amount of land than lot 1 even though both lots have equal amounts of frontage.

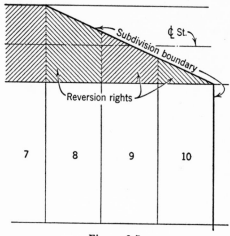

Figure 6-7.

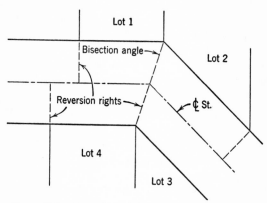

Figure 6-8. Reversion rights at angles in the street

221. Indeterminate Cases. Normally area X of Fig. 6-9 would by reversion become a part of lot 5. In one court case* it was held that an area similar to X belonged to the abutting owners who were entitled to road access. If area X were given to lots 1, 2, 3, and 4, how would it be divided?

* 149 Ky 409.

222. Exception and Discussion of the Rules of Apportionment.
In the states of Kansas* and Oklahoma,† the rule of apportionment
is similar to that of accretions to rivers.

Whenever any street, avenue, alley or lane shall be vacated, the same
shall revert to the owners of the real estate thereto adjacent to each side,
in proportion to the frontage of such real estate, except in cases where
such streets, avenue, alley or lane shall have been taken and appropriated
to public use in a different proportion in which case it shall revert to the
adjacent lots of real estate in proportion as it was taken from them.‡

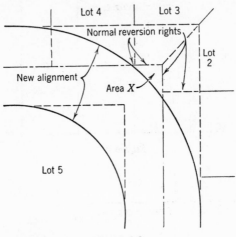

Figure 6-9.

This statute, in numerous cases, would be applied in accordance
with the rules given in the above Sections. In the case of a curve,
Fig. 6-3, the frontage of all lots remain in proportion to the new
frontage at the center line of the street provided radial lines are
used as shown. In Fig. 6-10, b is to B as c is to C, an exact
proportion. But troubles ensue, if the principle is strictly adhered to, at the termination of curves and at irregular boundary
lines of the subdivision as shown in Fig. 6-10. The proportion g
is to G as f is to F as e is to E is exact. Also d is to D as c is to C
as b is to B as a is to A. But d is to D as e is to E is not a proportion. Difficulty in applying the above statute is encountered at

* Showalter v. Southern Kansas Ry. Co. 49 Kan 421, 32 P 42.
† Blackwell, SW Ry. Co. v. Gist, 18 Okla 516, 90 P 889.
‡ Oklahoma statute law.

every intersection. How will lot 10 receive its share of the vacated street? The simple method of obviating such difficulties is to indicate on the subdivision map being filed the intended reversion rights of the adjoining lots. If dotted lines as shown in Fig. 6-10 were included as a part of the original map, no doubt could exist.

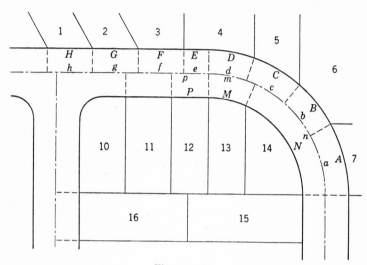

Figure 6-10.

223. Summary. The object of the principle for the distribution of land located within a vacated public way is to give each adjoining land owner an equitable share of the land.

If the ownership of the bed of the road is defined by deeds, that owner is given possession in accordance with his deed. If the ownership of the bed of the road is not defined by deeds, each adjoining owner is given an equitable share up to the center line of the road. The direction of the dividing line between adjoining owners is best defined by a line running at right angles to the center line of the road or on a radial line.

CHAPTER 7

Riparian
and Littoral Owners*

224. Riparian Rights. The privileges and rights conferred upon the riparian and littoral owner may take the form of rights to construct dams, docks, and mills, of rights to the bed of the stream, lake, or sea, of rights to land gradually and imperceptibly deposited by accretion, of rights of navigation, of rights to harvest ice, or of the right to appropriate water. If there is erosion or inundation due to rising waters, the riparian owner may suffer losses.

The legal aspect of water is voluminous and fills many books. Only a summary of that portion having a direct effect on the determination of boundary lines between adjacent property owners will be included within these pages. Laws controlling riparian rights differ materially from state to state. In Maine, New Hampshire, and Massachusetts, the littoral owner has rights to the ownership of tidal flats, whereas in California the upland owner cannot claim title beyond the mean high-tide mark. Because of the differences between state laws, this chapter includes opposite conditions enforced and found equitable by different states.

225. Definition of Terms

Riparian and littoral owners. Although Webster's *Dictionary* defines riparian as, "of, pertaining to, or living on, the bank of a river, of a lake, or of a tidewater," strictly speaking, those living adjacent to tidewater and lakes are "littoral" owners. Any strip of land, no matter how small, between an upland owner and the body of water deprives the upland owner from riparian or littoral rights. If the property of the upland owner abuts upon water and

---

* Reference: *Corpus Juris,* "Waters."

there are no words of exclusion in his deed, riparian rights by presumption are normally conveyed along with the property.

Navigable waters. "Navigable water" is not a term susceptible to precise definition.

Navigable waters are navigable in fact when they are used, or are susceptible of being used, in their ordinary conditions as highways of commerce, over which trade and travel are or may be conducted in the customary modes of trade and travel on water.*

The sovereignty of the bed of navigable fresh waters resides in the states, who may dispose of the bed as they see fit. But all navigable waters are subject to an easement as common highways for the use of the public. Although it has been held† that Willow River, Wisconsin, was a navigable stream because it was capable of floating logs and boats at times of high water, this case represents an extreme not usually recognized as navigable within the normal meaning of the word. The sole and final authority on what constitutes navigable waters rests with the Federal courts.

Accretion and alluvion. Where, from natural causes, land forms by imperceptible degrees upon the bank of a river, stream, lake, or tidewater, either by accumulation of material or recession of the water, the process and end result are called alluvion or accretion. The land formed as a result of accretion is usually called alluvium. The characteristic is that alluvial or other deposits are accumulated at a rate that cannot be perceived in each moment of time. Rivers and tidewaters, normally being in motion, carry sand, silt, pebbles, or stones that may be deposited at favorable locations to form accretion. Static or still lakes expose dry land by recession or drying up, and, if the process is imperceptible, it comes within the legal meaning of accretion. Ownership of accretions normally reside in the adjoining riparian proprietor.

Revulsion or avulsion. Revulsion is opposite to accretion. Accretion is an imperceptible gradual deposition of land that may be observed over a period of time, but not at any one instant; revulsion is the sudden and perceptible removal of considerable quantity of land by water such as a river changing its course in time of flood.

Reliction. Reliction is land left uncovered by the gradual receding of waters. The ebb and flow of tides is not reliction.

* United States v. Holt State Bank, 270 US 49.
† Willow River Club v. Wade, 100 Wis 86.

Thread of a river. The thread of a river is the line formed an equal distance from the shores, and is not to be confused with the center of the main channel which may be closer to one bank than to the other. The thread of a lake is the center line which passes through the thread of the inlet and the thread of the outlet. Where there is no inlet or outlet, the thread passes through the center of the lake on its longest axis. The thread of a river or lake is determined at its ordinary and natural stage.

Bed. The bed of a lake or river is normally that land which is covered by water sufficiently long to keep it bare of vegetation and destroy its value for agriculture.

Meander line. A meander line run by a surveyor is for the purpose of platting the size and extent of the body of water. Patents issued by the government are not limited to the meander line as run by the surveyor, but to the actual shore line where it exists.

It has been the practice of the government from its origin, in disposing of the public lands, to measure the price to be paid for them by the quantity of upland granted, no charge being made for the lands under the beds of streams or other bodies of water. The meander lines run along or near the margin of such waters are run for the purpose of ascertaining the exact quantity of the upland to be charged for, and not for the purpose of limiting the title of the grantee to such meander lines. It has frequently been held, both by the federal and state courts, that such meander lines are intended for the purpose of bounding and abutting the lands granted upon the waters whose margins are thus meandered; and the waters themselves constitute the real boundary.*

Until Dec. 2, 1930, an exception existed around the shores of the Great Lakes within the State of Michigan. In the case of Aimsworth v. Munoskong Club† the Michigan state supreme court ruled that the land between the meander line and the water line belonged to the state in trust for the people. But in the case of Hilt v. Weber‡ the court reversed itself.

226. Ownership of the Bed of Fresh Water and Tide Lands. Normally the law that determines the ownership of the bed of streams, ponds or lakes, and tidelands is regulated by the state; but such regulation cannot extinguish, without due process of law, a title already granted by a duly constituted body.§ Thus in Texas,

* Hardin v. Jordan, 140 US 371 and Foss v. Johnstone, 158 Cal 119.
† 159 Mich 61, Dec. 1909.
‡ 252 Mich 198, 233 NW 159.
§ Oklahoma v. Texas, 259 US 565; United States v. Utah, 283 US 64.

before the adoption of the English common law in 1840, land grants made by Spain, Mexico, or Texas reserved the bed of all perennial streams regardless of the conditions of navigability. Land grants made after 1840 included the bed of non-navigable streams. Those grants made before 1840 did not, by the adoption of the English common law, acquire rights not granted them at the time of their patent; i.e., the bed of the perennial streams was still vested in the state.*

The laws of the United States that regulated the disposal of the public domain granted to the riparian owner the bed of all non-navigable streams. Upon admission of a territory into statehood, the adoption of a law vesting non-navigable river beds in the state is not operative where the United States had previously patented such land in another.

Land grants made by the United States did not include the bed of navigable streams. Upon admission to the Union all sovereign rights to the bed of navigable streams, subject to a public easement for commerce, passed to the state. After having acquired the bed of navigable streams, each state has the right, by statute law, to dispose of the bed as it sees fit. Some states have retained ownership to the beds; others have vested title in the adjoining riparian owner. The limit of upland proprietors, as reserved by the United States for navigable streams, is the high-water mark, but some states have transferred to the riparian owner lands between the high- and low-water marks.

Lands not forming a part of the public domain, as the original 13 states, were not regulated by the rules of the United States. Although many of the original states adopted the common law of England, that of granting the bed of all waters except those subject to the ebb and flow of the tides to the riparian owner, some of the states by colonial ordinance and common law did otherwise. Maine, Massachusetts, and New Hampshire granted tidelands between low and high tidewater, but not more than 100 rods, to the riparian owner.

By virtue of the Massachusetts colonial ordinance of 1641–1647 and the common law adoptions by Maine and New Hampshire, title to ponds over 10 acres in extent, called great ponds, was vested in the state as a trust for public use. The littoral owner has no right to the water or soil nor control or use of the water

* State v. Grubstake Inv. Ass'n, 297 SW 202, 117 Tex 53.

except where there is an explicit legislative grant. But deeds granted before the ordinance and from the Plymouth Colony passed title to great ponds, thus creating a few cases of private ownership.

Under civil laws, which prevailed in Florida while it was a Spanish Colony, the limit of a subject's right was the mark of the highest winter wave. Upon the changing of sovereignty, that limit was regulated by the laws and policy of the new sovereign, and ordinary high water became the limit.*

From this brief discussion it can be seen that the question of ownership of the bed of water can differ significantly from state to state. For fresh water any one of the following laws may exist: (1) the bed belongs to the adjoining riparian owner; (2) the state owns the bed below the low-water mark, and the upland riparian owner has the remainder; (3) the state owns the bed up to the high-water mark; (4) the rule in each state may be different for navigable or non-navigable waters. Adjoining salt water, the tidelands may be owned by the state as in California, or it may be owned privately as in three of the New England states.

The limit of ownership in the bed of a stream or lake is sometimes modified by the location of the state line. Where the division line between states is "the center line of the main channel," and the riparian proprietor normally owns to the "thread of the stream," the ownership is extended or shortened to go to the state line as determined by the center line of the main channel.†

An Oklahoma law declaring that certain conditions make a stream navigable is of no avail against the United States. A grant of land by the United States to an Indian tribe before the admittance of Oklahoma as a state grants the rights to the bed of non-navigable streams and the oil contained therein. The condition of navigability is a question to be settled by the courts of the United States in accordance with the conditions existing at the time of the patent or grant and not according to Oklahoma or any other state law.‡

227. Control of Navigation. Navigable rivers, lakes, and tidelands are public highways free from interference of adjoining riparian owners in the interest of the public. Even though the upland owner may possess title to the bed of a navigable river, lake, or

---

* Alden v. Pimery, 12 Fla 365.

† Franzini v. Layland, 120 Wis 72.

‡ Brewer-Elliott Oil and Gas Co. v. United States, 260 US 77.

tideland, this must be taken as subject to the right of the public to pass over and along the water.

228. Boundary Line Shifts with Water Line

Where the water line is the boundary of a given lot, that line, no matter how it shifts, remains the boundary; and a deed describing the lot by its number conveys the land up to the shifting water line.*

The facts of ownership of the bed of the stream does not alter this principle. If the state owns the bed of a stream and land is deposited as accretions along the shore, such built-up lands, built up on the bed as owned by the state, belong to the riparian owner. Likewise an upland owner whose land is eroded away loses title to the bed of former lands now lying below water. In California, tidewater accretions caused by man-built barriers, such as jetties, belong to the state.

229. Ownership of Land Built Up by Accretion

Principle. *Land gradually built up by accretion, except where otherwise stipulated, belongs to the riparian owner to whose property it is attached, irrespective of whether the state owns the bed of the stream or not. Distribution of land formed by accretion is determined by the laws of the state wherein the accretion forms.*

Land added to the shore by imperceptible means presents complex problems in the distribution of the alluvium. Although the courts of different states have devised different means to arrive at a fair and equitable solution (see Section 233), they have agreed that the riparian proprietor has the right of ownership.

Land attached to a public highway by process of accretion becomes part of the road subject to the same easements.†

230. Ownership of Land Lost by Erosion and Inundation

Principle. *Land gradually eroded away or permanently inundated by water becomes part of the bed of the water and belongs to the owner of the bed.*

Land eroded away or submerged by water does not necessarily belong to the former owner. The land becomes a part of the bed of the water body; ownership of the bed is determined by the laws

* Jefferis v. East Omaha Land Co., 134 US 178.
† St. Louis v. Missouri Pac. R. Co., 114 Mo 13, SW 202.

of the state.   Figure 7-1 shows the conditions existing before and
after erosion removed part of the SW quarter of section 10.   The
area marked *ABCD* is now part of the bed of the river and belongs
to the owner of the bed of the river, whoever he may be.   If the
stream is non-navigable and if ownership is limited to the thread

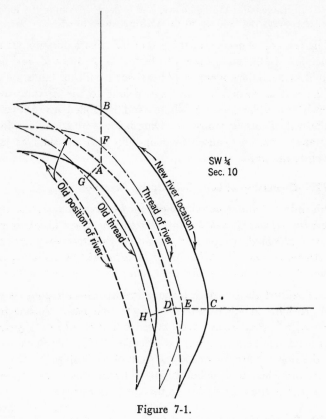

Figure 7-1.

of the stream, the owner of the SW quarter retains title to *BCEF*
but loses title to *FEDHGA*.   If the river is navigable and the state
owns the bed, the area *ABCD* is lost by erosion.

231. Ownership of Land Removed by Revulsion

Principle.   *Land detached from the land of an owner by the
sudden process of revulsion belongs to the person from whose land
it was detached.*

Land is not lost by revulsion, but is lost by gradual erosion. A river that changes its course by cutting a new channel and forming an island does not change the ownership of the new island. Likewise, a parcel of ground detached from the land of one owner and attached to the land of another by the sudden change of a river course is not lost by the former owner. In some states, a statute of limitations determines how soon the former owner must claim the detached land.* In all states, detached land can be lost by adverse possession.

232. Ownership of Salt Water Tidelands

Principle. *Ownership of the former public domain tidelands between average high tide and average low tide is vested in the state, which may dispose of it.*

Most of the original states not forming a part of the public domain adopted the English common law whereby lands below the average high-tide mark belong to the state. In Massachusetts, by the colonial ordinance of 1641–1647, and in Maine and New Hampshire by the adoption of the colonial ordinance as common law, the tidelands between average high and extreme low water, but not more than 100 rods, belong to the riparian owner in accordance with the law:

In all creeks, coves and other places about and upon salt water, where the sea ebbs and flows, the proprietor of the land adjoining shall have propriety to the low water mark where the sea does not ebb above a hundred rods, and not more wheresoever it ebbs further.†

This does not apply to fresh water but to open seashore, arms of the sea, and islands within the sea. In Massachusetts, the low water referred to is to be interpreted as extending to the lowest ebb. Grants made prior to the ordinance were held to extend only to high-water mark in Massachusetts and to low-water mark in Maine.

233. Methods of Determining Ownership of Land Exposed or Built Up by Reliction or Accretion

(*a*) Proportionate Shore-Line Method. Land that has been built up by accretion and apportioned among several riparian own-

---

* In California, one year, Sec. 1015, Civil Code.
† Emerson v. Taylor, 9 Me 35.

ers so that each owner has the same percentage of water frontage that he had formerly is said to be divided by the proportionate shore-line method.

Three conditions arise in the application of this principle; i.e., the shore is concave, convex, or straight as shown in Fig. 7-2.   In each

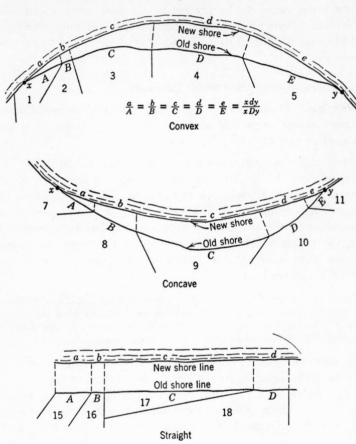

$$\frac{a}{A} = \frac{b}{B} = \frac{c}{C} = \frac{d}{D} = \frac{e}{E} = \frac{xdy}{xDy}$$

Figure 7-2.   Proportionate shore-line method

condition the length of the new shore line is in proportion to the length of the old shore line, or b is to B as the total length of xdy of the new shore is to the total length of xDy of the old.   Straight lines are drawn from the new point on the new shore to the old point on the old shore.   The equity of this method is based upon the fact that each riparian owner is entitled to the same proportionate amount of docking space. If there are deep indentations or sharp projections, the general trend of the shore line is used.

In Louisiana* the principle is: Proportionate area or acreage system for division of alluvion between adjoining riparian proprietors is excluded.

If an alluvion be formed in front of the property of several riparian properties, the division is to be made according to the extent of the front line of each at the time of the formation of the alluvion.†

The method as above stated represents the majority opinion for the division of accretions.

(b) PROPORTIONATE THREAD-OF-THE-STREAM METHOD. Land that has been built up by accretion and apportioned among several riparian owners in such a manner that each owner has the same percentage of footage in the thread of the stream as he had on the old shore line is said to be divided by the proportionate thread-of-the-stream method.

The method is best explained by the following quotation: ‡

Measure the entire river front of survey 759 as it existed in 1860, when the third subdivision of Cahokia commons was first laid out, and note the aggregate number of feet frontage as well as that of each parcel or lot. Then measure a line drawn as near as may be with the middle thread of so much of the stream as lies opposite the shore line so measured. Having done this, divide the thread line thus measured into as many equal parts as there are linear feet in the shore line, giving to each proprietor as many of these parts as his property measures feet on the shore line. Then complete the division by drawing lines between the parts, designating the lot or parcel belonging to such proprietor upon both the shore and the river lines.

This method is commonly used to determine pier rights.

(c) PIE METHOD. Where water has receded or land has built up along the shore of a circular body of water, and the land is divided in the manner in which a pie is cut, the land is apportioned by the pie method.

Circular lakes that have become dry by the receding of waters are best divided by the pie method as shown in Figs. 7-3 and 7-5.§

(d) COLONIAL METHOD. The method used in Maine to appor-

---

* Newell v. Leathers et al., 23 So 243.
† Statute law.
‡ Kehn v. Snyder 2 NE 68, 114, Ill 313.
§ See Scheifert v. Briegel, 90 Minn 125, 96 NW 44.

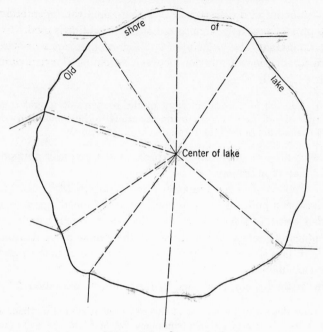

Figure 7-3. Pie method

tion tidelands (alluvial flats) by drawing a base line from one corner of each lot to the other, at the margin of the upland, and running a line from each of these corners, at right angles to the base line to low water will be referred to as the Colonial method.* In the case of Emerson v. Taylor (9 Me 35) the principle is stated with reference to Exhibit *B* Fig. 7-4 as follows:

Draw a base line from the two corners of each lot, where they strike the shore, and from those two corners, extend parallel lines to low-water mark, at right angles with the base line. If the line of the shore be straight there will be no interference in running the parallel lines. If the flats lie in a cove, of a regular or irregular curvature, there will be an interference in running such lines, and the loss occasioned by it must be equally borne or gain enjoyed equally by the contiguous owners, as appears in the following plan, marked *B*.

(*e*) LONG-LAKE METHOD. If a long lake is divided by erecting perpendiculars from the thread of the lake to the point of contact

* See Emerson v. Taylor, 9 Me 35; Treat v. Chipman, 35 Me 34.

of the property line with the shore and the ends are divided by the pie method, the lake is divided by the long-lake method.

Figure 7-5 shows the proper procedure for dividing the bed of a long lake.*

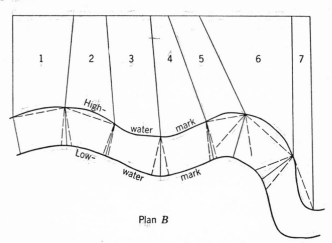

Plan *B*

Figure 7-4. Colonial method. Emerson v. Taylor 9Me35

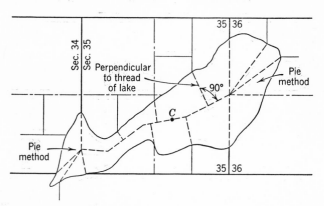

Figure 7-5. Long-lake method. Rooney v. County of Stearns, 130Minn176

The two ends of the lake were considered semicircular and were divided according to the pie method. Using point *C* as a center and adopting the pie method was rejected because of the inequities involved.

* Rooney v. County of Stearns, 130 Minn 176.

(f) COVES. No uniform rule exists for the division of coves. Within the same state different methods have been applied, depending upon the equities of the particular circumstances. Thus in Fig. 7-6 is shown the court's ruling for distribution of flats in a cove in Boston Harbor. The direction of the division lines between riparian owners extends at right angles to a base line drawn across the cove. All lines commence at the point of contact of the upland owners' line with the high-water mark and terminate at extreme low-water mark (but not more than 100 rods).*

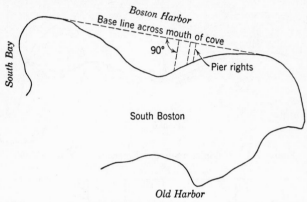

Figure 7-6.   Perpendicular method.   Gray v. Deluce, 59Mass9

Because of difficulties in applying the base-line principle as used in the previous case, the court followed a different principle for Coos's Cove, Gloucester, as shown in Fig. 7-7, whereby the proportionate shore line method (see Section 233a) was used.† The court noted,

The appropriate mode of division is to give each proprietor a front line at extreme low water mark proportionate in length to his shore line at ordinary high water mark, and to run the division line of the flats straight from high water mark to the low water mark.

In Blodgett and Davis Lumber Co. v. Peters et al.‡ and Rust v. Boston Mill Corp.§ a similar method was used. It appears from the majority of cases that the proportionate shore-line method is

* Gray v. Deluce, 59 Mass 9.
† Wonson v. Wonson, 96 Mass 71.·
‡ 49 NW 917, 87 Mich 497.
§ 23 Mass 158.

preferred. This gives each an equitable right to construct piers to the line of navigation.

(*g*) Perpendicular Method. Establishing the division line between properties by turning 90° from a line will be referred to as the perpendicular method. Since radial lines are perpendicular to their tangent of the curve, lines established radially to a curved shore line are herein considered variations of the perpendicular method.

Many adaptations of the perpendicular method are applied depending upon the circumstances of the case. The perpendiculars

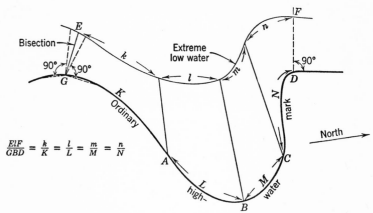

Figure 7-7. Distribution of rights to Coos's Cove, Gloucester, Mass.

may be erected to a base line across the mouth of a cove (Fig. 7-6), to the thread of a stream or lake, or to the shore of tidelands. The Colonial method (Section 233-*d*) is a rule of thumb used to arrive at a line that is nearly radial or perpendicular. The long-lake method, as illustrated in Fig. 7-5, is a special case whereby property lines are constructed at right angles to the thread of a lake. In Wood v. Appal, the court held that instead of continuing in the same course by the compass, the property deflects at the bank in a direction that is at right angles to the stream.

Starting from the bank, a direct course to the stream, or at right angles to the stream, must always afford the shortest and most certain boundary of river frontage.*

In Wells v. Bailey, it is stated,

* 63 Pa 210.

The land belonging to the new riparian owner is within lines drawn from the termini of its side lines at right angles to the channel of the river.*

(h) PROLONGATION OF PROPERTY LINES. Dividing accretions and relictions by prolonging the property lines will be referred to as the prolongation-of-property-line method. The weight of authority is against the use of this means as in the case of Grand Rapids Ice and Coal Co. v. South Grant Rapids Ice and Coal Co.† See Fig. 7-8. The owner of the fractional north half of section 34 claimed

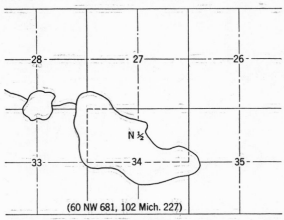

Figure 7-8.

all ice rights lying within the limits of the north half as it would exist if surveyed. The court ruled that the owner of a fractional section meandered by the United States survey is not limited in his riparian rights to the extended lines of his subdivision.

This is not the universal principle. Foss lake, a meandered lake, was divided by a section line as it would exist if run across the water.‡ In McCaman v. Stage (43 P 86) division of accretion follows the half quarter-section line extended. In Hubbard v. Manwell§, Fig. 7-9, shows the conditions as they existed. Hubbard claimed to the line that would give him a share of the accretion by the proportionate shore-line method or by the shortest distance to

* 10 A 565, 55 Conn 292.
† 60 NW 681, 102 Mich 227.
‡ Foss v. Johnstone, 158 Cal 119 P 294.
§ 60 Vt 235 14 Atl 693.

the stream in accordance with the court's previous ruling.* Both
were rejected in favor of extending the property lines as shown.

If a lake were so small that the section lines were run across the
lake and not meandered around the lake, the limits of ownership
were decreed to be the lines as run†

(*i*) Summary of Methods of Apportioning Accretions.
Three fundamental methods of dividing accretions exist, namely:
(1) The proportionate shore-line method; (2) the perpendicular

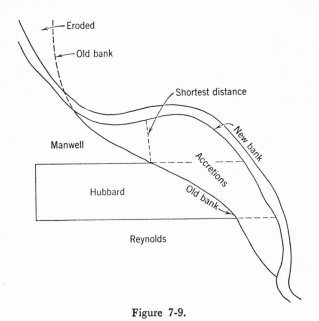

Figure 7-9.

method as used in a broad sense to include radial lines; and (3)
the prolongation of the property lines. Many variations applied by
the courts make it appear that there are many more. The proportionate shore-line method may be in proportion to the new shore
line, the thread of the stream, or low-water mark, depending upon
the peculiar circumstances of the case. In applying the proportionate shore-line method, the courts often resort to the perpendicular
method to determine the start and finish points for proportioning.

* **23 Vt 316.**

† Kirpatrick v. Yates Ice Co., 45 Mo App. 335; also see Kean v. Roby,
145 Ind 221.

Thus, in Fig. 7-7, the cove flats were divided by giving each a proportionate share of the frontage at low-water mark in proportion to their frontage at high-water mark. The points of commencement of the apportioning were determined by erecting a perpendicular to the straight shore at the right of Fig. 7-7 and by erecting a "radial" line marked *GE* in Fig. 7-7. The "radial" line was determined in a manner similar to that used in the Colonial method, Fig. 7-4. Two right-angle lines were erected from cords drawn to the right and left of *G*, and the line *GE* was formed by the bisection of the two right-angle lines. The Colonial method as shown in Fig. 7-4 is an empirical method for determining a "radial" line and is a variation of the perpendicular method. Any radial to a curve is a perpendicular to the curve itself. The pie-cutting method, involving radial lines from a center, is a modification of the perpendicular method. In the long-lake method, lines are run at right angles to the thread of the lake.

Extending the property lines across a body of water and/or accretions has been decreed proper in a sufficient number of cases to make one wonder what he should do under a given set of conditions. Since the states differ in their interpretation of the law, it is necessary for the person attempting to establish division lines extending through accretion to determine the law for his particular state.

234. Distribution of Land between Meander Line and Water Line.* Normally, the ownership of land lying between the meander line and the high-water mark is determined by prolonging the property line to the high-water mark.† In Minnesota,‡ it was held that the land between the meander line and the water should be apportioned similar to the principles for accretion. But this is a rare exception.

235. Land Lost by Erosion and Regained by Accretion. Land entirely eroded away or submerged ceases to be riparian, and the new land touched by the river becomes riparian. Upon reappearance of the land by accretion or reliction, ownership of the new accretion is vested in either the new riparian proprietor or the former owner, depending upon the state in which the land is located.

* Menasha Wooden Wane Co. v. Lawson, 70 Wis 600, 36 NW 412.
† City of Peoria v. Central National Bank, 224 Ill 43, 79 NE 296.
‡ Hanson v. Rice, 88 Minn 273, 92 NW 982.

In those states where title is extinguished permanently by complete erosion or submergence, not every disappearance of land extinguishes the title of the true owner. Submergence must be long continued so as to preclude identity upon reliction, and erosion must transport soil beyond the limits of ownership. Claimant must show the facts that deprive the true owner of his title and must assume the burden of proof.*

The bed of the Connecticut River gradually eroded away all the land of a riparian owner and encroached upon an upland owner. Later accretions built upon the land of the new riparian owner were held to belong to the new riparian proprietor irrespective of whether the alluvium formed extended beyond his former ownership lines or not.† Also in Yearsley v. Gipple,‡ the court held that, if lands become riparian by the eroding away of adjoining lands, the owner is entitled to the right of the riparian owner to accretions, even though they extend beyond the original boundary line of the land.

But this is not true in other jurisdictions where the principle is that title to land that becomes submerged is not lost, and, when the land reappears by some means, the original owner is entitled to the land.

On the Canadian River, a non-navigable stream, the patentee acquired title to the middle of the stream. If all of the land of a riparian proprietor washes away so that an upland owner becomes riparian and then the land reappears by the river abandoning the old channel, the upland owner does not acquire title to the bed of the river on the theory that the former owner's title was extinguished when he ceased to be riparian.§

The land in section 30, composed of lots 5 and 7 gradually eroded away by the Missouri River, a navigable stream, until the owner of land in section 31 became riparian. By accretion the waters receded and restored all of Section 31 and lots 5 and 7 of section 30. The lots of section 30 did not become the property of the owner of section 31 on the theory that the title to lots 5 and 7 were extinguished.‖

* Baumhart v. McClure, 153 NE 211.

† Wells v. Bailey, 10 A 565, 55 Conn 292.

‡ 175 NW 641 Neb; see also Peuker v. Canter et al., 63 P 617, 62 Kan 363.

§ Hunzicker v. Kleeden, 17 P 2nd Okla 384.

‖ Allard v. Curren, 168 NW 761, 41 SD 73; see also Baumhart v. McClure, 153 NE 211 (Ohio).

236. Ownership between States

Principle. *Unless there is a limitation provided by the admission act, the line of division between states bordering on a river is the center of the main channel of the stream.*

The main channel of the Mississippi may at one place be near the western shore and at another, near the eastern shore. The main channel is not the thread of the stream nor is it at an equal distance from each shore. It is evident that the main channel is a changing line. Special conditions stated in the admission act alter the general principle. The low-water mark on the Indiana side of the Ohio river is the division between Kentucky and Indiana.* The center of the north channel of the Columbia River is the division between Oregon and Washington.† The lower edge of the west bank of Chattahoochee River is the division between Georgia and Alabama.‡

237. Pier Rights and Apportionment of Navigable Water. The apportionment of the bed of navigable water for the purpose of constructing piers and docks has been the subject of many lawsuits. For the purpose of harvesting ice, numerous lakes have been pro-rated to adjoining riparian owners.

In the case of rivers, the principle outlined in Section 233b is usually applied. The actual shore line (not meander line) of the river and the line of navigation are measured.§ By dividing the line of navigation into parts proportionate to each riparian owner's shore length and drawing straight lines from the shore division lines to the proportionate division made on the line of navigation, the problem is solved.‖

The riparian owner, unless there is a reservation in the conveyance, is entitled to free access to the line of navigation. In general, the riparian owner may build piers or approaches., as long as he does not interfere with the public rights or obstruct navigation. The methods used to locate pier rights for navigation are not in complete agreement with the methods used to proportion dried beds of lakes and rivers. The theory should probably be the same, but the problem is not identical since in the one case a fair distribution

---

* Indiana v. Kentucky, 136 US 479.
† Washington v. Oregon, 211 US 127.
‡ Georgia v. Alabama, 23 How. '64 US 505.
§ Peoria v. Central Nat. Bank, 224 Ill 43.
‖ **Northern Pine Land Co. v. Bigelow, 84 Wis 157.**

of rights to the line of navigation is sought, whereas in the other case an equitable distribution of dry land is the object.

238. Swamp and Overflow Lands. Certain lands that were subject to inundation and were unfit for agriculture unless levees and drainage channels were constructed were granted to the states upon application and survey. The grants were limited to unappropriated lands whose character at that time would bring them within the limits of the law.

Patents to riparian land adjoining a non-navigable swamp-like lake carried title to the bed of the lake. The state's sale of land left dry by receding waters, said land not having been recognized as swampland by proper legal means between the state and the United States, does not convey a valid title as against the riparian owner.*

239. Ownership of Islands

Principle. *The ownership of an island forming in a river or lake belongs to the owner of the bed of the river or lake.*

If an island forms on one side of a stream and the riparian proprietor owns the bed of the stream, the island belongs to the proprietor on whose side of the stream it formed. If an island is formed in the middle of a stream and the riparian proprietors own the bed of the stream, the island is divided by a line drawn through the thread of the stream.

Where the state owns the bed of a stream or lake, the adjoining riparian owner is not entitled to an island that springs up from the bed of the stream or lake.† The right to new islands follows the right of the soil on which they were formed. If the course of a river changes and cuts off a parcel of land to form a new island, the island belongs to the former owner.

An island in a non-navigable stream and not legally appropriated belongs to the owner on whose side it is located.

240. Fraudulent Surveys and Erroneously Omitted Areas‡

In a number of cases, the Moon Lake case,§ the Ferry case,‖ and others, the original boundaries of lakes were grossly and probably

---

* Foss v. Johnstone 110 P 294, 158 Cal 49.
† Perkins v. Adams, 33 SW 778.
‡ Manual of Surveying Instructions 1947, pages 366–378.
§ Les Wilson & Co. v. United States, 245 US 24.
‖ Jeems Bayou Fishing and Hunting Club v. United States, 260 US 561.

fraudulently in error. In such circumstances the meander line and not the lake was held to be the true boundary of the upland owner. The remaining land, that lying between the false meander line and the lake, belonged to the United States as undisposed public lands. Moon Lake as originally meandered consisted of 835 acres, yet investigation on the ground showed that it was impossible for a lake to have existed at the time of the original survey. In the Ferry Lake case the original surveyors falsely ran a portion of the meander line so as to omit 230 acres of dry land.

241. Interpretation of Deeds with Respect to Ownership of the Bed of Waters

General Presumption:

Assuming that the bed of a water is subject to private ownership, that the grantor owned the bed, and that there is no clearly expressed intention that the bed is conveyed, the grantor is presumed to pass title to the center or thread of the water or in the case of open tide water, to the limits of private ownership.*

Unless a contrary intention is expressed or is clearly inferred from the terms of the conveyance, the grantee of land bordering upon rivers or lakes is presumed to acquire title to the thread of the stream or lake on the theory that the grantor would not reserve an inundated parcel of land of no practical value to him, particularly in the absence of access thereto. Such terms as "along the river," "by the river," "up the river," "bounded by the lake," "to the ocean and along the ocean," "fronting on the river," "with and by said river," "to and down said river," and "in line of the river" are indefinite and raise the presumption that the bed is conveyed. Where the description states that the side lines extend a stated distance that reaches to the bank of the river and then states "along the river," the conveyance is presumed to extend to the thread of the river.

Should the terms of the conveyance be definite in its exclusion or inclusion of the bed of waters, the force of the presumption is overcome and the grantee will be awarded title in accordance with the terms of the deed. Such terms as "on and along the bank of the stream" and "to the low-water mark and along the low-water mark" are definite statements that exclude the possibility of meaning

* See *American Law Reporter* 75-599.

"along the thread of the stream." Such a general statement as "along the *side* of a river" has been interpreted to indicate a definite side of the river, but not a clause limiting ownership to the *bank* of a river.

The surrounding circumstances may be used to overcome the presumption as in Carleton v. Cleveland,* where it was apparent that it would be very unlikely that the owner and operator of a mill would sell the bed of his mill pond. The court noted that a riparian owner can sever the upland from the bed of the river and a conveyance by metes and bounds, not calling for the river, was limited to the calls even though part of the land was submerged. On the other hand, if the bed of the river would have been of no value to the grantor, and he had no access to the bed of the river, the case would probably have been reversed.

242. Double Descriptions. Double descriptions such as "a parcel of land, bounded by the *shore* of Denny's River, being lot number 52 on the plan,"† are often ambiguous. Lot number 52 on the plan was riparian and automatically included in the land to the center of the river (Maine law), whereas the metes and bounds portion granted only to the *shore* of the river. The construction giving the greatest advantage to the grantee, i.e., the center of the river, prevailed; the first stated condition was rejected.

Contrasting this with a similar case in the same state‡ a deed reading "thence to a cedar post on the bank of Worromontogus at the southwest corner of the Neal lot, so called; thence westerly by said stream to the above named road" . . . and calling for "a plan made by Asbury Young" was interpreted to mean along the bank. The term "by said stream" means to the limit of private ownership (low-water mark in this case). But the plan by Asbury Young was the result of a survey wherein markers were set a few feet away from the bank to exclude riparian rights. Other surrounding circumstances and the survey made it unlikely that low-water mark was intended.

243. Changing Conditions. From the above discussion it is obvious that ownership lines adjoining waters are changing lines. But whatever the disadvantages of unstable property lines are, the necessity of maintaining rights to navigation and to usage of the water

---

* 92 Atl 110, 112 Me 310.

† Lincoln v. Wilder, 29 Me 169.

‡ Erskine v. Moulton, 66 Me 279.

is of greater importance. The direction of pier rights, as determined by the proportionate thread-of-the-stream method, may change with the shifting of the thread of the stream; the shore line and side property lines may change with erosion or accretion, but the undesirability of such conditions is overcome by the economic necessity of contact with the water.

The disadvantage of the proportionate shore-line method of distributing accretions is obvious in Fig. 7-10. The old shore line

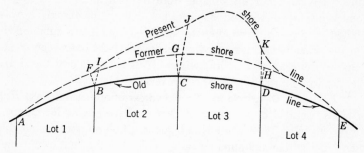

Figure 7-10.

ABCDE gradually moved to *AFGHE* by imperceptible means, and then, at a later date, to *AIJKE*. When the shore was located at *AFGHE*, the property line divisions were *FB*, *GC*, and *HD*; but when the shore moved to its present position, the division lines became *IB*, *JC*, and *KD*. The direction of the lines between the lots actually alters with every change in the pattern of the accretions. The permanence of property lines is thus lost. Why should the line *FB* change to *IB* and lot 1 acquire dry land once belonging to lot 2? A judge sitting on the bench must arrive at a particular problem solution on the basis of conditions existing at the time of the judgment. At best, a solution of a riparian problem is a temporary solution subject to change with changing conditions.

CHAPTER 8

Federal Mining Claims

244. Scope. When filing a valid mining claim, the prospector must comply with many regulations imposed by law. Methods used for posting notice, for recording the claim, for annual assessment work and other technical phases of mining, although interesting, cannot be considered within the scope of this book. Factors affecting the location and limits of boundaries will be discussed.

245. Mining Claims. A mining claim is a potential right to fee title to land and the minerals contained therein; said right may ripen into a fee title or patent by the use of a metes and bounds conveyance if certain acts and conditions are fulfilled. When a homestead patent is issued, any mining claim posted prior to the homestead claim has prior rights, even though a patent to the mining claim has not been issued. Although a claimant has exclusive surface rights within his valid claim, he does not acquire a fee title to the land until a patent is issued.

Two kinds of mining claims exist, a *lode claim* and a *placer claim*. The lode claim consists of a claim on minerals which exist as a fissure in rock filled with mineral matter, usually by deposition from solution by underground water. The term *placers* includes all forms of deposits except veins or lodes of rock in place. As used in the mining act, placers means ground within definite boundaries chiefly valuable for its deposits in earth, sand, or gravel, not in place, that is, in a loose state, upon or near the surface, or occupying the bed of ancient rivers or valleys, and it may be, in most instances, collected by washing.

246. Land Open to Appropriation of Minerals. Lands indicated as being held by the United States for disposal under the land laws are open to mineral location. Land specifically withdrawn, such as national parks, national monuments, military reservations, and Indian lands are not subject to location. Minerals found within a national forest are subject to location provided the discovery is such that it would justify an ordinary prudent person his expenditure of time and effort in developing a paying mine. Without the existence of commercial value, mineral claims within a national forest are not valid locations.

Since each state owns the bed of meandered lakes, the bed of navigable streams, and land between high and low-water mark, these lands are not subject to location under the Federal mining laws.

States whose land never belonged to the United States, and states specifically exempted from the Federal mining laws, are not open to location under Federal laws. They are Virginia, North Carolina, South Carolina, Pennsylvania, Rhode Island, New York, New Hampshire, New Jersey, Massachusetts, Maryland, Georgia, Delaware, Connecticut, Maine, Vermont, Kentucky, Alabama, Kansas, Illinois, Indiana, Michigan, Minnesota, Missouri, Ohio, Oklahoma, Wisconsin, Texas, and the territory of Hawaii.

247. Veins, Lodes, or Ledges. The terms veins, lodes, or ledges, though probably having different shades of meanings, are used synonymously by the mining act and the courts. A *vein* is a continuous body of ore or mineral-bearing substance found on or within the earth, having depth, width, and length, and being bounded on each side by country rock. It need not be straight or uniform, but it must be identifiable by vision or assay. The term *lode* often includes more than one vein. Tilted sedimental beds containing ores deposited by streams, and not by mineralizing agencies, come within the meaning of lode, vein, or ledge.

A vein or lode is continuous if it can be traced through the country rock. Ore found in disconnected pockets or cavities does not constitute a vein; but occasional pockets, connected by ore, constitute a vein. A vein may curve, vary in dip or strike, or divide into branches which may or may not reunite.

A "broad lode or zone" is one having the same genetic origin and lying within clearly defined boundaries. The broad zone may be fractured, or faulted. If a vein is traceable for a great distance and has definite walls, it is treated as a separate vein even though many veins are grouped close together. An extensive area, such as a limestone deposit, cannot be treated as a vein nor can a broad metalliferous zone.

A vein has an *apex, strike, dip,* and *walls.* The apex is the summit or top of a vein or lode at or below the surface. The strike or course of a vein is the direction of the vein across the land, the dip is the downward direction. A bearing is normally given to define the direction of the strike. Dip is measured by the downward angle formed with the horizon. The same vein may have variable

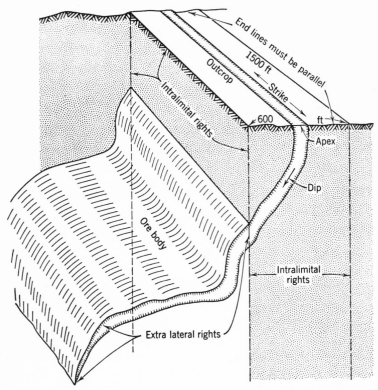

Figure 8-1.

dip or strike throughout its extent. The wall of a vein or lode is the line of demarcation between the vein and the country rock. The "hanging wall" and the "foot wall (wall walked on)" may be of different or the same material.

248. Extralateral and Intralimital Rights. *Extralateral right* is the right to follow the downward course of a vein, with certain limitations, to the end of its depth. (See Figs. 8-1, 8-2, 8-3, and 8-4.) The limitations are: (1) the apex of the vein must be within the

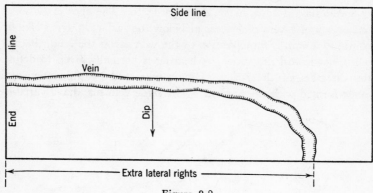

Figure 8-2.

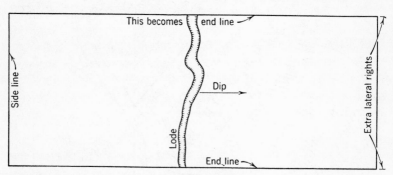

Figure 8-3.

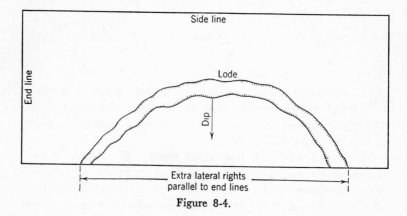

Figure 8-4.

boundaries of the claim; (2) only the dip or downward course may be followed; (3) the direction followed must be within the limits of the end lines of the claim extended vertically and outward; and (4) the vein must travel through land open to location. The vein may be followed whether irregular, curved, waving, faulted, broken, or brecciated, as long as the vein is continuous with the same mineralizing agent. Extralateral rights are not lost where the vein is found to run crosswise instead of lengthwise to the claim; the normal side lines become the end lines, and the end lines the side lines (see Fig. 8-3).

Intralimital rights to a claim extend downward within the limits of the claim to the center of the earth. All surface rights and everything within the limits of his intralimital rights, except the extralateral rights attached to other veins apexing in another's claim, belong to the owner of the claim. The owner of another vein has the right to follow the vein through the claim of another, but such rights are limited to that extent. There are no rights to explore in another's land nor are there rights to approach the vein from any other location than the vein itself. Country rock adjacent to the vein and within the limits of another's claim may be cut where the vein is too narrow or too crooked to mine. All the ore within the intersection of intersecting veins belongs to the senior claimant, but a right of way through the intersection is assured.

The issuing of a patent to a homesteader does not invalidate the extralateral rights of a prior vein or lode claimant. The date of discovery of minerals determines the extralateral rights of a claimant, not the date of patent.

249. Placer Claims. In the common meaning, placer deposits are thought of as gold, silver, or quicksilver found in sand, gravel, or earth. Within the meaning of the mining law, placer includes all mineral deposits other than veins of quartz or other rocks in place. Placer deposits may be hundreds of feet below the surface such as a petroleum deposit or a gold deposit found in a former river bed which is now covered with lava. Certain types of placer deposits, namely, petroleum, phosphate, potash, sodium, borax, oil shale and sulphur lands, have been withdrawn from location and may be obtained only by lease arrangements.

250. Mill Sites. In addition to lode and placer claims, mill sites of 5 acres or less may be claimed by either a vein or lode proprietor or by a mill owner for the purpose of processing minerals. Mill site locations are limited to mineral lands that do not contain valuable minerals.

251. Tunnel Locations. Tunnel sites are acquired in accordance with local rules and customs, but may not exceed 3,000 feet as imposed by Federal law. When a lode is discovered within a tunnel, the owner is called upon to make a surface location of the vein or lode as required by law. Discontinuing operations for 6 months constitutes abandonment of all rights to the veins along the line of the tunnel.

252. Size of Claims. Lode claims are limited to not more than 300 feet in width on each side of the center line of a vein and not more than 1,500 feet in length. End lines must be parallel to one another. The number of claims that a person may file is not limited. While lode claims may overlap one another for the purpose of determining extralateral rights, the overlapped portion normally belongs to the senior locator. Local legislation can be passed to limit the size of a claim to less than 600 feet by 1,500 feet, but such limitations cannot be less than 25 feet on each side of the middle of the vein.

Placer claims are limited in size to 20 acres or 160 acres for an association of not fewer than 8 people. Each placer claim, whether upon surveyed or unsurveyed lands, is required to conform as nearly as possible to the sectionalized system of surveys.

253. Discovery. Discovery of minerals occurs when there is reasonable evidence of the fact that there is a vein or lode containing valuable mineral or that there is valuable minerals in a placer deposit. Discovery cannot be based upon conjecture or the mere possibility of locating mineral. If reasonable prospect of success in developing a paying mine exists and sufficient evidence to justify a reasonably prudent person in making expenditures in money and labor exists, discovery is justified. Minerals in paying quantities at the time of location are not necessary, but there must be reasonable hope and assurance that there will be such minerals.

The amount and manner of the discovery work is not stated in the Federal law. Local laws often require posting of a notice of discovery and the sinking of a shaft of minimum depth or length.

254. Locations. In a broad sense there are four types of location: lode or vein, placer, tunnel, and mill site. There is a limitation on the size of a location, but there is no limit upon the number of locations. Discovery of minerals usually precedes location, but if the order is reversed and there are no intervening rights, it is immaterial that the statutory order is reversed since location becomes effective upon discovery.

The claim must be marked upon the ground as an indispensable condition of location. This does not mean that each corner of a claim must be monumented, only that the location must be marked so that the boundaries may be readily traced. Thus, if an unnavigable stream subject to location is marked by a notice on the bank stating the boundaries and limits of the claim, the claim is sufficiently marked.

Specific requirements by revised statutes, Sec. 2324 (30 USC Sec. 28), are "the location must be distinctly marked upon the ground so that its boundaries can be readily traced" and "all records of mining claims made after May 10, 1872, shall contain the name or names of the locators, the date of the location, and such a description of the claim or claims located, by reference to some natural object or permanent monument, as will identify the claim."

Many state statutes allow a period of time after discovery before it becomes mandatory to make a location. This gives the claimant time to explore and determine the direction of the strike of the vein. During such time the position of the claim may be laid in any direction from the discovery point, along the vein, a distance not exceeding 1,500 feet.

The monumenting of the boundaries of a placer claim location is not vital since the boundaries are usually described by the public survey system. Because lode claims are irregular in shape and size, monumenting of the boundaries is an essential part of final location. If there are any local laws in addition to the Federal laws concerning monumenting, they must be adhered to.

255. Possession. Exclusive possession follows location. Title of the locator, prior to discovery, is good against all except the paramount owner, the United States. Title of the locator followed by discovery in sufficient quantities to be profitable is good against all including the United States. Location without discovery does not confer a right to the minerals that might exist within a claim, but it does confer a right of possession as long as the claimant occupies the land to the exclusion of others and in good faith pursues the work of trying to discover minerals.

256. Annual Expenditures. The mining act provides that a minimum of $100 of labor or improvements for the purpose of development shall be expended annually upon each claim until a patent is issued. The amount required can be increased by local rule. If claims are contiguous, but not just touching on one corner, all of the annual expenditure of $100 per claim can be spent on any one of the claims.

257. Requirements for Patent. Application for patent to a lode mining claim must be accompanied by a request and deposit for survey along with a certified copy of the location notice. No survey is required for a placer claim described by the sectionalized system. An order for a survey will be issued and the survey will be administered by the government office cadastral engineer.

Prior to patent at least $500 shall be expended upon each mineral claim.* Only labor and improvements having a direct relationship to the development of the mine, such as shafts or tunnels, are included within the $500. Buildings, machinery, roadways, trails, and the like are excluded except where it is clearly shown that they are associated with actual excavations. Mills and equipment to transport ores are not included. If the application for patent embraces several locations held in common and adjacent to one another, the expenditures spent upon one claim can be prorated among all the claims.

258. United States Mineral Surveyors. United States mineral surveyors are appointed by the government after the applicant proves by extensive tests that he is proficient in the use of surveying instruments and has proper knowledge of mining surveys. The particular mineral surveyor selected for the patent survey and the fee paid to the surveyor are arranged for by the applicant.

259. Survey of the Claim. All mineral surveys must be made by the mineral surveyor in person. No observations or measurements previously made by himself or by others may be accepted as true. A transit with a solar attachment or other means of correctly determining the meridian and a steel tape graduated in feet are used to make mineral surveys. Bearings are referred to the true meridian, and distances are returned as the shortest horizontal measurement in feet.

The position of the claim is fixed by determining the bearing and distance of the claim to the nearest section or quarter-section corner. If no public survey corner exists within 2 miles, a location

* R. S. Sec. 2325, 30 USC Sec. 29.

monument is established on some prominent point having good visibility from every direction.

Monuments set by the original locator are used as the true location of the claim. However, the size of the claim cannot exceed 1,500 feet in length or 600 feet in width, nor can the end lines be other than straight and parallel. An error of closure in the survey must not exceed the statutory limit.

In addition to determining the size of a claim and setting permanent boundary corners, the surveyor records topography, location of shafts and tunnels, location of the vein where it crosses the end lines, conflicts with adjoining claims, and location of springs, salt licks and mill sites.

260. Summary. Mineral claims, unlike other property rights, are not necessarily limited to the downward projection of the property lines to the center of the earth. The right to follow an apexing vein through any neighboring property open to location places a cloud upon the rights of adjoining property. A mineral claim until patented is a partial right since title to the land is retained by the government.

CHAPTER 9

The Surveyor
and His Duties

261. Purpose of a Boundary Survey. A boundary survey may be for any one or all of the following purposes: (1) to mark an existing property description on the ground; (2) to establish new lines relative to existing title lines; (3) to determine the line of possession relative to title lines; (4) to file a permanent record of where an existing title description is located on the ground.

New lot boundaries established for the first time are often regulated by state laws. Such regulations may be for safety (maximum grade, minimum curvature, etc.), aesthetics, expense, future development, and like considerations. They involve the utilization of surveying equipment, the running of traverses, the computation of closures and areas, the measurements of angles and distances, the proper alignment of streets with acceptable grades, and the development of building sites. The scope of this book excludes a discussion of these factors.

If the purpose of the survey is to establish existing title lines, it must be remembered that, in the absence of adjoining property owners agreeing upon a disputed line, the only proper location of the disputed line is in the position that a court of competent jurisdiction would decree. Thus surveyors, when establishing boundaries, are obligated to familiarize themselves with the law as it exists. The client expects the surveyor to establish the correct legal position of his property lines. If a line is incorrectly delineated because of lack of experience and knowledge of law, the surveyor may be the cause of an aggravated condition between neighbors. And if the matter is disposed of by the courts, the client would plead upon a losing ground.

The possibility is always present that over a period of time another line, through action of law, has replaced the original property line. There may be occupancy over a period of time, a neighbor may be estopped from asserting the true line, or former owners might have agreed upon another line. The title to the old line is then gone. For the surveyor to re-run the original deed and mark the lines on the ground is of no avail; another line that may be entirely dependent upon unwritten conveyancing is the correct boundary. Thus the occasion might arise when it is unnecessary to establish the original deed lines; a survey for the purpose of describing where the line of possession exists may be sufficient to support litigation in matters involving unwritten conveyances.

262. Land Surveyor. The land surveyor is a professional man who has specialized in the application of law, mapping, mathematics, and instruments to the problem of positioning land boundaries. The ability to use instruments, measure angles, and locate objects relative to one another is not the sole qualification for claiming the title land surveyor. Carpenters in establishing building lines, aircraft workers in setting up jigs, and civil engineers in determining the position of bridge abutments all use surveying instruments; but this cannot be considered land surveying. Most engineers are qualified to make measurements, use instruments, design buildings and structures, but few of them have sufficient training in the laws that determine the location of property lines to be considered proficient land surveyors. To refer to an engineer as a land surveyor is similar to calling a surgeon a dentist. A land surveyor may also be an engineer; many are not.

The surveyor is a fact finder. He goes upon the land armed with all the documentary evidence that is available and searches for markers, monuments, and other facts. After all the evidence, facts, measurements, and observations are assembled, the surveyor must come to a conclusion from the facts. Which monuments can be accepted and which must be rejected? If there are conflicting terms in a deed, which is correct? If there are conflicts between measurements and monument positions, which hold? The ability to arrive at a conclusion and answer such questions elevates the land surveyor from the status of a technician to that of a professional man. He is exercising independent judgment.

263. Duties of the Land Surveyor. It is the land surveyor's duty to correctly locate and mark property lines as described in a deed furnished him and to relate lines of possession to title lines. The surveyor must be able to interpret the meaning of the terms of the deed and must be able to use surveying instruments to enable him to locate and mark the deed terms upon the ground. The surveyor cannot and does not assume the responsibility of proving that a given deed is correct and legal; that is a function of an attorney or court of law. But after a deed is furnished and he is told to mark the property on the ground in accordance with the terms of the deed as furnished, the surveyor must certify that his marks are in accordance with the terms of the deed. If there are conflicting terms within a deed and if the surveyor sets his marks in accordance with one of the conflicting terms, he is assuming responsibility for his decision. If the property lines, as described in the deed, encroach on others or if others encroach on the property lines described, the surveyor should note the encroachments.

264. Title by Possession. Many times in establishing boundaries, a surveyor will find others occupying his client's land as indicated by a fence, a house, a well, or cultivation. If a person occupies a parcel of land long enough and complies with certain acts of the law, or if there is an agreement over a disputed boundary, he may have the right of title to the land that he is occupying. Only by a court order or by a written agreement between the adjoiners can the written title be changed. The surveyor may not take over the judicial functions of the court and determine what the unwritten title rights are, but he may determine by measurements the relationship between the written title and the line of possession. If a surveyor is hired to establish the boundaries of a parcel of land in accordance with a legal description furnished him, he should follow the exact instructions written in the deed. If the adjoining owner probably has adverse rights to a strip of land which the written deed gives to his client, the surveyor may not establish the boundary so as to exclude that portion claimed by another. Likewise, a surveyor should not include within the boundaries of his survey, that portion of land that his client adversely claims. But if a surveyor is employed to measure and mark the line of possession, nothing should prevent him from so doing as long as he clearly indicates on a plat that the markers represent only the line of possession. Assuming that a surveyor may mark property in accordance with possession, and there is authority that under certain circumstances a surveyor should do so, what are the effects of such markers and what ethics are involved? Normally it is presumed by the public, and often by surveyors themselves, that all property markers found represent points set in accordance with written deed lines. If an owner, whose stakes have been set in accordance with a line of possession, points out to his neighbor a survey marker and states, "This is my property line," deception can occur. The adjoiner, assuming that the surveyor may not declare that a line of possession is the true title line, is apt to be misled. If the adjoiner discovers the truth, i.e., that the markers are merely lines of possession, he will more than likely seriously question the ethics of surveyors. The *Technical Standards for Property Surveys* as adopted by the American Congress on Surveying and Mapping states, "Every parcel of land whose boundaries are surveyed by a licensed surveyor should be made conformable with the record title boundaries of such land." That is a wise policy for every surveyor.

265. Liability of Surveyors. Liability results when the surveyor fails to do correctly the thing that he purports to do. If the owner instructs the surveyor to survey his land in accordance with his written deed, and the surveyor does precisely that without error, no liability can ensue. If the owner tells the surveyor to survey his land in accordance with his lines of possession regardless of the written title lines and the surveyor does just that, no liability can ensue. But in the event that the surveyor establishes lines in accordance with possession he should be prepared to prove that he properly notified the client of such fact since the burden of proof would probably be his.

The surveyor, as a professional man, is bound to exercise that degree of care that a skilled surveyor of ordinary prudence would exercise under similar circumstances. The surveyor is not liable for the absolute correctness of a property line; he is liable if he fails to establish the line as a reasonably prudent skilled surveyor would do. Where a surveyor is notified that a large building is being erected exactly on the property line, he would be expected to exercise greater care than under other conditions.

Normally it is presumed that the surveyor's liability is limited to the person who pays him the fee. Title companies limit their liability to those whose names appear on the face of their policy. To limit liability in a like manner, it is good form for the surveyor to state on his plat presented to the client "for the exclusive use of John Doe."

In Washington, where the surveyor erroneously marked a lot 5 feet into the street, the plea that the survey was not guaranteed was of no avail. The court observed,

It is also argued that the trial court erred in striking a portion of the answer, to the effect that it was the custom to guarantee the accuracy of surveys by certificate for which a larger fee was charged than in cases where the boundaries are ascertained without reference to the improvement of the lot, and that the survey made in this case was of the latter kind, and the smaller fee was charged, and, also, that the court erred in excluding evidence to the same effect. We think the court properly excluded such evidence. It was conceded upon the trial that the defendants were employed to make an accurate survey. Whether they gave a certificate or not, or whether they received a large or small fee, would not change the liability so as to relieve them from negligence. It was shown that the surveyor overlooked the parking strip or misread the figures upon the chain, and that in this way the mistake occurred. This was clearly not due care.*

For a fee of $12 (in 1911) the surveyor paid $1,267.50 to move an apartment house.

In Michigan† the commissioner of highways employed the county surveyor to survey properly the quarter line of section 31. The surveyor was said to have so negligently and unskillfully performed the work that he failed to ascertain said quarter line by his survey, thus rendering it necessary to make a new survey, and abandon a large amount of road constructed at large expense. The court in ordering a demurrer overruled noted,

Whether he was a professional or official surveyor, or represented himself as such, his undertaking was that he should bring to the work the necessary knowledge and skill to perform the same properly and correctly; and if he failed so to do, and the employer sustained damage in consequence of such failure, the plaintiff will be entitled to recover.

In Connecticut a surveyor, hired by Mr. Ferrie,‡ established the property lines in accordance with a written deed. After a building was commenced upon the line, the neighbor brought suit for ejectment and won on the basis of an old fence that formerly stood for 30 years. The fence was missing at the time of the survey. Mr. Ferrie, upon suing the surveyor, was awarded damages. The supreme court of Connecticut in ordering a new trial observed,

Having accepted the services of a client, the surveyor was bound to exercise that degree of care which a skilled surveyor of ordinary prudence

* Taft v. Rutherford, 66 Wash 256, 119 Pac 740.

† Commissioner of Highways of Thompson Township v. Arthur Beebe, county surveyor, 55 Mich 137.

‡ Ferrie v. Sperry, 85 Conn 337, 82 A 577.

would have exercised under similar circumstances. This being the rule, it was important that the jury should know what such an ordinarily prudent surveyor would do under the circumstances of the case. Might he simply examine the land records and monuments of title and observe the fixed monuments and evidences of present occupancy and ownership; or was he bound to scour the neighborhood to learn whether there had been adverse occupancy and claims of ownership of any part of the premises covered by his client's deed by others than the latter's predecessors in title appearing of record?

In this action against a surveyor for negligence in locating a boundary line, the exclusion of evidence as to what an ordinarily prudent surveyor would do under the circumstances, and as to what the requirements of such practice are, was erroneous.

When a surveyor fails to include all the land owned by his client, he is not liable for damages since the omitted land may be recovered; however, the client can sue to recover the fee paid for services rendered.

From the above cases it is obvious that to avoid liability the surveyor should err on the side of safety. This applies particularly to facts of record, evidence of occupancy, and other things that his eyes and ears can detect. In other words, try to do a little more than an ordinarily prudent surveyor would do under the circumstances.

TRESPASS RIGHTS OF SURVEYORS. The right of a surveyor to trespass upon another's land for the purpose of searching for monuments and recording measurements is presumed by all surveyors. It is common practice for the surveyors to enter upon a parcel of land, without the consent of the owner, and make those measurements that are necessary for the survey being performed. Foundation for this right is lacking in common law. In the absence of a statute law giving a surveyor trespass rights, a surveyor who enters upon the land of another without permission is an intruder without rights, and the mere trampling of herbage or grass may be sufficient cause for damages.*

266. Question of Law and Facts. In court cases the judge decides questions of law. Upon request of either party to a suit, questions of facts are determined by the jury, but, in the absence of a request for a jury trial, questions of facts are decided by the judge.

* Dougherty v. Stepp, 18 No Car 371.

What are the boundaries of a particular tract of land is a question of law, but where the boundaries of a particular tract are is a matter of fact.*

The surveyor determines facts when he identifies monuments, retraces former surveys, and measures angles and distances to known objects. If there is a conflict between a found monument and a measured distance, where the monument is located and its distance from other objects is a question of fact, but what are the boundaries, the monument, or the distance is a question of law. The surveyor must interpret many questions of law before he can correctly establish property corners. To refuse to establish a corner because the judge has the final authority on the question of law involved is like refusing to make a measurement because the jury makes the final interpretation of what the facts are. To try to interpret every question of law is asking for liability. Although a surveyor should know and be able to interpret most of the laws, it is doubtful if he will know them all.

In positioning a property the surveyor sets his lines in accordance with the location that he thinks the courts will uphold as law and fact. In court cases the surveyor's conclusions and testimony, as those of a man of science, are receivable in connection with the data of his survey. If a conclusion is stated, it is totally worthless without distinct proof of measurements, data, and observations; such proof will enable the judge and jury to decide for themselves what is the proper result. A surveyor cannot be allowed, under any circumstances, to fix private rights or lines according to any theory of his own. He must present a plan and/or testimony so as to enable any one else to test his accuracy, or to determine how far his conclusions were correct in accordance with the law.

EXPERT WITNESS. Any person skilled in any trade, occupation, and/or science may become an expert witness, who is permitted to testify to facts within his special field and knowledge, and who is permitted to give opinions based upon hypothetical or assumed facts. A surveyor of experience is eligible to act as an expert witness and is often asked to do so. An ordinary witness is permitted to testify as to facts and not permitted to give conclusions from facts.

Opinions may be given by experts where the opinion requires a person of particular skill or knowledge in a certain field such as surveying. Thus, if an original map recorded the fact that a 2

* 66 NE 63.

inch $\times$ 2 inch plug was set at a property corner and a 2 inch $\times$ 2 inch wooden stake was in fact found, the surveyor could give an opinion as to whether the word "plug" meant a 2 inch $\times$ 2 inch wooden stake and whether in his opinion the 2 inch $\times$ 2 inch wooden stake was old enough to be the original stake set by the original surveyor.

An expert may testify as to what might have caused something; but not what did cause it. Thus a surveyor may testify that the improper location of a house might be caused by measuring from an incorrect monument located 10 feet from the correct monument. He cannot say that it was the cause; that is for the jury to decide. To say that a 2 inch $\times$ 2 inch pine stake located at a property corner would completely disappear in 30 years owing to decomposition, termites, etc., would be improper. To say that at all locations where pine stakes were originally set none were found that were over 30 years old, and that those older than 10 years were in a bad state of decomposition would be proper. The question "whether the 2 inch $\times$ 2 inch stake found was the original property corner" is for the jury to decide.

EVIDENCE AND MONUMENTS. The connecting links between the written description and the boundaries as they exist on the ground are monuments. Every survey starts from a monument; the only question is, which monument? Most differences between surveyors arise from varying opinions as to which monument should be used for a particular description. If a surveyor uses a certain monument as his beginning point, he has the "burden of proof," that is, he must be prepared to present evidence of the correctness of his contention. A mere statement that a given monument is the one referred to in a deed, without valid reasons for the statement, is insufficient to prove the correctness of a monument. For every survey the surveyor must be prepared to prove by satisfactory evidence, usually in the form of monument evidence, that the precise positions in which he has established lines are correct and excludes other possibilities.

The following kinds of evidence are used to prove the position of a monument referred to: (1) physical characteristics of the monument itself; (2) testimony of a person or surveyor who saw the monument placed or in place; (3) hearsay evidence; (4) proximity of the monument to the theoretical location; (5) reputation evidence; (6) reference points set to mark an original monument.

The physical characteristics of the monument, i.e., its shape, size, the material of which it is composed, its apparent age, and its markings are the most common forms of evidence used to identify a monument. Such factors should be carefully and permanently recorded at the time of observation. The testimony of a surveyor who set the original monument or found the original monument is highly acceptable in the event of litigation. Persons who saw the original and remembered its position are given consideration by the courts. Even hearsay evidence, what one person heard another say, is admissible under limited conditions, such as the sayings of a deceased person.

Monuments found to exist in the vicinity of the measured distance are given greater consideration than those found in unlikely positions. If a monument is found considerably out of position, a greater amount of evidence is required to prove that it has not been disturbed and that it is in fact the original. A monument 1,000 feet out of position presents grave doubts, but one a half foot out of position presents no problem.

Often the only evidence that establishes a monument is reputation. Thus, if for years a monument has been accepted as the true section corner, and especially if surveyors have accepted it, the monument becomes the corner by common repute. In such cases it is important to show that many persons have used the monument in question.

Perhaps the best evidence of the position of an original corner is reference points set by surveyors to mark the position of a monument.

The identity of the position of an original monument is dependent upon the chain of records that describe where and what the original monument was and what has replaced the original monument. Titles are dependent upon a continuous chain of ownership records from the first sale; likewise, identity of an original monument's position is dependent upon a continuous chain of records. If a monument is reset, satisfactory proof of the fact that the new monument occupies exactly the same spot as the old monument must be preserved. Surveyors are responsible for identifying and determining the position of old monuments, and, if they replace an original monument, it is their duty to file a permanent public record of such fact. The laws require property owners to file all deed transactions and keep a continuous record of titles. Likewise, the law should require a surveyor to file public records when he resets a monument in place of an original monument and when he replaces any monument of record representing the position of a property line.

A property owner when requesting a survey wants permanent assurance that he is occupying the land to which he is entitled. The maintenance of secret survey records and secret original monument positions by surveyors assures future boundary disputes. Another surveyor, starting from a different point, will find a different location for a property.

The time to determine the position of a monument is when it is in existence, not after it has disappeared. The certainty of permanent land location is wholly dependent upon the certainty with which monuments can be replaced in the event that they are lost, and the certainty of replacement is wholly dependent upon the accuracy with which existing monuments are tied to other permanent monuments. If existing monuments are related accurately to a network of Lambert or Mercator grid monuments, and if the coordinates of the existing monuments are made a public record, permanency of location and freedom from dispute by other surveyors at any future date are probable.

267. Initial Steps in Making a Survey. Prior to a property line survey, the surveyor must obtain from the owner a copy of the description of the property to be surveyed and obtain from various sources copies of all maps, adjoiner deeds called for, and records of other surveys in the vicinity. It is the duty of the property owner to furnish a written description of the land to be surveyed, and it is the duty of the surveyor to locate properly the land described.

268. Research An examination of all maps and documents called for in the deed together with an examination of all adjoiner maps, city or county surveyors' records, township plats and filed notes, if any, utility maps, record of surveys, and all other known records must be completed before the start of the field work. Knowledge of the order of seniority of deeds is essential, if lines are to be correctly run. The surveyor locates the property described, but does not guarantee the title. A title insurance policy states the order of seniority of deeds and should be used, if available, as a foundation for a survey.

269. Legal Description. The landowner, not being a surveyor, has little or no concept of the necessity of furnishing a correct and complete legal description of the land being surveyed. Because deeds are usually stored in a safe deposit box, the owner frequently attempts to use a tax statement or other incomplete document to define the deed terms. The surveyor should insist on the true deed, or, what is better, the title of policy insurance. A deed may have a perfect perimeter description of land yet be in error because of the existence of senior rights determinable from an inspection of a title insurance policy.

270. Tie-In's. Every survey plat of a boundary survey should show the relationship of the land to all monuments called for, to all roads and easements mentioned, and to all senior properties. The relationship should be shown by bearing and distance ties and a note of the bearing equation, if any, that exists between the adjacent and instant property.

271. Basis of Bearing. No other factor has caused more confusion than the omission of the basis of bearings on many survey plats. In old deeds the usage of the magnetic compass was common; yet many of the deeds gave no basis of bearings. Even in modern surveys where the deflection method of survey is normally used, the surveyors are often guilty of failure to state on what basis they derived their bearings.

272. Arbitration In the vast majority of surveys no difficulty with the adjoining property owners is encountered by the surveyor. If an overlap on another's line of possession occurs, or if there is an argument between neighbors, it should be the duty of the surveyor to attempt to bring the parties to a reasonable understanding before diplomatic relations rupture. It is far easier to prevent an argument than it is to stop one. If an agreement can be reached, proper deeds can be negotiated. In the event that no solution can be attained and the matter is referred to the courts for final judgment, the surveyor will find himself spending considerable court time, often without the benefit of fees. Except for very valuable lands in litigation derived from boundary disagreements, even the winner loses financially.

273. Oaths and Parole Evidence. Since monuments as set by the original surveyor are usually considered correct, whether set in accordance with the recorded distances and bearings or not, it becomes essential that their location be preserved. A monument that has disappeared from view cannot be considered lost, if a person who had knowledge of its position can testify to its correct position. Occasionally it becomes necessary to determine a location from some old resident who can positively state a corner's former location. In such a case, the surveyor takes an oath from the person stating the following facts: (1) What the corner looked like. (2) The number of years that he resided in the area. (3) His name, age, and whether he is a citizen. (4) The date. (5) How he knew that it was the corner. (6) When he last saw the corner. These statements should be written in a field book, signed by the person and followed by a notation by the surveyor that: (1) The person was placed under oath. (2) The person made the above statements. (3) The person is believed to be of sound mind and of good character. (4) What the surveyor placed at the spot pointed out. The surveyor then signs the statement along with the date of the oath. After taking an oath the surveyor should file a record of survey showing a copy of the oath as recorded in the field book.

Although such an oath is hearsay and not admissible in court as long as the person is living, it serves two purposes: (1) the oath is admissible after the death of the person and (2) it prevents the changing of testimony at a later date.

274. Quasi-Judicial Functions of Surveyors. Judicial functions in this country are vested in the courts; surveyors cannot assume the authority of a judicial officer. The taking of testimony from witnesses placed under oath and acting as an arbitrator in boundary disputes are quasi-judicial functions. When determining property lines the surveyor places his stakes and presents a plat showing where he believes that the property lines should be, said belief being founded upon what he thinks the court will uphold in the event of litigation involving his survey. He is constantly interpreting what the statutes say and what the courts have determined to be right and wrong, but such interpretation is correct only to the extent to which the courts will uphold it. He is in the unfortunate position of being the middle man who must determine for a client what he thinks the court will accept.

275. Summary. The duty of a land surveyor in making a survey is to locate the land in the position that a court of competent jurisdiction would decree. He must exercise the degree of care that an ordinary prudent surveyor would use under the circumstances. Although the degre of care required may vary from state to state, it is advisable for the surveyor to do a little more than is necessary within the particular area in which he is working.

CHAPTER **10**

Writing Deeds

1. caption
2. body
3. qualifying clause
4 augmenting clauses

276. Contents. Previous pages were devoted to an explanation of the legal interpretations placed upon deed terms. This chapter will include the purpose, forms, and contents of the descriptive parts of deeds.

277. Purpose of a Deed Description. *The purpose of a deed description is to* (1) *describe by words the exact location, geometric shape and size of the land intended to be conveyed by the seller and purchased by the buyer, and* (2) *identify the land for title purposes.*

The aims are not identical. A description may be precisely locatable on the ground by definite Lambert coordinates quoted or by other means, yet may be entirely uninsurable because of a failure to state the relationship between the instant property and the adjoiners. Again, a property may have an insurable title giving the exact relationship to adjoiners, yet not be locatable without court aid because of the uncertainty of monuments on the ground. A deed that perfectly defines the geometric shape and size of a property but fails to state the vicinity wherein the land is located is ambiguous. Likewise, a deed description that exactly defines the point of beginning and the vicinity of the conveyance, but fails to define a closed geometric shape is uncertain. The essential elements of a deed description are intent, title identity, location, geometric shape, and size.

278. Intent. Much has been said about the intent of the parties to a conveyance; its importance cannot be over emphasized. The courts interpret the intent as it is expressed in the deed; they do not create it. The scrivener by his words states what the intent is. The intent may be land enclosed by known monuments, or by defi-

242

nite area, or by definite distance, or up to an adjoiner, but, whatever the intent is, it should be expressed with clear precision of statement utilizing a minimum of words.

279. Title Identity. An insurable title risk is one that has freedom of title conflict with all senior properties. Unfortunately most deeds are composed with this single purpose in mind; whether a deed is locatable seems to be the least concern of many title authors. From the title insurer's viewpoint a call for an adjoiner or monument with omission of unnecessary bearings and distances is the safest method of describing land. A valid title description may be written without bearings and distances such as "bounded on the south by Jones's land, on the east by 12th Ave., on the north by Brown's land, and on the west by Smith's land," but such a description is unsatisfactory to the tax assessor, new owner, surveyor, and those concerned with mapping the land. Even though bearings and distances do not control a call for an adjoiner or monument, and may only be informational, they should be inserted if they are known with reasonable certainty; but if they are doubtful quantities, they should be omitted.

Deeds that are to be free of conflict with an adjoiner must always (1) show the relationship of the deed with that of the adjoiner or (2) be written with identical calls in the adjoiner. The safest procedure is to insert the call for the senior deed whether necessary or not. When both deeds call for identical monuments or when both deeds start from the same point of beginning and use identical calls for bearings, distances, and area, conflict cannot exist. A new line being described for the first time (a free boundary), or an agreement deed, need not carry adjoiner calls.

Informative terms in a deed transformed into controlling terms in an adjoiner may cause conflict. A deed written "beginning at the northeast corner of lot 4; thence S 0° 05' W, 200 feet to an iron pin; thence S 89° W, 300.00 feet to an iron pin; thence, etc." and a junior adjoiner deed written "beginning at the northeast corner of lot 4; thence S 0° 05' W, 200 feet; thence S 89° W, 300 feet; thence, etc.," usually results in a conflict. In the second description the omission of the call for monuments transforms the informative terms of distance and bearing into controlling terms; and, if the monuments were set in error, conflict or a gap exists. Other conflicts have been discussed previously and will not be repeated here.

280. Location. Deeds recite the state, county, city, and the particular part of the city or county in which the land is located. All metes and bounds descriptions require a point of beginning, and practically all points of beginning refer, somehow, to a fixed monument such as a stake, tree, river, road, ocean, parcel of land, or any other physical object.

The days of free surveys, when a surveyor selected his point of beginning and surveyed out a parcel to his liking, are over. New boundary surveys are started from the monuments of older surveys. Monuments mark the land; they tell the layman where his boundaries are; they are the physical example of possession. The certainty of location of a deed description is entirely dependent upon the certainty of the monument marking the points called for in the deed. A conveyance may be free from ambiguity, may be concise in its statements, may describe a perfect perimeter and yet not be locatable because of the uncertainty of the point of beginning. Thus, a deed description stating "commencing at the southwest corner of Rancho . . . ; thence . . . " is not locatable because the original Rancho corner was described as a sycamore tree that disappeared years ago and no records exist indicating its former position. A deed description that is permanently locatable needs monuments that can be accurately and readily replaced in the event that they are destroyed. The futility of unrelated boundary monuments was discovered by the Egyptians during floods of the Nile River. The development of geometry is partly attributed to their efforts to find means of replacing lost markers.

New construction and changing conditions make the destruction of many monuments a probability. Trees grow old and die. Stones may be moved by ploughs, bulldozers, frost, or people. Waters change their location by erosion or accretion. Permanency is lacking. If with reasonable certainty a monument can be replaced after it is destroyed, location will be preserved.

Subdivision maps offer a system whereby lots are locatable by a network of monuments tied together by numerous measurements in various directions. The position of any one lot within a subdivision is related to the position of all the other lots within the same subdivision. If one monument is destroyed, other monuments may be used to re-establish the lost monument. A metes and bounds description is related to few other properties, often only its adjoiners. The destruction of one point of beginning in a metes and bounds description may be fatal to the certainty of its boundary location.

Subdivision descriptions are local in area. They are often unrelated to other subdivisions or other parts of a city or state. If the controls in a local area are lost owing to extensive cultivation, flooding, or other causes, the exact location of a deed description is endangered. The Lambert coordinate system with many monuments tied together allows the accurate replacement of lost monuments in their correct former position.

Property must be located by means of monuments, but this does not mean that property needs to be dependent upon one destructible monument. Property that is assured of a permanent location is tied by engineering measurements into numerous other monuments so that its position, if lost, may be re-established.

281. Geometric Shape and Size. Every property has a definite geometric shape that is definable by the use of geometry, trigonometry, and mathematics. Land may be described by monuments alone. The usual landowner is incapable of making correct measurements and, to avoid expenses, monuments are substituted for measurements. As an immediate expediency this clearly defines the intent and may describe a definite and exact parcel of ground of unknown size. Lands solely dependent upon monuments to mark their limits are unsatisfactory to the cadastral engineer who cannot plot the land on his maps and are unsatisfactory to future property owners who have no means of replacing lost monuments. It is obvious that to mark property boundaries on the ground, monuments must be used, and, to replace monuments that marked a property, correct measurements of the boundaries must be determined before the destruction of monuments.

Mathematics is used to prove measurements. If a surveyor starts at the point of beginning of a deed, correctly marks each course given, and fails to return to his original starting point, the deed has an *error of closure*. If the bearings and distances are given for each course in a deed, mathematics can be used to prove whether the figure is a closed geometric shape. After a surveyor has made his measurements around a closed figure, if it does not close mathematically, he knows that he has made an error. For a conveyance to be satisfactory to all it should be mathematically correct. Unfortunately many are not.

Modern subdivision maps are an engineering approach to a

boundary control problem.   Each lot is properly measured, monumented, and proved to be a geometrically closed figure.

Some descriptions, poorly written, are indefinite in location, and land, junior in character and adjoining the indefinite conveyance, must of necessity have an ambiguous line adjoining the indefinite conveyance; however, it is not necessary to make the new adjoiner conveyance entirely dependent upon the indefinite conveyance for its location.   The scrivener can, by carefully selecting terms, confine the indefinite portion of the new deed description to that line adjoining the ambiguous description.   To commence a description at an adjoiner's corner, the position of which might be in alternate places depending upon whom you ask, is dedicating a legal battle to future generations.

282. Scrivener.   One problem frequently encountered in legal descriptions is that of a defective title composed by an incompetent person who believes that he has sufficient knowledge of deed terms to formulate conveyances.   Each and every term inserted in a deed has a meaning, and, if the meaning of a word does not conform to the intent of the parties, or if it conflicts with other terms, the language used may alter the amount of land conveyed.   For example, if the intent is to convey exactly 5 acres and a perimeter description is written followed by the statement, "containing 5 acres," the deed will be construed by the perimeter description whether it contains 5 acres or not.

Unfortunately the qualifications of the persons who write deeds are seldom regulated by law.   The person who offers land for sale is usually a novice, incapable of knowing how to describe land and ignorant of the meaning of deed terms.   To avoid expenses he may attempt describing the land himself, thus avoiding monetary payments but creating potential litigations.   The old adage, "a little knowledge is a dangerous thing," is apt.   If the owner calls in an expert, the public and all future purchasers will benefit as long as the deed endures.

When a new deed is being written, specialized knowledge is required.   An attorney knows the proper words to convey legally to another a particular interest in land.   An easement, grant deed, warrant deed, quit claim deed, estate for life, lease, or other interest may be conveyed, depending upon the selected words.   To know whether a person owns a particular parcel of land and is legally qualified to convey a valid title requries an abstract of deed conveyances going back to the inception of the title. Engineering and surveying knowledge is vital to describe correctly the geometric shape, size, and mathematical correctness of a particular parcel of land. Deeds with simple geometric shapes are subject to little or no engineering calculation; others demand extensive analyses.

The surveyor because of his special training is best qualified to determine the location, shape, and mathematical correctness of a designated parcel of land. The words selected to describe a parcel of land is properly that of the surveyor since he knows what monuments are existing and what lines are certain and definite. But he is not competent to compose a deed in its entirety nor should he attempt to supplant the attorney by attaching a particular description to a deed form or legal document. His function is to survey the parcel of land and to describe what he surveyed, but not to write a legal document for conveyancing.

Likewise a title searcher searches a title. He states what the facts are, but he does not compose deeds. Deed conveyances should be the result of the teamwork of the attorney, the surveyor, and the title searcher.

TERMS OF A DEED

283. General Statement. The general statement, usually preceding the body of the deed, should indicate the vicinity in which the land is located by giving the state, county, city, township, range, and section or subdivision number or name. The purpose of the general statement, often called the caption, is to acquaint the interested parties with the approximate location of the land; but not to give a specific location. The body of a deed gives the exact location, and, when it is in conflict with the caption and unambiguous, it normally becomes controlling over the caption.

284. Body of a Deed. The body of a deed exactly pinpoints the location of the land on the ground. It may be long or short, depending upon the absence or presence of maps of record, the certainty and nearness of the starting point, or the number of lines described. An ideal deed body uses a minimum of words, imparts the exact intent of the parties to the deed, yet causes no uncertainty or conflict in defining the location and shape of the land. If a map of record may be referred to, all the data on the map referred to are incorporated into the deed, thus giving a maximum of information with a minimum of words.

285. Form of Body of Deed. In a written perimeter description there must be a point of beginning, a sequence of courses, and a statement, "thence to the point of beginning." This may take many forms; the more common types are: (1) Beginning at a point on the south line of lot 12, distant thereon S 89° W, 100 feet from the southeast corner of said lot; thence . . . ; thence . . . ; thence to the true point of beginning. (2) Beginning at the southeast corner of lot 12; thence S 89° W, 100 feet to the point of beginning (or commencement); thence . . . ; thence . . . ; thence to the point of beginning (or commencement). (3) Beginning at a point on the south line of lot 12 from which the southeast corner bears N 89° E, 100 feet; thence . . . ; thence to the point of beginning.

The boundary recital form, more commonly used in the east than the west, has the general statement changed from "described as follows" to "bounded as follows" or "bounded and described as follows" and also has bound recitals for each side; thus, "bounded as follows: on the east by the Arizona Railroad; on the north by Broadway Street; on the west by Cedar Street; on the south by Jones's land."

Other body forms are conveyance by proportion, conveyance by a distance in a direction, and conveyance by area (see Section 4).

286. Qualifying Clauses. Reservations and exceptions are qualifying clauses that modify the meaning of the body of the deed. By the description in a deed a person is given a parcel of land; by the qualifying clauses a portion of the land given to the buyer is taken back by the seller or an easement is reserved by the seller. Qualifying terms may appear in the body, caption, or as a separate statement.

An exception to an exception often results in ambiguity. By rearranging the description, double exceptions can be avoided.

287. Basis of Bearings. Astronomic north is north as determined by an observation of the stars. The word "true" as originally used was to distinguish between astronomic north and magnetic north, but of late it has been overworked and often misused. When a deed is based upon a bearing derived from a star or sun observation, the word "astronomic north" conveys the specific meaning and is preferred. Lambert or Mercator grid bearings, other than on the central meridian, are *never* true or astronomic bearings. The further east or west that the property is located from the central meridian, the greater is the difference between the grid bearing and the astronomic bearing.

As pointed out previously, surveyors measure angles by the deflection method and then compute bearings from the angles turned. If the deed terms are to describe the lines as measured by the surveyor, they must, in addition to stating a bearing, give the basis from which the bearing was computed. In many instances, but not all, the basis of bearings is defined in an indirect manner by the

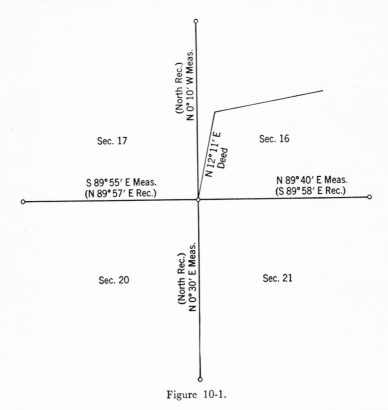

Figure 10-1.

terms of the deed; thus, a call for a plat includes a call for the basis of bearings as shown on the plat. A call naming the bearing of a fixed line forms a basis of bearing for the next line deflected from the fixed line. A deed written "beginning at the southwest corner of section 16, thence N 12° 11′ E, 1301.00 feet; thence, etc.," has no basis of bearing, since the direction of N 12° 11′ E is not fixed by monuments. See Fig. 10-1. If the original surveyor deflected the angle from the section line and computed the bearing N 12° 11′ E by assuming the west line of the given section to be north, the fact must be stated in the deed thus, "beginning at the southwest corner of section 19 from which the west quarter corner of section 19 bears north; thence, N 12° 11′ E, 1301.00 feet, thence, etc." If the basis of bearing were omitted and the conditions were as shown in Fig. 10-1, the surveyor could use as a basis of bearing any one of the four section lines shown or an astronomic observation. Even though the original deed author probably adopted a bearing of one of the section lines bordering on section 16, two alternate bases would still exist. The turned angle from the west line of section 16 could be 12° 21′ or 12° 03′, depending upon whether the record bearing for the west line of section 16 or the record bearing for the south line of section 16 were adopted. Ambiguity exists.

If a line is defined by monuments, by calls for an adjoiner, or by other physical means on the ground, the bearing of the line is not an absolute necessity for the validity of the deed. But if a monument is to be replaced after it is lost, or if a basis of bearing is essential for the next course, a bearing must be given. A deed reading "beginning at the southwest corner of lot *D* according to map 25, thence northerly along the westerly line of lot *D*, 13 feet; thence easterly parallel with the southerly line of lot *D*, 20.00 feet; thence S 50° 20′ E to the south line of lot D; thence to the point of beginning" is devoid of a basis of bearings. Map 25, an old one, gave no bearings. Who can say what the S 50° 20′ E was relative to?

288. Brevity. A deed should utilize a minimum of words, but brevity at the expense of clarity and certainty is to be avoided. Such phrases as "to a point" can often be eliminated. Every deed is recorded or registered permanently. Superfluous words and phrases only add to the volume of storage space required by the recorder.

289. Directional Calls. Every line in a description has two directions, depending upon the direction of travel along the line. On a north-south line you can go either north or south. For every line lacking a definite bearing or azimuth, there must be a general directional call that may take the form of "thence southerly along the westerly line of Jones's land" or "thence southwesterly, southerly, and southeasterly along the creek." Never omit the directional call where a bearing or other suitable direction call is not given.

290. Order of Importance of Conflicting Terms. The order of importance of deed terms must be known to the scrivener; otherwise erroneous intent may be written. A conveyance intending to convey to a specific monument will be construed to go to the monument only if the monument is called for. The insertion of a measured bearing and distance and the omission of the call for the monument alter the meaning. Generally speaking, but with some exceptions as previously noted, conflicting calls are given the following order of importance: (1) monuments, (2) distance, (3) bearing and (4) area.

291. Closing Terms. "To the point of beginning," "to the point of commencement," or "to the true point of beginning" are proper phrases used to insure that a deed does close mathematically. Included in the last term is usually the precautionary statement "more or less" or "plus or minus" to indicate that the distance and bearing quoted are secondary calls.

292. Changing the Form of a Deed. The form of a deed description should not, except in unusual circumstances, be changed. An obvious typographical error or the like may be corrected, but only upon good authority. In the event that such a change is made it is wise to include a statement that the deed is the same as that conveyed to the grantor by a specific recording, or, in other words, a "being clause."

If a surveyor by his observations and measurements determines which conflicting term in a deed is correct, or if he discovers an error in the written deed, he should not attempt to change the deed. He may attempt reforming the deed with the consent of the adjoiners. If the deed is not reformed, he should file a public record of his survey showing the discrepancies and errors found.

Glossary of Deed Terms

About. "About" often indicates a lack of knowledge and should be avoided in descriptions. A deed to land being "about" 30 feet wide was insufficient to pass title (Tinelite v. Sinnott, 5 NYS 439). "About" has been interpreted to mean "nearly," "more or less," "in close correspondence to," and "in the immediate neighborhood," depending upon the contents of the remainder of the description. "About north" was interpreted as astronomical north when nothing else limited the word (Shipp v. Miller, 15 US 316).

Abstract. A bare or brief statement of facts written in abbreviated words; a statement of the important parts of a deed, trust deed, or other legal instrument.

Abstract of Title. A compilation of abstracts of deeds, trust deeds, and other pertinent data which affect the title to a piece of real property, all bound together in chronological order, constitutes an abstract of title. It is a form of title evidence made for the purpose of title examination.

Abstracter. The individual who takes the information pertaining to a title in its full form and puts all facts into an abbreviated form, the form being called an abstract.

Access Rights. In acquiring freeway, turnpike, or throughway lands, ingress and egress of the abutter, called access rights, are often denied.

Accession to Real Property. Title to real property can be acquired by accession which is the addition to property by growth, increase, or labor. Land gradually deposited on the bank of a stream by imperceptible means becomes the land of the upland owner by accession.

Accretion. The process by which new soil is accumulated; growth. The imperceptible addition of land to the shore of the ocean or bay, or to the banks of a river.

Acknowledgment. A formal declaration before some competent officer declaring it to be his act or deed; usually declared before a notary public.

Adjacent. "To be near," "close or contiguous," "in the neighborhood or vicinity of," or "adjoining or contiguous to" are the common meanings of the term "adjacent."

Adjoining. The word "adjoining" in a description of a premise conveyed means "next to" or "in contact with" and excludes the idea of intervening space (Yard v. Ocean Beach Ass'n., 24 A 729).

Affidavit. A sworn statement made before a notary public or other authorized person. The one who makes the statement is called the "affiant."

Agreement. Usually a written instrument executed by two or more parties in which the parties agree to do or not to do certain things; a contract.

Alluvion. Where, from natural causes, land forms by imperceptible degrees upon the bank of a river or stream, navigable or not navigable, either by accumulation of material or by the recession of the stream, such land, called alluvium, belongs to the owner of the bank subject to any existing right of way over the bank. The process of land formation is called alluvion.

Along. "Along a line" means on and in the direction of the line. "Along the road" means along the center line or thread of the road unless qualified as, for example, "Along the east side line of the road." "Along a line" may be changing in direction by curves or angles. Avoid "with a line," "by a line," or "on a line" where "along a line" is meant. The term "along" may mean "on"; thus "along" the shore means "on" the shore and includes the shore (Church v. Meeker, 34 Conn 421).

American Title Association. A.T.A. Loan Policy differs from the standard type policy, in that the standard type policy insures by the record only, whereas the A.T.A. insures against off-the-record information which may be disclosed by an inspection and survey of the property. A.T.A. Loan Policy insures lender only but gives greater coverage than the standard loan policy.

Approximate. "Approximately," "a little more than," "not quite," "not more than" are all terms of safety and precaution. Approximate often denotes uncertainty of dimensions to a greater degree than "more or less" and to a lesser degree than "about." Reasonable knowledge of dimensions is indicated by "approximate."

Appurtenances. A word employed in deeds, leases, etc., for the purpose of including any easements or other rights used or enjoyed with the real property, which are considered to be so much a part of the property that they automatically pass to the grantee under the deed conveying the real property.

Arbitrary Map. An office "subdivision" or map made by a title company, assessor, or others for their own convenience in locating property in an area in which all the descriptions are by metes and bounds. On this "subdivision," the "lots" are given "arbitrary" numbers. The deeds and other instruments affecting these "lots" are posted to what is called an "arbitrary account."

At. The word "at," when applied to the place or location of an object, is not treated as definitely locative. It denotes nearness or proximity, and is less definite than "in" or "on." A boundary of land described as "at" a road, without qualifying terms means "to the center of the road." "To," "on," "at," and "by" a stream, unqualified, means to the limit of private ownership. The word "at" may have elasticity of meaning, depending upon how it is used.

Avulsion. The sudden and perceptible tearing away or separation of land by violent action of water.

Azimuth. Azimuth is a direction measured clockwise from a given meridian. The army uses north as the assumed meridian; the Lambert system uses south. If azimuths are used in a description, the assumed meridian must be defined.

Bank of a Stream, Right or Left. When one is facing downstream, the right side is the right bank and the left side is the left bank.

Base Line, Sectionalized Land. Base line is a parallel of latitude or approximately a parallel of latitude running through an arbitrary point chosen as the starting point for all sectionalized land within a given area.

Batture. A term used to denote a bed of sand, stone, or rock rising towards the surface of a body of water. As used in Louisiana, it is applied to portions of the bed of the Mississippi River that are exposed at low water and covered at high water.

Beach. Used in conjunction with boundary lines, the word "beach" may mean the sea side or the land side of the beach. The meaning intended in a deed depends upon the other words used in the deed and upon the surrounding circumstances. In the absence of qualifying terms, "beach" often conveys to the limits of private ownership, thus giving the greatest advantage to the buyer.

Being. "Being" usually denotes a secondary call as "to the northeast corner of Brown's land, being also a 2-inch iron pipe." The 2-inch iron pipe is usually the secondary or informative call, whereas Brown's corner is normally the superior call. A "being clause" is frequently a controlling call.

Being Clause. The "being clause" of a deed denotes the origin or history of the present deed, such as "being the same land conveyed to Brown in Book 1237, page 672, of Official Records." If a change is made in the wording of a deed, there should always be inserted a being clause. Reference to a being clause generally does not operate to enlarge or restrict a particular and sufficient description of land conveyed (26 CJS 372).

Bisection of a Line. Bisection of a line is not the cutting of the line into two equal parts. Where mid-point is meant, use mid-point.

Blaze. Blaze is a mark on a tree caused by cutting off the bark and a portion of the live wood.

Block. A block is a square or portion of a city enclosed by streets, whether it is occupied by buildings or composed of vacant lots. In addition, blocks are often enclosed by the boundary of the subdivision.

Border. "Border" is synonymous with "boundary."

Bounded. Land sold and described as "bounded" by a highway is construed to extend to the center line of the highway unless other limits are given.

Bounds. Bounds are the lines by which different parcels of land are divided. "Butts and bounds" or "butted and bounded" are phrases sometimes used to introduce the boundaries of land. "Buttal" means along the ends of the land.

But. "That which follows is an exception to that which has gone before" is the common meaning of "but" in a sentence. "But" may mean "except," "except that," "on the contrary," or "yet."

By. In a deed, "by a road" is construed as including the land to the center of the street, but "by the east side of a road" means "along the east side" and not "along the center line." "To," "on," or "by" a stream means to the limits of the grantor's land.

Cadastral Map. Strictly, a map for the purpose of making a cadastre. A cadastre is an official register used to apportion taxes. Hence it is a map to show the value and relationship of lands for taxing purposes.

Call. A "call" within a deed is the designation of visible natural objects, monuments, course, distance, or other matter of description as limits of the boundaries. Locative calls are particular or specific calls exactly locating a point or line. Descriptive calls are general or directory calls which merely direct attention to the neighborhood in which the specific calls are to be found.

Cardinal Direction. Cardinal direction is either due north, east, south, or west.

Center Line of a Street. Center line of a street usually applies to the center of a street prior to widening, or closings; i.e., the center line of the original street midway between the sides. To avoid ambiguous conditions, if the street has been narrowed or widened on one side or unequally, the center line should be defined.

Central Angle or Delta. Central angle or delta defines the angle subtended by the arc of a portion of a circle. "Through an angle" or "through a central angle" is clear in meaning when a course along an arc is described.

Chain of Title. A chronological list of documents which comprise the record history of title of a specific piece of real estate.

Chainmaker. A person who assembles a chain of title.

Color of Title. If a claim to a piece of real property is based upon some written instrument, although a defective one, the person is said to have "color of title."

Common Law. Common law represents the determination of what is right and wrong as found by the courts to which various cases have been submitted by parties to legal actions (see **Unwritten Law**).

Concave. The inside of a curve; towards the center of the circle.

Conditions. Restrictions created by a qualification annexed to the estate by the grantor of a deed, upon breach of which the estate is defeated and reverts to him.

Consideration. The inducement, either money or other consideration, which moves a party to enter into a contract.

Convex. Outside of a curve.

Conveyance. The term "conveyance" embraces every instrument in writing by which any estate or interest in real property is created, aliened, mortgaged, or encumbered, or by which the title to any real property may be affected, except wills.

Conveyed. "Conveyed" means all the land transferred in fee title. "That land conveyed to Brown" would include the lot described plus adjoining streets.

Cord, Long (see Fig. 1-2).

Course. "Course" as used in surveying includes both bearing and distance. "Course and distance" where "bearing and distance" is meant is a common error. Because, when a ship is set on a "course," a bearing is implied, the word "course" is sometimes used in land description utilizing that meaning.

Covenant. A word used in deeds for the purpose of creating restrictions; imports an agreement on the part of the grantee to make, or to refrain from making, some specified use of the land conveyed.

Curves (see Fig. 1-2). (1) **Center Line of a Curve** is the mid-point along the arc of the curve and is not the "center of the circle" describing the curve. (2) **Parallel Curves** are curves that are concentric. (3) **Radius of a Curve** stops at the arc of the curve. A description intending to extend beyond the arc should state "and on the prolongation of the radius." (4) **Compound Curves** are tangent at the point of compounding (changing of radius). (5) **Reverse Curves** are tangent at the point of reversal. (6) **Tangent Curves** have a common tangent where the curves meet.

Decree. A judgment by the court in a legal proceeding.

Decree of Distribution. The judicial decision made by a probate court determining who is legally entitled to the real and personal property of a decedent.

Deeds. A deed is evidence in writing of an executed contract for the sale of land. Its purpose is to define location and title to land. Several types exist. (1) **Grant Deed.** A grant deed conveys the fee title of the land described and owned by the grantee. If at a later date the grantor acquires a better title to the land conveyed, the grantee immediately acquires the better title without formal documents (after rights). In some states, by law, the grantor warrants the deed against acts of his own volition. (2) **Quit Claim Deed.** A quit claim deed passes on to the grantee whatever title the grantor has at the time at which the transaction is consummated. It carries no after rights; i.e., if the grantor acquires a better title at a later date, it is not passed on to the grantee. The deed carries no warranties on the part of the grantor. (3) **Agreement Deed.** An agreement deed is an agreement between owners to fix a disputed boundary line. (4) **Warranty Deed.** A warranty deed conveys the fee title to the land described to the grantee and in addition guarantees the grantor to make good the title if it is found lacking.

Degree of Curve. Along railroads the degree of curve is the central angle of a curve subtended by a 100-foot chord on the said curve. Along highways the degree of curve is usually, but not always, defined as the central angle subtended by a 100-foot arc of said curve (see Fig. 1-2).

Description. The exact location of a piece of property stated in terms of lot, block, and tract, or by metes and bounds.

Distance between Points. Distance between points is always assumed to be the shortest possible horizontal distance unless otherwise specified.

Due. Where monuments or other deed terms do not limit the calls, "Due north" means "astronomical north." A deed reading "thence N 65° 10′ 24″ W along said southwest line (Cuyama Rancho) as shown on said record of survey map a distance of 2,877.60 feet; thence due north 13,295.04 feet to the true point of beginning" was interpreted as though "due" meant "astronomical." The deflection method, whereby an angle of 65° 10' 24" was turned from the Rancho, was rejected. The "due north" was determined by observation on Polaris and resulted in a difference of approximately 11 feet east and west (Richfield Oil Corp. v. Crawford, 249 Pac 2nd 600). "Due north" as originally used meant "true north" as determined by a declination correction to a magnetic reading. The word has become ambiguous in meaning because of careless usage. If astronomical north is meant in a deed, use "astronomical north," but not "true north."

Easement. An interest in land created by grant or agreement which confers a right upon owners to some profit, benefit, dominion, or lawful use of or over the estate of another; it is distinct from ownership of soil. Example: an easement for road purposes.

Eminent Domain. The right or power of government to take private property for public use on paying the owner a just compensation.

Escheat. The lapsing or reverting of land to the state.

Escrow. A grant may be deposited by the grantor with a third person, to be delivered on performance of a condition, and, on delivery by the depositary, it will take effect. While in the possession of the third person, and subject to condition, it is called an escrow.

Estoppel. A preclusion in law which prevents a man from alleging or denying a fact in consequence of his own previous acts.

Et Al. And others, and another.

Et Con. And husband.

Et Seq. And following.

Et Ux. And wife.

Examiner. A person who analyzes a chain of title to land and passes on validity of various instruments and then renders his opinion.

Exception, Excepting. An exception withdraws a part of the thing described as granted, and which would pass but for the excepting clause. The word "except" means "not included." "Lot 12, excepting the east 30 feet" clearly conveys that portion of lot 12 lying westerly of the east 30 feet. "Lot 12 and lot 13, except the east 30 feet" is not clear since the exception might apply to either one lot or both. "Lot 12 and lot 13, except the east 30 feet of lot 13" is better.

Exception Doubled. Double exceptions should always be avoided. "Lot A, except the east 50 feet, except the south 50 feet" conveys two meanings, namely, (1) "lot A, except the easterly 50 feet of all of lot A and except the south 50 feet of all of lot A," or (2) "lot A, except the east 50 feet of all of lot A, except that the south 50 feet of the east 50 feet is reserved by the grantor." In a double exception the second exception may refer to the exception or to the lot.

External (see Fig. 1-2).

Extrinsic Evidence. Extrinsic evidence is evidence of matter not contained in the writings, but offered to clear up an ambiguity.

Fee. An estate of inheritance in land.

Fee Simple. An estate of inheritance in land without qualifications or restrictions as to the persons who may inherit it as heirs. Also called an "Absolute Fee or Fee Title." Denotes absolute ownership.

Fractional Lot. A fractional lot is a portion of a section not subdivided in the regular manner and may be more than or less than the smallest division (40 acres). It is meaningless to refer to a lot in a subdivision, other than government sections, as being a fractional lot.

Fractional Section. A fractional section is one reduced in size due to a land grant, body of water, etc.

Free Boundary. A free boundary is one that is not limited by a call for a monument as "thence north 12° east, 120 feet." "Thence North 12° East, 210 feet to Brown's south line" is not a free boundary.

Grant. The transfer of real property by deed.

Grant Deed (see Deeds).

Grantee. The person to whom a grant is made, the one who acquires property.

Grantor. The person by whom a grant is made, the one who transfers the property.

Guide Meridians. Guide Meridians are true north lines usually run at 24-mile intervals along a standard parallel. Guide meridians terminate in the next northerly standard parallel.

Habendum Clause. That part of a deed which follows the legal description and limits and defines the rights that the grantee is to have in the property conveyed.

Hack. A hack is a mark on a tree made by cutting out a V notch well into the live wood.

Heirs and Assigns As Used in Deeds. Unless the words "and his heirs" are used, the estate conveyed is only for the life of the grantee (estate for life). "And his heirs" is not necessary in most states because of statutes abolishing the necessity. "And assigns" is included to take care of corporations, trustees, etc., who cannot have heirs.

High-Water Mark. High-water mark is the line which the water impresses on the soil by covering it for sufficient periods of time to deprive it of vegetation (Raide v. Dollar, 203 P 469). In the absence of any statement to the contrary, it must be construed to mean "ordinary" high-water mark (Rondell vs. Fay, 32 Cal 354).

Incumbrances. The term "incumbrances" includes taxes, assessments, and all liens upon real property.

Joint Tenants. An estate owned by two or more persons in equal shares created by a single transfer. Upon the death of a joint tenant, the surviving joint tenant takes the entire property and nothing passes to the heirs of the deceased.

Juxtaposition of Numbers. Figures used in a description which have differing units as "thence easterly along the north line of lot 21, 21 feet" can easily be changed to "2,121 feet or 2121 feet." Insertion of a phrase as "thence easterly along the north line of lot 21, a distance of 21 feet" is better.

Lis Pendens. A notice of a pending suit. A person dealing with property after a lis pendens has been recorded takes the property subject to the decree of court which may be rendered.

Lot Excludes Street. "However clear it may appear that the owner of a lot holds title to the center of the adjoining street, subject to the public easement, and that the boundary of the lot is technically, therefore, the center of the street, in view of the fact that the owner of such lot or land has no right to the possession or occupancy of any portion of such street, the word 'lot' as generally and customarily used does not include that portion of the street." (Earl v. Dutour, 181C 58).

Lot Line. Lot line is the line shown upon the map creating the lot. A lot line is permanent and does not change with street openings.

Low-Water Mark. Low-water mark is the line to which a body of water receded, under ordinary conditions, at its lowest stage.

Mean High-Tide Line. The average height of the tide between all the lowest high tides and all the highest tides.

Meander Line. Meander line is a traverse of a body of water for the purpose of determining the size and location of the body of water. Meander lines do not represent the boundary line; the body of water where it exists represents the true boundary lines.

Meridian Line. Meridian line is any line run due north and south. Since meridian lines converge at the North Pole, no two meridians are parallel. Practically within the limits of a property survey, all lines shown as north or south are considered parallel.

Metes and Bounds. As commonly understood, descriptions of real property which is not described by reference to a lot or block shown on a map, but is described by starting at a known point and describing the bearings and distances of the lines forming the boundaries of the property are called metes and bounds deeds. Parcels of land created in sequence by conveyances, but not all delineated on a map at one time, have senior and junior deed considerations. Within the limits of this book all descriptions having junior and senior considerations are discussed under metes and bounds descriptions.

Monuments. Monuments are tangible landmarks indicating boundaries. (1) **Physical Monuments.** A physical monument is an existing feature such as a stone, stake, tree, hill, ocean, river, or lake, but not the line of an adjoiner. (2) **Natural Monuments.** A natural monument is a naturally occurring object such as a lake, river, tree, boulder, or hill. Although the courts sometimes refer to a record monument as a type of natural monument, such a broad meaning is excluded in these pages. (3) **Artificial Monument.** An artificial monument is a man-made object such as a stake, fence, set stone, etc. (4) **Record Monument.** An adjoiner property called for in a deed such as a street or particular parcel of land. Frequently the boundary line of the adjoiner is referred to as the record monument; actually the entire property, rather than the line, is the monument. Physical monuments may or may not mark a record monument. In court reports, record monuments are often referred to as natural monuments, but such a meaning is excluded in these pages. (5)

Legal Monument. Any monument controlling in a legal description. It is often limited in meaning so as to be synonymous with record monument.

More or Less. The words "more or less" in their ordinary use are to be taken as words of caution, denoting some uncertainty in the mind of one using them and a desire not to misrepresent. When used in connection with quantity and distance, "more or less" are words of safety and precaution, intended merely to cover some slight or unimportant inaccuracy (Russo v. Corideo, 102 Conn 663). When "125 feet more or less to the point of beginning" is used in a deed, the "more or less" indicates that the 125 feet is an informative term whereas "to the point of beginning" is the controlling term. "About 12 acres more or less" is indefinite and should be avoided since the word "about" is very broad in meaning.

Normal. Normal to a line is 90° to the line. Normal to a curve is a radial line.

North. "Though the word 'North,' as used in the descriptive call of a deed, may be controlled or qualified in its meaning by other words of description used with it, yet when it is not qualified by other words, it must be construed as meaning due North" (96 Cal 505). **Due North** means geographical or astronomical north.

Northerly. Where nothing is given to limit the exact direction, northerly means due north.

Parallel Lines. Parallel lines are two straight lines that are an equal distance apart. Parallel curves are always concentric curves. East-west lines are parallel. Technically, north-south lines converge at the poles and cannot be parallel; however, in a legal description or on a map, where two lines are shown with the same bearing, it is implied that the lines are parallel. The same bearing on different maps does not imply parallelism. On township plats, parallel lines may have different bearings due to convergence towards the North Pole. A line is parallel *with,* not to, another line. By mathematical definition, "parallel lines" are straight lines; but, in common speech about boundaries, the words are often used to represent lines that are not straight lines, but photographs of each other, and courts in passing on questions of boundaries, often use them in the latter sense.

Parallel of Latitude. Parallel of latitude is any line that is run due east and west and that is at every point at right angles to the meridian. A parallel of latitude is a curved line on the face of the earth; however, within the limits of a boundary as shown on a map, parallels of latitude are considered straight lines. Only where large tracts are surveyed is curvature consideration necessary.

Parcel. Parcel generally refers to a piece of land that cannot be designated by lot number.

Parole Evidence. Parole evidence is evidence gathered by testimony of witnesses.

Patent. The title conveyed by the government describing land disposed of by the government is called a patent.

Plaintiff. The one who complains and brings action at law on a charge against another.

Plat. Same as plot, map, or chart.

Point. "Point" in a boundary is the extremity of a line. "To a point" in a description is often meaningless, since the end of a line is a point. If the point is to be referred to later, "to point A" or "to point #1" gives an easy later reference.

Principal Meridian. Principal meridian is a meridional line running through an arbitrary point chosen as a starting point for all sectionalized land within a given area.

Prolong. A line is prolonged but a curve is continued. Prolongation of a curve is the extension of the tangent to the curve.

Property. The ownership of a thing is the right of one or more persons to possess and use it to the exclusion of others. The thing of which there may be ownership is called property.

Quiet Title. An action at law to remove an adverse claim or cloud on the title of property.

Quit Claim Deed. A deed in the nature of a release containing words of conveyance as well as release. It conveys any interest that the maker may have in the property described without any representations or liability of any kind as to title conveyed or incumbrances that may exist thereon.

Real Property. Land and generally whatever is erected, growing, or affixed to the land.

Rear. A deed reading "thence running to the rear of the said land" does not always mean that the land extends to the rear line, but may mean "towards the rear" (Moran v. Lezotte, 19 NW 757).

Remainder. An interest in real property which does not give the right of possession until rights of the person in possession have been terminated either by his death or by lapse of time. One example is when A conveys real property to B reserving in the deed a life estate to A. A (life tenant) has the right of possession and enjoyment of the property for his lifetime, and at his death B (remainder-man) acquires this right of possession, thereby giving him the entire interest in the property. During A's lifetime, B's interest is a remainder.

Reserving. When a thing granted is taken back, it is reserved. Easements are usually reserved as "reserving a 20-foot easement for road purposes, etc." Reserving is used when a new incumbrance is being created. A reservation creates some right or privilege for the grantor in the land described as granted.

Restrictions. Provisions in a deed which limit the use of the land.

Reversion. The estate or interest that will revert to, or be returned to, the grantor in a deed should restrictions be violated or the term of the conveyance end.

Right-of-Way. Right to use or cross over property of another.

Riparian Rights. The right that an owner of land bordering on a river has in the water flowing in the river or underneath the land. Also the rights of a person owning land bordering on a body of water in or to its banks, bed, or water.

Said.   Said refers to one previously mentioned with the same name.

Scrivener.   Professional writer, deed author.

Searcher.   A person who assembles all the facts concerning the title to real estate for submission to a title examiner.

Shore.   Shore is the land lying between the high-water and low-water marks.

Slope Rights.   Adjacent to highways the right to extend fills or cuts beyond the side lines of the road easement as dedicated.

Spiral.   A spiral is used to change the curvature of a curve gradually to a straight line. Since many types of spirals exist, unless the type is defined, ambiguity results.

Standard Parallels.   Standard parallels, or correction lines, are parallels of latitude at intervals of 24 miles north or south of the base line.

Statute Law.   Statute law consists of laws passed by the proper legislative bodies. A statute generally repeals all earlier conflicting laws whether statute or common law.

Subdivision.   A tract of land divided, by means of a map, into lots, or lots and blocks, for the purpose of resale, generally for residential or agricultural purposes.

Subject To.   "Subject to" refers to something already existing as "subject to an easement."

Tangent.   A tangent to a curve is a line that touches the curve at one point and is also at right angles to the radial line at the point of contact with the curve.

Tax Sale.   An official sale of lands by the state for the nonpayment of taxes assessed on them.

Thence.   "Thence" means "from that place."

Thereon.   A deed that granted a passageway and specified that the grantor must fence the same but reserved the right "to erect gates thereon" implied the right to erect gates either on the side or across the passageway (Gossett v. Chandler, 264 SW 853, 204 Ky 402).

Thread.   "Thread of a road" is a line midway between the side lines. "Thread of a stream" is the line midway between banks.

Tidelands.   Tidelands mean lands covered and uncovered by the ordinary tides (Rondell vs. Fay, 32 Cal 354).

Tie Points.   Offset monuments set by the city engineer to mark street lines are commonly called tie points.

Tied.   As used in surveying, monuments are tied together by measurements. A property corner is tied to offset monuments or to other property corners.

Title.   Ownership.

Title Insurance.   Insurance against loss due to any defect or hazard insured against in a policy of title insurance.

Title Policy.   A policy insuring the title to real property, issued for the protection of persons acquiring interests in real property either as owner, lender, or lessee; it insures against forgery, incompetents, insanities, and other matters that are not shown by the County Recorder's office records; it insures the actual title to property as distinguished from the record title, such as is guaranteed in a guarantee of title.

Title Search. The checking or reviewing of all documents affecting the ownership of a piece of property.

To. "To," "on," "by," "at," and "along" a road carry title to the center line unless otherwise qualified. "To" implies contact. "To" does not always include an object, as "to a certain property" does not include the property. But "to a stone" usually means "to the center of the stone." "To" is directional, as "90° to (not with)" or "at right angles to." "To" is a word of exclusion rather than inclusion. If you go to an object, you exclude other objects.

Township. Township is a nearly square area of land usually containing 36 sections of land.

Trees, Ownership of Line Trees. Trees whose trunks are wholly upon the land of one owner belong exclusively to him, although their roots grow into the land of another. Trees whose trunks stand partly on the land of two or more coterminous owners belong to them in common.

Trust Deed. A written instrument by which a borrower (trustor) conveys his land to another (trustee) for the benefit of the lender (beneficiary) as security for the repayment of the money lent. In the event of a failure of the trustor to repay the money, the trustee conducts a foreclosure sale of the real property.

Unwritten Law. Unwritten law is the law not promulgated and recorded, but which is, nevertheless, observed and administered in the courts of the country. It has no certain repository, but is collected from reports of the decisions of the courts and from the treatises of learned men.

Vest. To give title to or to pass ownership to property.

West. West is a curved line following a latitude. Practically it is at right angles to due north since most descriptions are too small in area to have noticeable curvature.

With. "With" shows an association, as "parallel with," not "parallel to."

Words of Exclusion. "To," "from," "by," "between," and "on" are words of exclusion unless there is something in the phrase that makes it apparent that the words were used in a different sense. "To a stone mound," "on Brown's land," and "by the river" exclude other terms.

Bibliography

1. *Description and Survey in Title,* William C. Wattles, Title Insurance and Trust Company, Los Angeles, Calif.
2. *A Treatise on the Law of Surveying and Boundaries,* Frank Emerson Clark, Bobbs-Merrill Company, Indianapolis, Ind.
3. *The Legal Elements of Boundaries and Adjacent Properties,* Ray Hamilton Skelton, Bobbs-Merrill Company, Indianapolis, Ind.
4. American Mining Law, *Bulletin* 123, State of California, Division of Mines, San Francisco, Calif.
5. *Elementary Surveying,* Charles B. Breed and George L. Hosmer, Volume I of *Principles and Practice of Surveying,* John Wiley and Sons, New York, N. Y.
6. *Elementary Surveying,* Brinker and Taylor, International Textbook Company, Scranton, Pa.
7. *Surveying: Theory and Practice,* John C. Tracy, John Wiley and Sons, New York.
8. *Public Land Statutes of the United States,* Government Printing Office, Washington, D.C.
9. *Corpus Juris Secundum,* The American Law Book Company, Brooklyn, N. Y.
10. American Law Reports, The Lawyers Co-operative Publishing Co., Rochester, N. Y., and Bancroft-Whitney Company, San Francisco, Calif.
11. *Words and Phrases,* West Publishing Company, St. Paul, Minn.

Index